Use of Vegetation in Civil Engineering

CIRIA, the Construction Industry Research and Innformation Association, is an independent non-profit-distributing body which initiates and manages research and information projects on behalf of its members. CIRIA projects relate to all aspects of design, construction, management, and performance of buildings and civil engineering works. Details of other CIRIA publications, and membership subscription rates, are available from CIRIA at the address below.

This book is the outcome of a CIRIA research project aimed at providing technical guidance to practising engineers on the use of vegetation as an engineering material, with particular reference to the UK construction industry both at home and overseas. The project was carried out under contract to CIRIA by Richards Moorehead & Laing Ltd, consulting engineers and environmental scientists, in association with Silsoe College and Geostructures Consulting.

The photograph on the cover shows a timber retaining wall with concrete piers, planted with willow.

CIRIA's research managers for water engineering and environmental management are Owen Jenkins and Garry Stephenson

CIRIA
6 Storey's Gate
Westminster
London SW1P 3AU
Tel. 01-222 8891
Fax. 01-222 1708

Use of Vegetation in Civil Engineering

Project Coordinators and Editors

N. J. Coppin, MSc, MIBiol, MIEnvSci, ALI
Wardell Armstrong

I. G. Richards, BSc, CEng, MICE
Richards Moorehead & Laing Ltd

Construction
Industry
Research and
Information
Association

Butterworths
London Boston Singapore
Sydney Toronto Wellington

PART OF REED INTERNATIONAL P.L.C.

First published 1990

© CIRIA, 1990

British Library Cataloguing in Publication Data

Coppin, N. J.
  Use of Vegetation in civil engineering.
  1. Civil engineering. Environmental aspects
  I. Title   II. Richards, I. G.
  624

ISBN 0-408-03849-7

Library of Congress Cataloging in Publication Data

Use of vegetation in civil engineering/N. J. Coppin,
    I. G. Richards.
        p.   cm.
    "Construction Industry Research and Information
        Association."
    Bibliography: p.
    Includes index.
    ISBN 0-408-03849-7
    1. Soil stabilization.   2. Slopes (Soil mechanics).
3. Soil-binding plants.   4. Landscape architecture.
I. Coppin, N. J.   II. Richards, I. G.   III. Construction Industry
Research and Information Association.
TA710.U82   1989
624.1′51363—dc20   89-35566
                                              CIP

Composition by Genesis Typesetting, Borough Green, Kent
Printed in Great Britain at the University Press, Cambridge

Acknowledgements

Research team

Manager
I. G. Richards   Principal, Richards Moorehead & Laing Ltd

Authors
N. J. Coppin[1]   formerly Associate, Richards Moorehead & Laing Ltd,
                              now Partner, Wardell Armstrong Environmental
                              Consultancy Unit, (principal author and co-ordinator)
D. H. Barker   Principal, Geostructures Consulting
R. P. C. Morgan   Professor of Soil Erosion Control, Silsoe College
R. J. Rickson   Lecturer in Soil Erosion Control, Silsoe College

Research manager

M. E. Bramley   Water Engineering and Environmental Management
                              Section, CIRIA

Subject contributors

D. H. Bache   Department of Civil Engineering and Environmental
                              Health, University of Strathclyde (watercourse and
                              shoreline protection)
N. Bayfield   Institute of Terrestrial Ecology, Banchory Experimental
                              Station (surface protection and trafficability)
L. A. Boorman   Institute of Terrestrial Ecology, Monks Wood
                              Experimental Station (sand dune stabilisation)
S. McHugh   Industrial and Applied Biology Group, University of
                              Essex (seed mixtures and cultivars)
R. Stiles   School of Landscape, Department of Planning and
                              Landscape, University of Manchester (European
                              practice in bio-engineering)
N. Ward   Landscape architect, Richards Moorehead & Laing Ltd
                              (contractual arrangements)

Responsibilities for liaison with other organisations:
[1] Landscape Institute

The CIRIA project drew together information from a review of published technical literature; a survey of and discussions with UK practitioners, researchers and organisations involved with bio-engineering; a limited number of site inspections; discussions/correspondence with key European and US experts; and the experience of the authors and the Steering Group.

The project was carried out with the guidance and assistance of the Steering Group listed below:

M. E. Bramley, Chairman	CIRIA
C. L. Argent[2]	Ardon International Ltd
D. J. Ayres	British Railways Board
D. H. Bache[3]	University of Strathclyde
L. A. Boorman	Institute of Terrestrial Ecology
C. Booth	MMG Civil Engineering Systems Ltd
C. S. Dunn	Travers Morgan & Partners
J. H. Franks	British Seed Houses Ltd
C. D. Hall	Netlon Ltd
S. Hobden	Property Services Agency
I. Mackenzie	Central Electricity Generating Board
G. T. Naylor[4]	Hydraseeders Ltd
B. L. Simpson	Comtec (UK) Ltd
C. Smart	Welsh Office (Highways Directorate and Landscape Adviser)
R. A. Snowdon	Transport and Road Research Laboratory
D. K. Young	Mott MacDonald

The project was funded by:

Department of the Environment (Construction Industry Directorate)
Department of Transport (Transport and Road Research Laboratory)
Ardon International Ltd
British Seed Houses Ltd
Comtec (UK) Ltd
Hydraseeders Ltd
International Trade Centre UNCTAD/GATT
Manstock Geotechnical Consultancy Services Ltd
Netlon Ltd

Responsibilities for liaison with other organisations:
[2] International Trade Centre UNCTAD/GATT
[3] Institution of Civil Engineers, Ground Engineering Group Board
[4] British Association of Landscape Industries (BALI)

Acknowledgement is also made to the following for supply of information:

J. R. Greenwood (Department of Transport, Eastern Region)
R. G. Hanbury (British Waterways Board)
P. A. Inwood (Ministry of Agriculture, Fisheries and Food, York)

and to the following for supply of photographs:

A. Luke (Cambridge Bio-Soil Engineering Ltd)
Comtec (UK) Ltd
Hunters of Chester
Hydraseeders Ltd
MMG Civil Engineering Ltd
P. A. Inwood (Ministry of Agriculture Fisheries and Food, York)
Netlon Ltd
Richards Moorehead and Laing Ltd
R. Stiles (University of Manchester, School of Landscape)
N. J. Coppin (Wardell Armstrong)

Contents

Glossary

Amenity (vegetation)	Not grown as a commercial or edible crop
Biomass	The total mass of living and dead biological material
Community (plant)	Particular assemblage of plant species reflecting the prevailing environment, soil type and management
Cultivar	Cultivated variety of a plant species, usually bred from a wild 'ecotype'
DIN standards	West German standards similar to those of BSI
Ecotype	Naturally occurring variant of a species which is adapted to a particular set of ecological or environmental conditions
Establishment period	1) Time between sowing of the seed and the stage at which the plant is no longer reliant on the nutrient supply in the seed; 2) Time between planting and the stage at which special care is not required to ensure that all parts of the plant are functioning normally
Eutrophication	Nutrient enrichment of a habitat by natural or artificial means; leads to dense and uncontrolled vegetation growth
Evapotranspiration	Moisture loss from a vegetated ground surface due to transpiration via the leaf and evaporation from the vegetation and soil surfaces
Geotextile	Synthetic or natural permeable fabric used in conjunction with soil and vegetation; principally for erosion control, filtration, soil reinforcement and drainage
Grass	Member of a distinct botanical family, widely utilised by man; includes rushes, sedges and reeds; non-woody usually short-lived individuals which can withstand grazing and trampling
Growth habit	The physical form and geometry of a plant
Herb	Generally non-woody flowering plant; no specific definition but covers a very wide variety of small plants; excludes grasses but merges into shrubs

Humus	Organic fraction in the soil, decomposed plant (and animal) material
Hydroseeding	The rapid application of seeds and fertilisers in a water suspension onto an area where, for reasons of access, speed of application or ground condition, conventional techniques cannot be used
Litter layer	Layer of undecomposed plant debris on the soil surface
Management (of vegetation)	The control of vegetation for a specific purpose, to achieve a required growth habit or to manipulate the plant community
Metabolic activity	The internal biochemical processes which are necessary for plant growth and function
Monoculture	Artificial plant community (sown or planted) which is composed of a single species
Mulch	Layer of synthetic or natural material applied to the soil surface primarily to conserve moisture or suppress herbaceous growth
Nurse species	Plant species which are included in a sown or planted mixture, to shelter the slower growing components or to provide some quick protective growth; usually only lasting a short time before being superseded by long-term components
Nutrient harvesting	The control (reduction) of nutrient levels in the soil by the regularly cutting and removal of the vegetation cover
Parent material	The original sediment or rock from which a soil is formed by weathering
Pioneer species	Those species which are particularly well adapted to be the first to colonise bare ground
Poaching (soil)	Damage caused to soil as a result of trampling by livestock or machinery in wet conditions
Propagation	Multiplication and establishment of plant material using seeds, cuttings, offshoots, etc.
Reinforced soil	The inclusion in a soil mass of layers of metallic, synthetic or natural materials to facilitate construction of steep slopes and retaining structures
Rhizome	Stem growth which creeps beneath the soil surface, rooting at nodes to form new individuals; found in many grasses and herbs
Seed bank	The store of dormant seed in the soil
Shrub	Woody plant of substantial stature, smaller than a tree but some overlap with this group
Soil horizon	Layer or zone within the surface soil formed by natural processes of weathering, humus accumulation and plant/animal activity; usually distinguished as topsoil and subsoil

Stolon	Stem growth which creeps over the ground surface, rooting at nodes to form new individuals; found in many grasses and herbs
Succession	Natural sequence or evolution of plant communities, each stage dependent on the preceding one, and on environmental and management factors
Sucker	Root (or stem) growth which eventually separates from the parent plant and forms a new individual
Tiller	Specific to grasses; a shoot branching from the base of an existing grass plant; will form clumps or spreading mats depending on the growth habit
Tree	Woody plant of large (generally >3 m) stature

Notation

A	Area of soil under consideration; leaf area per unit volume
A^C	Air capacity of soil
b	Transverse width of crown of tree in windthrow analysis; width of slice in slope stability analysis
c	Apparent soil cohesion
c'	Effective soil cohesion
C	Crop and soil conservation factor; Rational runoff coefficient; Penman root constant
C_D	Drag coefficient; bulk drag coefficient
C_d	Vegetation drag coefficient
c_R	Increase in soil cohesion due to root reinforcement
c'_R	Increase in effective soil cohesion due to root reinforcement
c_S	Increase in soil cohesion from soil suction due to evapotranspiration
c'_S	Increase in effective soil cohesion due to evapotranspiration
CI	Vegetation retardance index
d	Thickness of rooted zone in segment of slope; average stalk diameter; shear stress from windblow
e	Void ratio
E_a	Actual evapotranspiration losses arising from ground surfaces covered with vegetation
E_o	Equivalent evaporation arising from an open water surface
E_t	Potential evapotranspiration losses from ground covered with standard reference vegetation (usually a grass sward)
H	Height of shelterbelt; thickness of soil and decomposed rock mantle
I	Intensity of erosive rain; soil erodibility by wind
L	Moment arm of centroid of vegetation within critical slip circle about centre of rotation; distance to flow re-attachment point downstream of shelterbelt barrier
L_d	Packing density (soil)
MD	Average potential maximum soil moisture deficit; disturbing moment of slope
pF	Soil suction expressed as common logarithm of suction or negative hydraulic head measured in centimetres of water
pH	A measure of soil reaction (acidity or alkalinity) on a logarithmic scale of 1–14
P	Rainfall interception factor
R	Radius of failure plane of segment of slope; annual rainfall
S	Soil shear strength
T	Total pore space; tensile root force acting at base of slice
T_R	Average tensile strength of root in fibre
t_R	Average tensile strength of root fibre per unit area of soil
u	Pore water pressure at slip surface
u_r	Decrease in pore water pressure due to evapotranspiration by vegetation at slip surface

ε	Porosity (soil)
γ	Unit weight of soil
γ_d	Dry unit weight of soil
γ_{sat}	Unit weight of saturated soil
γ_w	Unit weight of water
ρ	Density of soil
ρ_a	Density of air
ρ_b	Bulk density of soil
ρ_d	Dry bulk density of soil
ρ_s	Particle density
ρ_w	Density of water
ΔS	Increase in soil shear strength
$\Delta S'$	Increase in effective soil shear strength
ϕ	Angle of internal friction or shearing resistance
ϕ'	Effective angle of internal friction or shearing resistance
σ_n	Normal stress
σ'_n	Normal effective stress
τ_R	Maximum bond stress or pull-out resistance between root and soil

1 Introduction

1.1 Background

Vegetation is widely used in civil engineering as a way of reducing the visual impact of civil engineering works and enhancing the quality of the landscape. It can also perform an important engineering function because of its direct influence on the soil, both at the surface, protecting and restraining the soil, and at depth, increasing the strength and competence of the soil mass. Vegetation can also very significantly affect soil moisture. All these effects may be adverse or beneficial, depending on the circumstances, and most have direct engineering relevance; *see* Figure 1.1.

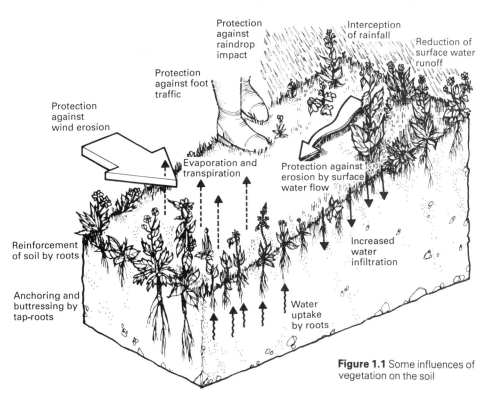

Figure 1.1 Some influences of vegetation on the soil

1

The engineering use of vegetation is termed 'bioengineering' and this Guide introduces a range of bioengineering applications relevant to the UK construction industry. The majority relate either to the restraint of surface soil particles or the stabilisation of a soil mass. These applications are summarized in Box 1.1.

Box 1.1 The applications of vegetation to related engineering situations

Applications	Mining and reclamation	Highways and railways	Construction sites	Waste disposal and public health	Airfields and helipads	Waterways	Land drainage	Reservoirs and dams	Coastal and shoreline protection	Buildings	Recreation	Pipelines	Site appraisal
Slope stabilisation – embankments and cuttings	●	●	●					●	●				
– cliffs and rockfaces	●	●							●				
Water erosion control – rainfall and overland flow	●	●	●	●		●	●	●			●	●	
– gully erosion	●	●	●			●	●	●	●		●	●	
Watercourse and shoreline protection – continuous flow channels						●	●						
– discontinuous flow channels	●	●	●			●	●		●	●			
– large water bodies (shorelines)								●	●				
Wind erosion control	●		●	●	●				●		●	●	
Vegetation barriers – shelter	●	●	●		●				●	●	●		
– noise reduction		●	●							●			
Surface protection and trafficability			●		●	●			●	●	●	●	
Control of runoff in small catchments	●	●	●	●			●	●		●			
Plants as indicators	●		●			●			●			●	●

The Guide is written primarily for the practising civil engineer and therefore assumes some familiarity with the engineering context of bioengineering applications. However, many engineers are unfamiliar with the use of vegetation as an engineering material. This is because bioengineering requires both an understanding of engineering principles and a knowledge of vegetation and the way it interacts with soil, water and climate. Such knowledge is not generally a part of civil engineering training and practice, which tends to emphasise the use of inert materials such as steel, concrete and timber, rather than live vegetation. The Guide provides the reader with an understanding of the principles and procedures involved in bioengineering and how these can be employed. It also identifies areas where the engineer must seek specialist advice on the selection and establishment of vegetation. In this context, it is expected that the Guide will also be helpful to the vegetation specialist in indicating the kinds of situations in which advice may be sought.

The principles and procedures brought out in the Guide are applicable to a wide range of climates and soils, but the applications presented, together with specific information on climate, soils and plant species, have been selected to reflect UK conditions. In some cases, procedures are set out on a formal basis for the first time.

Some of the information contained in the Guide comes from experience in central Europe and North America where physical and institutional conditions have led to the more widespread practice of bioengineering than in the UK. The book *Sicherungsarbeiten im Landschaftsbau* by Hugo Schiechtl, (1973), quickly became a standard work on the European approach to bioengineering and was translated into English in 1980 at the University of Alberta Press. *Biotechnical slope protection and erosion control* by Donald H. Gray and Andrew T. Lieser (1982) is the standard work dealing with North American practice. In 1984 David Bache and Iain MacAskill produced their book on *Vegetation in civil and landscape engineering,* and this marked a new departure for engineers in the UK. *Specification for highway works* (HMSO, 1986) deals in a more comprehensive way with the completion of earthworks than *Specification for road and bridgeworks* (HMSO, 1976), which it replaced. This progression points to a growing awareness of the importance of vegetation in construction.

Despite many years of experience in Europe and North America, however, the engineering role of vegetation is still imperfectly understood. There are many questions to be answered. For example, to what extent can this role be quantified? Is the level of quantification sufficient to enable design procedures using vegetation to be established? Can vegetation provide economic and environmental advantages over conventional engineering materials, and can it extend or enhance the performance of these materials? How much engineering experience is there on which to base designs using vegetation? This Guide attempts to help the engineer answer these and other related questions.

Some uses of vegetation for engineering purposes have been well researched and documented, such as the design of grassed waterways. Other aspects are understood only qualitatively and the practice of bioengineering is very much an 'art', based on engineering experience and judgement, rather than an exact 'science'. This Guide provides an overview of present knowledge for a whole range of applications, from cases where the vegetative element can be 'designed' on a rational scientific or empirical basis, to instances where the use of vegetation is largely based on an intuitive feel for what is right. The information and technical content of the report have been selected to demonstrate the present 'state-of-the-art' and also to illustrate its limitations.

While bioengineering will necessarily continue to encompass both art and science, future research will undoubtedly develop further the scientific base and extend the frontiers of engineering knowledge and practice. Whatever the scientific basis of a bioengineering design, however, the engineer should recognise that its results will be judged by others as much on its environmental attractiveness as on its engineering suitability. In reality, it is often difficult to draw a clear distinction between the engineering and landscaping roles of vegetation. In all cases the engineer must seek to satisfy both engineering and environmental design criteria.

Three specific aspects related to the effects of vegetation in engineering are not covered.

1. Vegetation in relation to buildings: damage due to water removal on shrinkable clay soils; root penetration of foundations and drains; risk of toppling onto buildings.
2. Vegetation in relation to water quality: choking of waterways with plant growth as a result of eutrophication; the use of reed beds for land treatment of effluents and nutrient harvesting.
3. Vegetation growth on structures: adverse effects on weathering, corrosion or performance of concrete and steel.

It is not the intention of this Guide to provide a design manual, or to convert the engineer into a vegetation specialist. Instead, the aim is to bridge the gap between the various disciplines that combine to make up bioengineering and to promote discussion between the engineer and the vegetation specialist. Thus this publication is an educational document as well as a practical guide.

1.2 Structure of the Guide

Following this Introduction, the Guide is divided into five sections. These are ordered so that readers approaching the subject for the first time are taken logically through the basic aspects of plants and their growth, the principles of the engineering effects of vegetation, methods of vegetation establishment and management, and applications of bioengineering. Readers with a specific application in mind, and using the Guide as a source of reference, may prefer to use it in the reverse order, identifying the application and design guidelines, deciding on the method of approach and its implementation, and then referring to the techniques of vegetation establishment and management. Cross-referencing to the basic principles of the engineering effects of vegetation and the aspects of plant growth can be made as necessary, making particular use of the information presented in 'boxes' rather than in the text.

The sections of the Guide are summarised below:

1. Introduction. Background to the Guide; its aims and objectives.
2. Basic aspects of vegetation. Theory and understanding of the structure and growth of vegetation and its interaction with the soil, water and climate.
3. Physical effects of vegetation. Theory and understanding of the properties and functions of vegetation in an engineering role; adverse and beneficial effects.
4. Vegetation selection, establishment and management. Techniques of site preparation, vegetation establishment and management; guidance on quality control.
5. Method of approach and implementation. Strategy, approach to planning, investigation, design, construction, establishment and maintenance; contractual implications; check list for comparing costs.

6. Applications. Practical applications of vegetation by the UK construction industry (*see* Box 1.1).

A full Bibliography and list of references is included for those who require more detailed information on any subject covered in the Guide. A list of plant species appropriate to the UK, with their bioengineering properties and the roles they can perform; relevant standards; and sources of independent advice and information are given in Appendices.

A Glossary contains definitions of key technical terms, particularly those where conventional use differs between the engineer and the vegetation specialist. A Notation list is included to help the reader, particularly where conventions differ between different disciplines or where the same symbol is used to denote different terms, depending on the context. In general, technical terms and notation conform to civil engineering convention.

2 Basic aspects of vegetation

To appreciate how vegetation functions and should be managed, engineers need an understanding of the requirements of plants and plant communities, and of their behaviour under different conditions and circumstances. This Section reviews those aspects which are relevant to the performance and use of plants in an engineering context.

2.1 Plant form and structure

Plants exhibit many different forms and structures, but in general those elements that an engineer is likely to work with can be considered to comprise:

Roots, to provide anchoring and absorb water and nutrients from the soil
Stems, to support the above-ground parts
Leaves, to trap energy in the form of sunlight for the manufacture of carbohydrate compounds
Flowers for reproduction.

Some typical growth habits and structures are illustrated in Figure 2.1. Four plant groups will be considered here: trees, shrubs, grasses and herbs.

2.1.1 Trees

The growth habits of trees can vary considerably, even within one species growing in different environments. Most trees grow from a single upright main trunk which branches in the upper part to form a crown, the size of the crown determining the overall stem spacing. Densely-spaced plantations will tend to grow as a mass of tall thin stems with small crowns. Some species can spread by root suckers and form dense thickets. Coppicing and less severe forms of pruning are the usual ways of manipulating and perpetuating the above-ground growth of trees (Section 4.7).

2.1.2 Shrubs

Typically, shrubs have a fairly dense, woody, perennial growth, with many well-branched stems. Some shrub species are quite low-growing, for example cotoneaster grows to a height of about 300–400 mm, whilst others, such as gorse, broom and hawthorn, can grow to over 2 m.

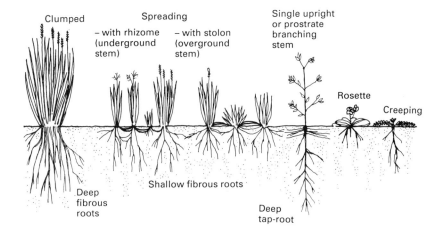

(a) Grasses and herbs

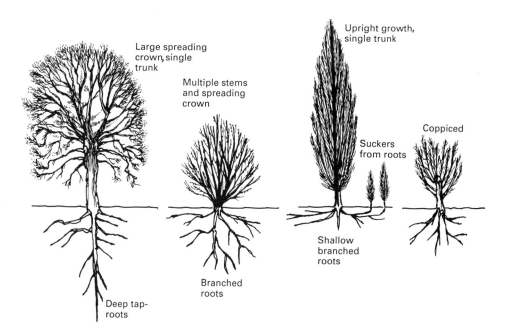

(b) Trees and shrubs

Figure 2.1 Some typical plant growth habits (not to scale)

2.1.3 Grass

The grasses are a widespread and versatile family of plants, widely used by man for a variety of purposes. A grass sward is the commonest use of vegetation in an engineering context, and usually contains a variety of grasses together with herbs such as clover. Grasses give quick establishment and dense ground cover, respond well to many different management techniques and allow a range of land-uses.

Grasses spread vegetatively by tillering, that is by producing new stems from the bases of existing ones. The new tillers either cluster at the base of the existing plant, forming large clumps of densely packed plants, or they form on rhizomes or stolons to produce a spreading sward (*see* Figure 2.1). Rhizomes and stolons are stem structures, the former growing below-ground and the latter spreading across the surface. Rhizomes are particularly useful in bioengineering, as they can form a mass of tough underground stems with considerable structural strength, but in grasses they rarely grow very deeply.

The single most important factor in the growth habit of grasses is that the main growing points are at ground level. This means that moderate mowing, grazing, burning or abrasion does not do any lasting damage to the plant.

2.1.4 Herbs

Herbs are broad-leaved plants of which the above-ground parts are generally non-woody. They include what are generally referred to as wild flowers and weeds, together with cultivated and forage plants such as legumes (e.g. pea, clover, vetch and lupin). Growth habits vary from upright single-stemmed or multi-stemmed individuals to spreading, creeping individuals.

2.1.5 Root systems

Root systems are of particular interest to engineers because of their fundamental importance to most of the functions that vegetation can perform. They vary from very fine fibrous systems through branched systems to a vertical taproot. All plants have a mat of surface roots, the main function of which is to collect nutrients, and which grow in and around the surface soil layers because this is where mineral nutrients are generally available. Deeper roots are used for anchorage and for absorbing water. Large taproots are often associated with the storage of food for over-wintering plants, especially where the above-ground parts die back substantially. The taproots are thus perennial structures whereas fine fibrous roots are subject to annual cycles of decay and renewal.

The greater part of the root system has one purpose: to extract water. A range of common forms is illustrated in Figure 2.2. Individual species vary in their rooting behaviour but soil type and the groundwater regime strongly influence root development. Roots in well-drained soils therefore have to go deeper and exploit a much larger volume of soil than those in moister soils, while a high groundwater level or a layer of densely-compacted soil will force roots to spread laterally; *see*

Figure 2.3. The majority of roots are usually found within 300–400 mm depth in herbaceous vegetation, and up to 3 m deep in vegetation dominated by trees and shrubs. Although much greater rooting depths are often quoted, the proportion of roots at lower depths is usually very small.

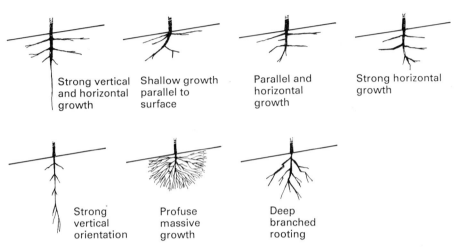

Strong vertical and horizontal growth Shallow growth parallel to surface Parallel and horizontal growth Strong horizontal growth

Strong vertical orientation Profuse massive growth Deep branched rooting

Figure 2.2 Different patterns of root growth (after Yen, 1972)

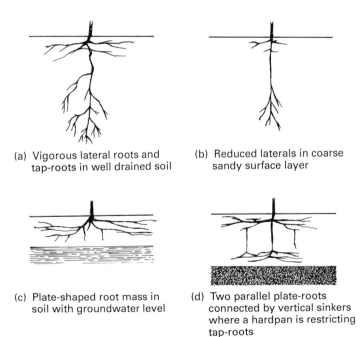

(a) Vigorous lateral roots and tap-roots in well drained soil

(b) Reduced laterals in coarse sandy surface layer

(c) Plate-shaped root mass in soil with groundwater level

(d) Two parallel plate-roots connected by vertical sinkers where a hardpan is restricting tap-roots

Figure 2.3 Modification of root distribution by site conditions

Plate 2A Soil permeated with fibrous roots of grass and clover. Note that the densest root growth is in the top 50 mm or so

As grasses are widely used as ground cover, it is worth considering the characteristics of their root systems in more detail. Some 60–80% of the grass root mass is found in the top 50 mm of soil, and requires three to four years to become fully developed. The root systems, as shown in Plate 2.A, are highly branched and fibrous, forming a mass of fine roots most of which are short-lived, lasting only a year or so. There is a constant cycle of renewal, but the part of the root system which is active is greatly reduced during the winter period (*see* Section 2.1.6).

The extent of root systems, especially of trees, can be considerable. Helliwell (1986) proposes a method of estimating the extent of tree roots, summarised in Box 2.1. The 'zone of influence' of trees on shrinkable clay soils is considered to be about 1.5 times their height for high water demand species, 0.75 times for medium water demand species and 0.5 times for low water demanders (NHBC, 1985). These estimates give some indication of the potential extent of tree root systems but they need to be modified to take account of different soil types and groundwater conditions (*see* Figure 2.3).

The application of tensile or compressive forces to roots stimulates them to thicken. For example, it has been observed that on slopes the thickest roots run obliquely up-hill, functioning as anchors. Root tensile strengths have been measured, and typical ranges of values are given in Table 2.1, but there is great variation according to size and age, plant species and site conditions.

Box 2.1 A method for estimating the extent of tree root systems (After Helliwell, 1986)

This is based on the rule of thumb that a tree requires a root system occupying a volume of soil equal to one-tenth of the volume occupied by the crown (branches and foliage).
  This estimate is then modified by multiplying it by:

1) (average maximum potential $SMD/200$) + 0.2
   where SMD is the soil moisture deficit,
   to allow for the effect of likely drought.
2) 15% of the available water capacity
   to allow for the soil droughtiness.
3) a figure related to the soil fertility:
   – very fertile soil   0.6
   – moderately fertile soil   0.8
   – low fertility   1.0
4) a figure related to the degree of wind exposure:
   – sheltered climate   1.0
   – windy climate but tree in a large group   1.5
   – single isolated tree in moderately windy area 1.5
   – isolated tree in a windy area   2.0

The actual depth and spread of rooting will depend on soil and groundwater conditions as well as species.
  This method is very approximate, and does not allow for the difference between species in density of foliage, rate of moisture loss and nature of the root system.

The density of roots in a volume of soil is a significant parameter and can be assessed by a number of methods:

Measuring Root-Area-Ratio (RAR), the proportion of the cross-sectional area of a sample section of soil that is occupied by roots.
Weighing the mass of root separated (by washing and sieving) from the soil volume. This will tend to underestimate the quantity of finer roots.
Estimating the length of root in a sample using the line intersection method of Newman (1966).

Methods of investigating root systems are reviewed by Bohm (1979).

2.1.6 Seasonal growth pattern

Seasonal patterns in plant growth and distribution are very significant in relation to engineering function. All vegetation follows an annual cycle of growth, reproduction, die-back and dormancy. Plants are generally dormant over the winter period, and the way in which they cope with this period is important in considering their engineering behaviour. A typical annual cycle of active plant growth is illustrated in Figure 2.4.

In annual species, the cycle of germination, growth, flowering, seeding and senescence is completed in one growing season. Perennials persist from year to year by a variety of strategies, illustrated in Figure 2.5. Evergreen plants such as pines do not shed their leaves for the winter but have other mechanisms to reduce activity

Table 2.1 Tensile strengths of roots of selected plant species (after Schiechtl, 1980; O'Loughlin and Watson, 1979)

Grasses and herbs	Tensile strength (MN/m^2)
Elymus (Agropyron) repens (Couch grass)	7.2–25.3
Campanula trachelium (Bellflower)	0.0–3.7
Convolvulus arvensis (Bindweed)	4.8–21
Plantago lanceolata (Plantain)	4.0–7.8
Taraxacum officinale (Dandelion)	0.0–4.4
Trifolium pratense (Red Clover)	10.9–18.5
Medicago sativa (Alfalfa)	25.4–86.5

Trees and shrubs	
Alnus incana (Alder)	32
Betula pendula (Birch)	37
Cytisus scoparius (Broom)	32
Picea sitchensis (Sitka Spruce)	23
Pinus radiata (Radiata Pine)	18
Populus nigra (Black Poplar)	5–12
Populus euramericana (Hybrid Poplar)	32–46
Pseudotsuga menziesii (Douglas Fir)	19–61
Quercus robur (Oak)	32
Robinia pseudoacacia (Black Locust)	68
Salix purpurea (Willow)	36
Salix cinerea (Sallow)	11

The figures given above for live roots are the ranges measured by various workers. When roots die there is some residual strength which will persist. Figures given by O'Loughlin and Watson (1979) indicate this for one species (*Pinus radiata*) as follows:

	Minimum		Maximum	
	Tensile strength (MN/m^2)	Diameter (mm)	Tensile strength (MN/m^2)	Diameter (mm)
Living trees	7.6	0.13	37.5	1.4
3 months since felling	2.9	0.2	33.3	1.1
9 months since felling	2.9	0.2	43.3	1.5
14 months since felling	2.7	0.2	30.9	1.5
29 months since felling	0.3	0.3	14.3	1.8

Tensile strengths of roots will vary considerably with age, size and season. The overall strength of roots penetrating soil will depend on the density and orientation of the roots as well as their individual strengths. For these reasons the figures given should be interpreted with caution. There is no comprehensive list of species which gives root strengths. Further data are quoted by Stiny (1947), Turmanina (1965), Hiller (1966), Kassif and Kopeloritz (1968), Chang (1972), Hathaway and Penny (1975), and Waldron and Dakessian (1981).

during dormancy. Their leaves are usually stiff and waxy in order to survive the cold and reduce transpiration. Deciduous species shed leaves and may die partially or completely back to ground level during the winter.

The ability of a plant to function satisfactorily as an engineering component during the dormant period is most important. It is then that the above- and below-ground plant biomass is at a minimum, reducing the shielding and root reinforcement effects. As an example, the seasonal root growth and distribution

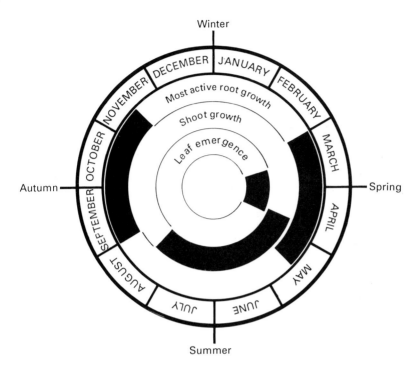

Figure 2.4 A typical annual cycle of active plant growth (shaded) for southern UK

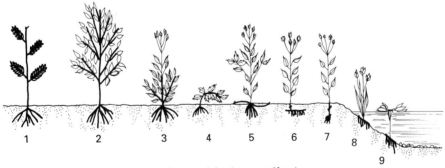

1   Evergreen plants that reduce activity (e.g. conifers).
2   Deciduous plants that shed leaves.
3, 4 Perennating parts, borne very close to the ground, the
      remainder dying.
5   Perennating parts at ground level, all above ground
      herbage dies back.
6 to 9 Perennating parts below ground or submerged in water

Figure 2.5 Various strategies for overwintering of perennial plants (after Raunkiaer, 1934)

below a grass sward are illustrated in Figure 2.6. Metabolic activity and transpiration are also lower during winter, reducing the effects of the plant on soil/water relationships. As growth is reduced, so is the ability to self-repair in the event of damage. It may be necessary to maximise the growth of a certain part of a plant, such as the roots, during the active growing season, so that the carry-over effect into the dormant season is sufficient to fulfil the functional requirement, which may be more pressing in the winter.

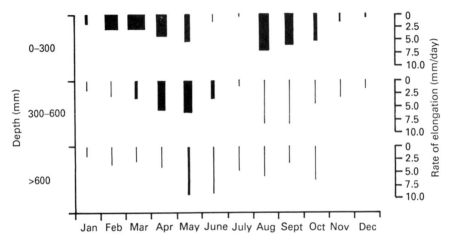

(a) Mean daily rate of elongation of ryegrass roots (width of symbol is proportional to the number of roots).

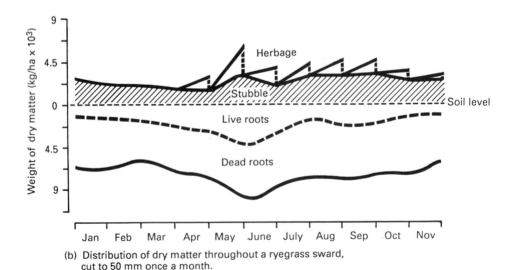

(b) Distribution of dry matter throughout a ryegrass sward, cut to 50 mm once a month.

Figure 2.6 Root growth and distribution with season for a ryegrass sward (from Garwood, 1967a)

2.2 Vegetation and plant communities

Plants not only exist as individuals but interact with each other to form dynamic communities. It is therefore important to consider the structure and function of plant communities.

2.2.1 Community structure

Natural assemblages of plants which are recognisable as a unit are termed 'communities'. These are defined by their species composition and are associated with specific characteristics of climate, soil and management. Although apparently stable, communities are dynamic with a continual turnover of individuals. When some factor changes, such as climate, ground conditions or grazing, the community will adapt accordingly.

A recently-established plant community, such as a sown grass sward or a tree plantation, may consist of a small number of species and bear little relation to a natural or semi-natural community. The extent to which a community will change depends largely on management. For example the species composition of a football pitch is maintained by a high level of management. If that management should cease, then species composition will change, quite rapidly at first but more slowly as it approaches a more natural composition.

2.2.2 Vegetation structure

Vegetation has a three-dimensional structure. In plan there is a spatial distribution of individual plants of different shapes and sizes, with some degree of overlap in both above- and below-ground parts. In vertical section there are usually distinct layers which are characteristic of the type, age, status and management of the community.

Swards of grass and herbaceous vegetation have a fairly simple structure, as shown in Figure 2.7 and Plate 2.B. When they are not grazed or cut very frequently they become a tall-grass community with a fairly dense growth; a litter layer usually accumulates and a dense root mat develops. Grazed or frequently cut swards have a much shorter, more compact growth, with a higher shoot density but less root mass. The litter layer is less well developed, as defoliation removes much of the above-ground biomass.

Woody vegetation with trees and shrubs can have a well-developed stratification, with a dense canopy, an open shrub layer and a generally sparse ground cover. Structure in a tree plantation depends on the age and maturity of the plantation, as illustrated in Figure 2.8. The dense shade beneath some tree species, such as beech, limits the development of the shrub and ground flora. The structure of very young plantations resembles that of swards, until the canopy closes over. Shade then becomes a dominant factor in controlling the stratification beneath it.

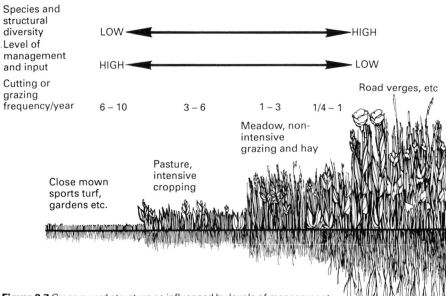

Figure 2.7 Grass sward structure as influenced by levels of management

Plate 2B Typical short grass and herb community

The litter layer is an important component of the vegetation structure, forming a continuous protective layer over the soil surface. The system of roots, rhizomes and suckers is stratified in a way similar to the above-ground parts as shown in Figure 2.9.

2.2.3 Succession

The concept of vegetation as being dynamic has already been introduced. Change can occur in response to a changing climate, soil environment, or management

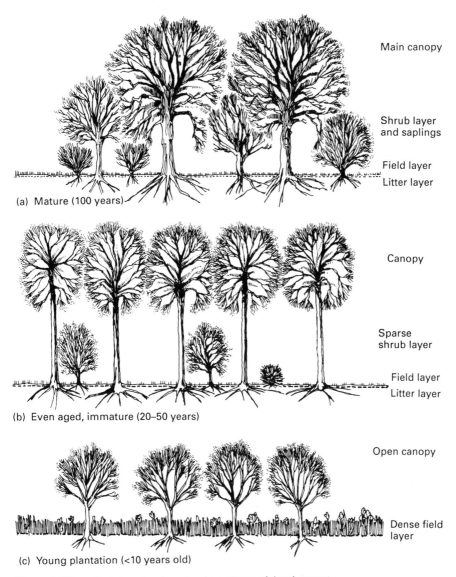

Main canopy

Shrub layer
and saplings

Field layer
Litter layer

(a) Mature (100 years)

Canopy

Sparse
shrub layer

Field layer
Litter layer

(b) Even aged, immature (20–50 years)

Open canopy

Dense field
layer

(c) Young plantation (<10 years old)

Figure 2.8 Tree plantation structure at various stages of development

regime. A more important type of change is a natural succession towards a climax community, through a number of progressive (seral) stages. The theoretical climax or *potential natural vegetation* is that which would develop under the prevailing climatic, soil and historical conditions, including any previous man-made changes, if all current human influences were removed (Tuxen, 1956). From this notional climax, it is possible to make deductions about the associated pioneer and successional plant communities and the individual species which they comprise.

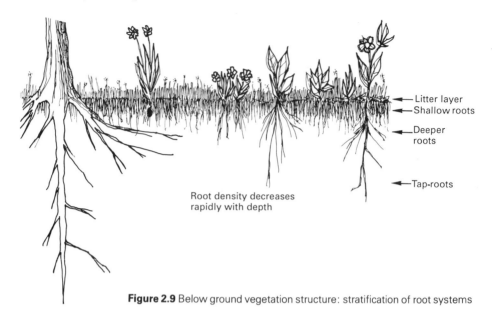

Root density decreases
rapidly with depth

Figure 2.9 Below ground vegetation structure: stratification of root systems

For most of the UK the theoretical climax or potential natural vegetation is woodland, mainly oak but also beech, ash and, in the north, pine and birch. Given sufficient time, and the absence of any interference by man, the progress of succession, starting from bare ground, is one of herb and grass, scrub and then tree cover, as shown in Figure 2.10 and plate 2.C. In very exposed locations, close to

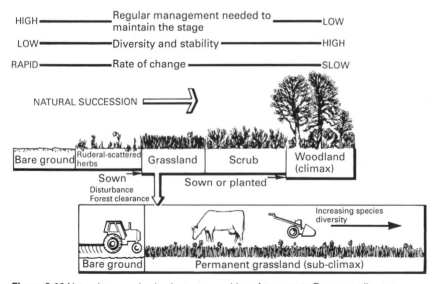

Figure 2.10 Natural succession in plant communities of temperate European climates

(a) Young mixed plantation on a road cutting

(b) Mature tree growth (Sycamore) on a railway cutting

Plate 2C Succession to tree cover

coasts and in very mountainous or cold regions, the tree cover stage may not be reached.

Interference can deflect the natural succession from its usual path to produce a sub-climax. The most significant form of interference is due to man, who manages and manipulates the vegetation to maximise the benefits which can be gained from it. Examples of these sub-climaxes are grassed areas, maintained by grazing or cutting, and heather moorland maintained by burning. Herbaceous communities comprised mainly of grasses have been widely manipulated by man, and their character varies considerably with the management they receive (*see* Figure 2.7).

Succession implies a change in soil characteristics as well as species composition. Beginning with a subsoil or mineral spoil the following changes will occur progressively:

1. organic matter content will increase;
2. plant roots and soil animals will open up the soil, increasing water infiltration;
3. weathering of large particles will reduce coarse particle sizes;
4. soil structure will develop and clay flocculation will increase effective particle size in the finer fraction.

These changes generally result in a reduction in soil density and an increase in permeability.

This brief discussion of succession has been included to underline the extent to which management of vegetation is important. Rarely will an engineer embark on an engineering design relying totally on a climax vegetation because of the time needed to reach that stage. He might, however, anticipate a progression to this state, making use of earlier intermediate stages, or alternatively a management strategy (e.g. grass cutting) might be adopted which seeks to ensure that natural succession does not take place. In either case the engineer must be aware of what changes can take place, and the natural forces on which they depend.

2.2.4 Plant strategies and competition

Plants have a number of strategies for exploiting their particular environment. A plant community is made up of species which compete with each other in various ways for sources of light, water and nutrients. The external factors which species have to deal with can be summarised in two categories:

1. stress, brought about by restrictions in light, water, mineral nutrients, temperature;
2. disturbance, arising from the activities of man, herbivores, pathogens, damage, erosion and fire.

It has been suggested (Grime 1979) that plants have adopted three strategies for dealing with various intensities of environmental stress, such as infertile or drought-prone soil, and disturbance. *Competitors* exploit conditions of low stress and low disturbance; *stress-tolerators* exploit high stress and low disturbance; and *ruderals* (e.g. weeds) exploit low stress and high disturbance. In reality many different plant species exhibit various degrees of each strategy, being intermediate between the three extremes. A review of plant strategies for a wide range of UK species is given in Grime *et al* (1988).

The practical implications of the concepts of plant strategies and niches within a community are that mixtures of species have to be designed to take account of plant community dynamics and the characteristics of a site. In general, the first colonisers of bare ground will be ruderal plants, and the direction in which vegetation will develop subsequently depends on the relative stress due to climate or soil. Where stress is not very great, such as where good topsoil is used, progression will be from ruderal to competitive communities. Where stress is greater, due to the soil or climate, the plant community will progress towards stress-tolerant species.

2.3 Basic requirements of plants

Plants need light, air, water and nutrients, as shown in Figure 2.11. Since even healthy vegetation growing in topsoil may not be performing ideally in an engineering sense, all aspects of the soil/plant system and the various interactions involved need to be considered. For a detailed consideration of plants and soil, refer to Wild (1988). Deficiencies in plant requirements are most apparent in hostile environments. Most construction sites can be considered hostile to plants in some way. Box 2.2 summarises the main problems which occur and these are described in detail in Bradshaw and Chadwick (1980) and Coppin and Bradshaw (1982). The environmental requirements relevant to plant growth are considered under two headings:

1. plants and soil: the capacity of the soil to support vegetation;
2. plants and climate: the bioclimate affecting the choice and performance of plants.

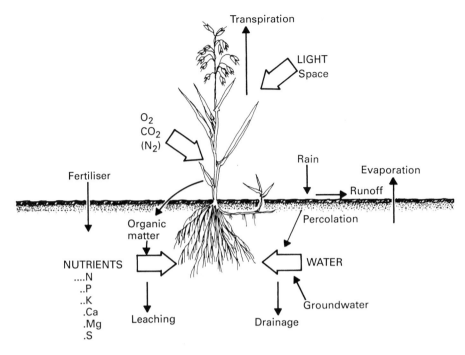

Figure 2.11 Basic needs of plants

Box 2.2 Plant growth problems on hostile sites

Problem	Consequence
Physical	
Shallow rooting depth	Drought effects, poor root development
Coarse soil texture	Poor water holding capacity
High soil density, compaction, fine soil texture	Low water infiltration, high runoff, poor root penetration
Steep slope	Surface instability, high water runoff
Chemical	
Low nutrients	Infertility, especially nitrogen
Low exchange capacity	High leaching of nutrients (c.f. coarse soil texture)
Low pH	Acidity, nutrients unavailable
Toxicities	Salt, heavy metals
Climatic	
Low rainfall	Drought
High rainfall	Erosion, soil loss, leaching of minerals
Cold	Slow plant growth, short growing season
Aspect	Other effects modified, e.g. drought and cold
Exposure	Erosion, physical damage to vegetation, growing season reduced

Box 2.3 Soil physical parameters (definitions relating to plant growth)

Parameter	Definition	Assessment
Soil texture	Description based on proportions by weight of sand, silt and clay as percentages of fine earth fraction <2 mm in size	Field estimations or laboratory measurement
Stoniness, % vol	Proportion of large particles, >2 mm	Direct measurement, or field estimation
Dry bulk density* (ρ_d) Mg/m^3	Apparent density of soil *in situ* (on a dry basis)	Field measurement, either removal of undisturbed core or replacement method (sand or water)
Particle density* (ρ_s) Mg/m^3	Density of the soil particles	Laboratory measurement by displacement. Most soils are consistent with a value about 2.65 Mg/m^3
Void ratio (e)	Ratio: volume of soil voids to volume of solids	$e = \rho_s/(\rho_b - \rho_s)$
Porosity (ε) %* (total pore space, *T*)	Volume of soil voids expressed as a percentage of total *in situ* soil volume *note* – voids occupied by air and water.	$\varepsilon = (1 - \rho_b/\rho_{sl}) \times 100$
Soil erodibility factor	The risk of erosion by air or water due to the nature of the soil itself	Direct measurement or estimation based on soil texture, *see* Sections 6.3.2 and 6.5.2
Packing density (L_d)* (rooting potential)	A more reliable indicator of the effects of compaction than bulk density alone: allows for clay content	$L_d = \rho_b + (0.009 \times \% \text{ clay})$

* see Hall *et al.,* (1977), Jarvis and Mackney (1979).

2.4 Plants and soil

The terms 'topsoil', 'subsoil' and 'soil' are used throughout this Guide in their accepted engineering sense (such as I.C.E. 1976), except that the definition of soil is extended to include unnatural loose materials such as mine spoil and quarry waste, materials which figure frequently in earthworks. Soil scientists and vegetation specialists sub-divide the engineer's simple topsoil and subsoil description into soil horizons, features which have developed from the parent material or rock (*see* Section 2.4.4).

Many of the physical properties of soil which are of interest to the engineer are equally important to the soil specialist, for example bulk density, moisture content, particle size and organic content. The latter's traditional interest in these properties generally extends to the topsoil and subsoil only, and these are materials which the engineer has tended not to examine in such detail.

2.4.1 Physical properties of soil

Box 2.3 summarises the important physical parameters of the soil. The soil characteristics which affect vegetation establishment and growth, their principal determinants and the ways in which they can be modified are given in Box 2.4. Soil

Box 2.4 Soil physical characteristics

Important soil characteristics	Principal determinants				Modifiers					
	Particle size	Packing density	Porosity	Organic matter	Vegetation cover	Topography	Cultivation	Compaction	Additions	Time
Texture	●									
Soil structure	●		●	●			O	O		O
Rooting potential	●	●	●	●			O	O		
Soil water capacity	●		●	●				O	O	
Permeability and water acceptance			●		O	O	O	O		O
Ion exchange capacity	●			●	O				O	
Erodibility	●		●	●	O	O	O	O		
Ease of cultivation	●	●	●			O		O	O	

contains water, air, fine earth, stones and organic matter. The proportions of these components are illustrated in Figure 2.12.

Soil texture describes the particle size distribution and gives an indication of the likely behaviour of a soil in respect of handling, root growth or drainage. Descriptions such as sandy loam or clay are based on measured proportions and mixtures of clay, silt and sand in the fine earth (<2 mm) fraction, as shown in Box 2.5.

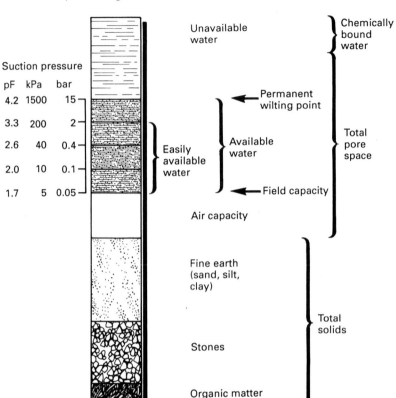

Figure 2.12 Representation of the relative proportions (by volume) of various fractions soil

Rooting potential indicates the resistance of the soil to root penetration, which depends mainly on the soil's bulk density and on mechanical strength. Roots have great difficulty penetrating soil with strengths greater than 2.0 to 2.5 MN/m², though higher limiting values have been suggested for coarse-textured soils. Generally, root growth is enhanced by greater moisture content and voids, and is retarded by higher bulk density and clay content. Critical dry bulk densities for soils, above which root growth is severely restricted, are about 1.4 Mg/m³ for clay soils and 1.7 Mg/m³ for sandy soils. As clay content is so important in determining the rooting potential, a term *packing density* (L_d) is often used to determine the maximum density to which a soil can be compacted and still permit root growth (*see* Box 2.3).

Soil structure is a characteristic which describes the arrangement and size of particle aggregates or 'peds'. Structure develops over time, as fine soil particles aggregate into crumbs and blocks. This increases the number of large pore spaces and thus the permeability and rooting potential of the soil. The presence of organic matter and plant roots plays a major role in developing and maintaining soil structure. Structure is easily damaged by handling or cultivation during wet conditions, when the soil is weaker.

Box 2.5 Soil texture

The usual particle grading curves prepared to BS 5930:1981 are familiar to most engineers. Soils are described according to the British Soil Classification System for Engineering Purposes.

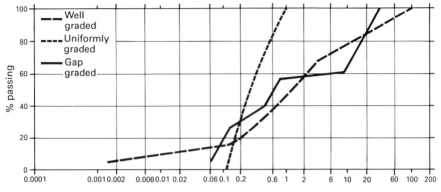

Particle size distribution (grading): mm

Clay fraction	Fine	Medium	Coarse	Fine	Medium	Coarse	Fine	Medium	Coarse	Cobbles
	Silt fraction			Sand fraction			Gravel fraction			
Fine earth							Stones			

For soil survey work, texture descriptions are based on the fine earth fractions, that is <2 mm size. The overall proportion of gravel and cobbles defines the *stoniness*. The proportions of sand, silt and clay in the fine earth soil matrix define the texture classes as given in the triangular diagram.

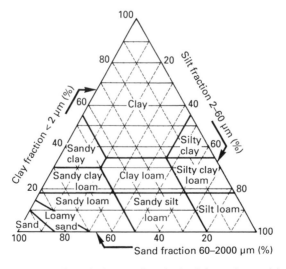

The proportions of sand, silt and clay can be obtained from the particle grading curve, calculating the quantity of each size fraction as a percentage of the <2 mm fraction.

Box 2.6 Soil water parameters

Parameter	Definition	Assessment
Soil water potential, N/m^2 or pF (soil suction and pore water pressure)	A measure of the suction power needed by roots, to extract water at a given soil moisture content. Defined as a function of the difference between the potential of water in the soil to that of pure free water at the same temperature, elevation and atmospheric pressure. The same measure as soil suction or pore water pressure	Direct measurement in soil using tensiometer
Field capacity (FC), % vol	The maximum equilibrium moisture content under free drainage, i.e. after excess water has drained away under gravity. Corresponds to a suction pressure of 0.05 bar	Measured using suction apparatus (sand bath) at 0.05 bar ($5kN/m^2$). Estimated from regression equation, topsoil $FC = 47 + 0.25(C) + 0.1(Z) + 1.12(X) - 16.52\,\rho_b$ subsoil $FC = 37.2 + 0.35(C) + 0.12(Z) - 11.73\,\rho_b$
Permanent wilting point (PWP, % vol (Retained water capacity)	The minimum moisture content which will sustain plant growth. Corresponds to a suction pressure of 15 bar	Measured using suction apparatus (pressure membrane) at $1.5\,MN/m^2$. Estimated by regression equations: topsoil $PWP = 2.94 + 0.83(C) - 0.0054(C)^2$ subsoil $PWP = 1.48 + 0.84(C) - 0.0054(C)^2$
Available water capacity (AWC, % vol	The difference between FC and PWP, theoretically the water available for plant growth under ideal conditions	Subtract measured/estimated values of FC and PWP. Estimate directly from equations: topsoil $AWC = 46.4 - 21.42(\rho_b)$ subsoil $PWP = 36.94 + 0.11 (Z') - 18.45(\rho_b)$ or: $AWC = 1.25 - 0.01(CS + FS) + 0.25(X)$ mm/cm depth or from tables of typical values.
Air capacity (AC), % vol	The volume of air in a soil at FC (ie. at 0.05 bar suction)	Subtract FC from total pore space. Or, from sum of typical values

Box 2.6 *(Continued)*

Parameter	Definition	Assessment
Profile available water (*PAW*), mm	Integration of the available water values for several horizons in a soil profile	*PAW*, mm = $(A_1H_1 + A_2H_2 + A_3H_3$ etc)/10 (where *A* is the *AWC* and *H* is the thickness of the horizon in mm). Integrate to 1 m depth or to impermeable horizon, whichever is shallower
Potential evapotranspiration (*E$_t$*), mm	Calculated water loss from a soil vegetated with a grass sward, assuming no limitations as a soil dries out	Penman equation, results published by Meteorological Office (*see* also Section 3.4.1)
Actual evapotranspiration (*E$_a$*), mm	Corrected *E$_t$* to allow for reduced water loss as a soil progressively dries out	
Soil moisture deficit (*SMD*), mm	Extent to which a soil dries out as *E$_a$* exceeds rainfall during the summer. Equivalent to the amount of rainfall needed to bring the soil back to *FC*	*See* Section 3.4.2 on estimating a soil moisture deficit. Data available from the Meteorological Office.
Average potential soil moisture deficit (*MD*), mm	Measured/estimated value of *SMD* from long-term meteorological data.	Published tables and plans (e.g. Bendelow and Hartnup, 1980)
Droughtiness	The likely intensity of moisture stress in a soil, based on *PAW* and *MD*	*PAW* – *MD*

C = clay %, *Z* = silt %, *Z* = %(2–100 μm grade).
CS = coarse sand % (0.2–2 mm grade).
FS = fine sand % (0.02–0.2 mm grade).
X = organic carbon %.
ρ_b = bulk density, Mg/m^3.
All % expressed as of fine earth fraction <2 mm.

2.4.2 Soils and water

Only the soil/water relations that affect plant growth are discussed here. The effects of vegetation on the overall soil moisture balance are discussed in Section 3.4.2. The implications of these effects on pore-water pressure and soil suction, and thus on soil strength, are considered in Section 3.6.

Soil water is usually defined in terms of water potential, being the difference between the chemical potential of water in the soil and that of pure free water at the same temperature, elevation and atmospheric pressure (Etherington 1982). Soil water potential is made up of two components:

1. the solute potential, i.e. the osmotic effect of dissolved salts; this is usually very small;
2. the matric potential, a function of the porous soil matrix in which water is held by capillary effects.

The soil water potential is therefore determined mainly by the physical properties of a soil, as shown in Box 2.6. Roots will only take up water when their water potential is less than that of the soil. Different plant species vary considerably in their 'water potential'. Water potential is usually measured in terms of pressure/suction: bars, kN/m^2 (kPa) or head of water. This is sometimes given in units of pF, defined as $pF = \log_{10}$ (negative hydraulic head of water in centimetres). However pF is no longer widely used.

The implications of soil water content as soil suction, or pore-water pressure, on the strength of a soil mass is discussed in Section 3.6. The influence of vegetation on the soil moisture balance, through rainfall interception, evapotranspiration and effects on soil permeability, is discussed in Section 3.4.

The *Available Water Capacity* (AWC) of a soil is the proportion of soil water normally available to plants (*see* Figure 2.12). It is the difference in water content between field capacity, the moisture content remaining when a soil has drained under gravity, and the permanent wilting point, the moisture content at which plants will not normally recover if soil moisture is further reduced. Even in freely draining soils, not all the AWC is readily available to plants and 'easily available water' is considered to be about two thirds of the AWC of a profile. The relationships with soil texture are shown in Figure 2.13, and further data can be obtained from Jarvis and Mackney (1979).

The *Profile Available Water* (PAW) is the total water over the whole soil profile, and represents the quantity of water available for plant growth. The limiting depth for the soil profile in calculating the PAW is frequently and arbitrarily assumed to be 1.0 m, but the maximum rooting depth of the vegetation or the depth to an impermeable horizon is used if either of these is clearly less than 1.0 m. Available water is thus closely related to the depth of root development, and plants are considerably more susceptible to stress through lack of moisture in the early stages of establishment, when the rooting depth is limited.

The *Soil Moisture Deficit* (SMD) is the cumulative reduction in soil moisture content below field capacity as potential evapotranspiration exceeds rainfall over

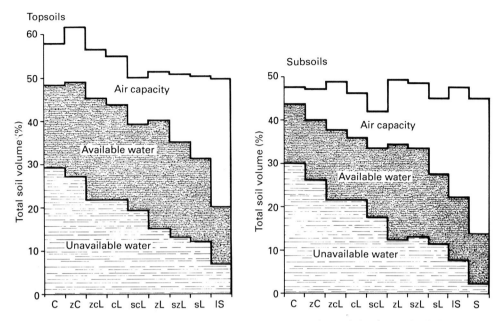

Key: C, clay; zC, silty clay; zcL, silty clay loam; cL, clay loam; scL, sand clay loam; zL, silt loam; szL, sandy silt loam; sL, sandy loam; IS, loamy sand; S, sand

(a) Air capacity and water retention for a range of soil textures

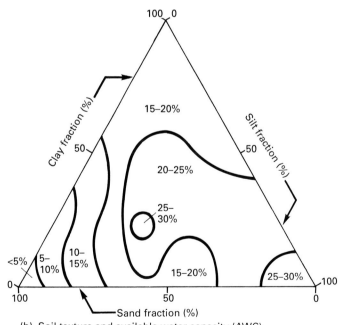

(b) Soil texture and available water capacity (AWC)

Figure 2.13 Relationships between soil texture, available water capacity (AWC) and air capacity (AC) (after Jarvis and Mackney, 1979; Etherington, 1982)

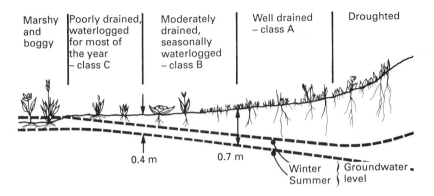

| Marshy and boggy | Poorly drained, waterlogged for most of the year – class C | Moderately drained, seasonally waterlogged – class B | Well drained – class A | Droughted |

Figure 2.14 Typical soil wetness classification

the summer months. SMD is discussed further in Section 3.4.1. Data on rainfall, potential evaporation and soil moisture deficit can be obtained from the Meteorological Office, and from Hall *et al* (1977), Robson and Thomasson (1977) and Bendelow and Hartnup (1980).

Droughtiness is a characteristic derived from the PAW and the potential SMD, the latter being calculated from potential evapotranspiration and rainfall. It is a measure of the likely intensity of moisture stress which a plant will experience. The soil moisture regime is also influenced by the natural drainage and the variation in the groundwater level, particularly the frequency and duration of waterlogging. A typical soil wetness classification is given in Figure 2.14.

2.4.3 Chemical properties of soil

The soil provides the plant with a chemical as well as a physical environment. The parameters used to define the properties are given in Box 2.7. Major chemical factors which affect plant growth are: pH, plant nutrient concentration and supply, and substances in toxic concentrations. The soil properties which determine or modify these are summarised in Box 2.8.

The pH of many soils lies in the range 5.5 to 7.5, though there are soils outside this, more especially at the acidic end. Excess acidity in soils is one of the most frequently encountered problems, especially when dealing with peaty topsoils or mineral soils and spoils which have developed from acidic rocks.

There are three types of acidity in soil: active, reserve and potential. The *active acidity* is simply the free H^+ ion content as determined by the pH measurement of the soil solution. *Reserve acidity,* which is related to the H^+ ions which are stored on the exchange complex of the soil, determines how much the soil resists changes in pH when a neutralising agent such as lime is added. *Potential acidity* is the acid-generating capacity of the soil due to chemical reactions such as the oxidation of pyrite (FeS_2) to form sulphuric acid. Significant potential acidity is a rare

Box 2.7 Soil chemical parameters (definitions relaating to plant growth)

Parameter	Definition	Assessment
pH, (soil reaction)	Measure of soil acidity (pH<7) or soil alkalinity (pH>7)	Direct measurement of soil in water suspension using a pH meter
Conductivity, mmho/cm	Content of soluble salts which can be toxic at high levels	Direct measurement of soil in water suspension using a conductivity meter
Total nutrients (nitrogen, phosphorus, potassium, calcium, magnesium), %	Content of all fractions in the soil, regardless of their availability to plants	Laboratory measurement involving digestion with standard extracting solutions
Available nutrients (phosphorus, potassium, calcium, magnesium), mg/kg (=ppm)	Content of fractions easily available to plants using an extractant of similar chemical extracting power to plant roots	Laboratory measurement involving extraction with standard extracting solutions
Mineralisable nitrogen, mg/kg (=ppm)	The quantity of nitrogen mineralisable to plant-available form by micro-organisms	Incubation of sample for 14 days, then extraction of nitrogen
ADAS Index	System used by the Ministry of Agriculture, Fisheries and Food (Agricultural Development and Advisory Service) for available nutrient level.	Extraction using standard ADAS techniques and reference to tables
Cation exchange capacity meq/100g	Ability of soil minerals to absorb charged ions into the surface of soil particles, which might then be available to plants	Laboratory measurement involving saturation with known ion and then extraction
Pyrite, %	Content of active sulphide (usually iron sulphide) which can oxidise in air to produce sulphuric acid. Applies to subsoils and strata of deep origins when they are exposed by earthworks	Laboratory measurement of 'active' pyrite

Reference for soil chemical analysis: Allen *et al.*, (1974), ADAS (1981)

Box 2.8 Soil chemical characteristics affecting plant growth

Important soil characteristics	Principal determinants				Modifiers			
	Particle size	Clay	Organic matter	Parent material	Fertilisers and manures	Rainfall	Vegetation cover	Time
Nutrients			●	●	○		○	
Ion exchange capacity		●	●				○	○
Fixation capacity				●	○			
Leaching	●		●			○		
pH			●	●	○	○		
Toxicities	●			●	○			○

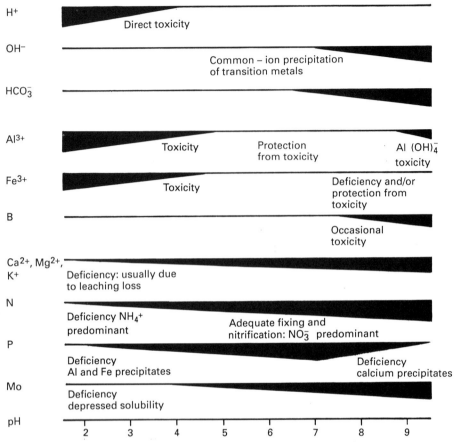

Figure 2.15 Variation in soil properties and availability of nutrient ions with pH (after Etherington, 1982)

occurrence and would normally only be found in sulphide-rich soils derived from certain geological strata, e.g. the coal measures and some sandstones which contain iron pyrites.

Alkalinity in soil depends mainly on the content of calcium and magnesium minerals, mostly as carbonates. Soils derived directly from limestone rocks have a naturally high pH of about 7.5 to 8.2. Spoil materials from some industrial processes can also have a high pH. The main significance of soil pH is that it affects the availability of certain minerals, as shown in Figure 2.15. This applies particularly to the availability of essential mineral elements, such as phosphorus, and potentially toxic ones, such as aluminium.

Plants need nutrients which they absorb from the soil via the roots, as shown in Box 2.9. On infertile soils the addition of nitrogen is usually the most significant element controlling plant growth and productivity, but phosphorus and potassium are also important, together with a range of other minerals needed in smaller quantities. Fertilizing is discussed in Section 4.2.6. Inorganic minerals are taken up

Box 2.9 Mineral nutrients essential for plant growth

Nitrogen (N) Phosphorous (P) Potassium (K)	Major nutrients, essential in substantial quantities
Sulphur (S) Calcium (Ca) Magnesium (Mg) Sodium (Na)	Minor nutrients, required in small quantities
Iron (Fe) Manganese (Mn) Boron (B) Copper (Ca) Zinc (Zn) Molybdenum (Mo)	Trace minerals, required in very small quantities for healthy growth

Note Mineral nutrients are sometimes referred to by their oxide, i.e. Phosphate (P_2O_5), Potash (K_2O), CaO and MgO. Fertilisers are usually given as the proportion (%) by weight of N:P_2O_5:K_2O, eg 20:10:10 contains 20% nitrogen, 10% phosphate (about 4.3% phosphorus) and 10% potash (about 8% potassium).

by plants and subsequently returned to the soil as organic matter when they die. Minerals in this organic matter become available to plants again when they are decomposed by micro-organisms. The last process of this cycle is known as mineralization. In fertile topsoils there is a large amount of organic matter cycling in this way; Figure 2.16 illustrates a typical nutrient cycle and indicates where problems can occur.

The lack of available nutrients in infertile soils such as subsoils and mine spoils results in poor plant productivity and function. Management of these soils so as to encourage the development of a self-sustaining nutrient cycle is vital, and can take several years.

Plant nutrients such as ammonium, potassium and calcium are found as free ions in the soil water, or bound by electrical and chemical bonds to the soil particles. The ability of a soil to yield bound ions is called the *exchange capacity*. As these bound ions are less easily leached than those in solution, the exchange capacity is an important factor in determining the fertility of a soil. The exchange capacity of a soil is largely dependent on its clay or humus content. A coarse-textured soil with a low humus content will therefore have a much lower capacity to store and supply plant nutrients than one with a high humus or clay mineral content.

Toxicity is uncommon in soils unpolluted by man. Some soil strata and spoil materials such as colliery spoil, pulverised fuel ash (PFA) and metalliferous mine wastes can contain elements, mainly metals, which are toxic to plants. Man-made pollution which affects plant growth includes contamination of air, soils and waters with spilt oils and fuels, industrial discharges, landfill leachates, sulphur dioxide and sewage effluent.

One frequently-encountered form of toxicity is due to a high salt content, mainly sodium chloride. This is rare in natural soils in the UK, except around the immediate coastal fringe, but is associated with particular environments, such as

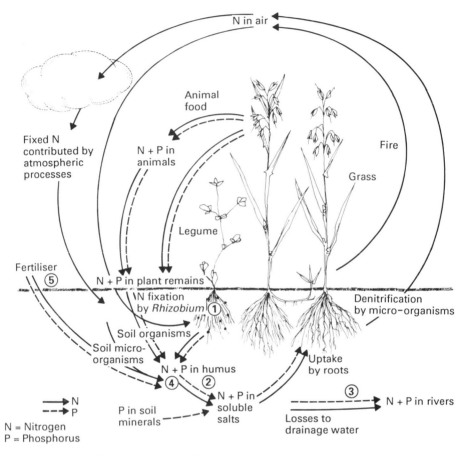

Where problems can occur in the cycle:

1 Nitrogen fixation by *Rhizobium* bacteria in legume roots can be inhibited by low pH or nutrient deficiency. Legumes may not be present in the sward.

2 Release of nutrients in organic matter by micro-organisms may be inhibited by low pH or a high carbon : nitrogen ratio in the organic matter. If release is blocked, humus will accumulate and the minerals become locked up and unavailable.

3 In areas of high rainfall and/or porous soil, many soluble minerals will be quickly leached away.

4 The organic matter/humus store can be very small in 'young' soils, so that the amount of nutrients released by micro-organisms can be almost insignificant.

5 Fertiliser inputs are essential in the early years; this will be the only source of nutrients until the humus fraction has built up sufficiently for natural cycling to be adequate.

Figure 2.16 Typical nutrient cycle for N and P and the problems that can occur in infertile or hostile soils (after Bradshaw and Chadwick, 1980)

roadside verges, and can also result from persistent irrigation. Specialised plants can grow in soils directly affected by salt, and only in very extreme cases is the salt content actually toxic. Salt is easily washed from the soil and so does not persist or accumulate. Salt in spray drift will affect plants at greater distance from the source, scorching leaf growth, and may eventually kill the plant if it is heavy or persistent.

Soil fertility is a complex interaction of all the above factors. Soil nutrients can be provided by using fertilisers or manures but, in the interest of long-term economy, it is necessary for the soil/plant system to be managed so that fertility becomes largely self-sustaining.

2.4.4 Soil horizons

In civil engineering, topsoil is defined as the upper humic part of the soil profile, as shown in Figure 2.17. This is the A horizon, as recognised by the soil scientist, and is not simply a single layer above the subsoil. The process of soil formation gives rise to a number of discrete but integrated horizons, the nature and properties of

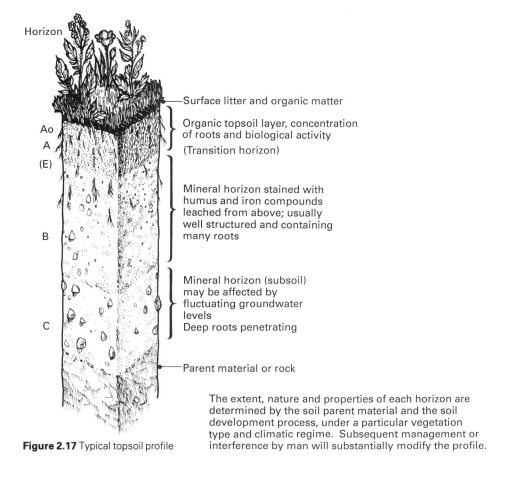

Horizon

Surface litter and organic matter

Ao

Organic topsoil layer, concentration of roots and biological activity

A

(E)

(Transition horizon)

Mineral horizon stained with humus and iron compounds leached from above; usually well structured and containing many roots

B

Mineral horizon (subsoil) may be affected by fluctuating groundwater levels

C

Deep roots penetrating

Parent material or rock

The extent, nature and properties of each horizon are determined by the soil parent material and the soil development process, under a particular vegetation type and climatic regime. Subsequent management or interference by man will substantially modify the profile.

Figure 2.17 Typical topsoil profile

which are determined by the parent material and the development process under a particular vegetation type and climatic regime. The topsoil and subsoil horizons should be examined carefully and described fully in all site appraisals and investigations. Ideally a specialist soil surveyor should advise on the removal, storage and handling of soil as well as on its physical characteristics. This topic is discussed further in Section 4.2.

Many subsoils and mine spoils can support adequate vegetation, and with careful management will eventually become good topsoil material. It is not necessary to specify topsoil as the surface finish in every situation.

2.4.5 Soil potential

The physical, water and chemical characteristics of the soil can be combined into an overall assessment of soil potential for plant growth. A scheme for this is given in Box 2.10.

Box 2.10 Assessment of soil potential

Class A is the highest quality and suitable for situations where good quality fertile topsoil is necessary. However, class C, whilst of poorer quality, would still be suitable for many situations (*see* Section 4.2.1). In many cases it would be possible to modify or manage a class B or C soil to improve its quality.

Parameter	Unit	Suitability class			Unsuitable
		A	B	C	
Soil type					
Texture	description[1] and clay%	fLS,SL SZL,ZL	SCL,CL, ZCL,LS	C<45% SC,ZC,S	C>45%
Stoniness	% vol	<5	5–10	10–15	>15
Available water capacity (at packing density 1.4–1.75)	% vol	>20	15–20	10–15	<10
pH		5.7–7.0	5.2–5.5	4.7–5.5	<4.7
			7.0–7.3	7.3–7.8	>7.8
Conductivity	mmho/cm	<4	4–8	8–10	>10
Pyrite	% weight	–	<0.2	0.2–3.0	>3.0
Soil fertility					
Total nitrogen	% weight	>0.2	0.05–0.2	<0.05	
Total phosphorus	mg/kg	>37	27–37	<27	
Total potash	mg/kg	>360	180–360	<180	
Available phosphorus	mg/kg	>20	14–20	<14	
Available potassium	mg/kg	>185	90–185	<90	

Notes: 1. f = fine, S = sand, C = clay, L = loam, Z = silt

Such a scheme can be used in several ways:

1. to select suitable soil materials for use as a surface covering in which to establish vegetation (*see* Section 4.2.1);
2. to determine how the soil should be placed and cultivated, and, for example, its optimum density requirements;
3. to design a soil profile to suit the site and vegetation required (*see* Section 5.4.1);
4. to predict the potential plant productivity and performance;
5. to establish the necessary management regime needed to maintain the required plant performance and function.

Soil suitability and potential for a range of specific purposes are discussed more fully in Jarvis and Mackney (1979) and other publications on soil use and management (such as Russell, 1973).

2.5 Plants and climate

The climatic factors which affect plant behaviour and performance, comprising growing season, moisture regime, exposure and rainfall seasonality, make up the bioclimate. The main parameters of the bioclimate are summarised in Box 2.11. Bioclimatic classifications are published by the Soil Survey of England and Wales

---

Box 2.11 Bioclimate: parameters and definitions

Rainfall, (mm)	Precipitation recorded on daily basis and compiled monthly, seasonally, yearly or for long-term averages
Potential evapotranspiration, E_t (mm)	Estimated water loss from a grassed surface calculated from records of sunshine, temperature, wind and humidity
Rainfall erosivity, R	Estimate of the power of rainfall to erode soil, based on records of intensity and rainfall energy
Growing season	An estimate of the length and intensity of the growing season, based on the accumulated average daily temperature above 5.6°C
Exposure	Relative elevation and aspect

Bioclimatic factors are estimated from long term meteorological data.

Sources of climatic/bioclimatic data

1) The Meteorological Office produces statistics for rainfall, wind, E_t, soil moisture deficit, temperature, etc., as long term averages or over specific periods for the whole of the UK.
2) The Ministry of Agriculture, Fisheries and Food publishes long term data for agricultural climate and for drainage and irrigation design (Smith, 1976).
3) The Soil Survey of England and Wales (Bendelow and Hartnup, 1980) and The Macaulay Institute for Soil Research in Scotland (Birse and Dry, 1970; Birse and Robertson, 1970; Birse, 1971) publish maps of bioclimatic parameters and maintain detailed climatological records.
4) Standard text books such as Chandler and Gregory (1976).

Box 2.12 Bioclimatic classification of the UK (after Bendelow and Hartnup, 1980; Chandler and Gregory, 1976)

1. Thermal regions

Symbol	Description	Accumulated temperature (day °C >5.6)
A	Moderately cold	825
B	Slightly cold	825–1375
C	Moderately cool	1375–1650
D	Moderately warm	1925

2. Moisture regime

Symbol	Description	Moisture deficit, mm (annual)
1	Moderately wet	<40
2	Slightly wet	40–60
3	Moderately moist	60–100
4	Slightly moist	100–180
5	Slightly dry	>180

3. Rainfall seasonality

Symbol	Description
w	Areas with a rainfall maximum in the winter half of the year
2	Areas in which the maximum is during the second half of the year
s	Areas where there is a slight tendency for a summer rainfall maximum (in the UK mainly East Anglia and Thames Valley)

4. Exposure categories

Symbol	Description	Approximate mean annual wind speed (m/s)	Vegetation effect
m	Unexposed	<4.8	Tree growth moderate to good
p	Exposed	4.8–6.6	Tree growth poor
v	Very exposed	>6.6	Heather very short, trees absent

5. Growing season

A	9 or more months
B	7–8 months
C	5–6 months
D	4 or less months

and the Soil Survey of Scotland, and are given in Box 2.12. The maps give a useful guide to regional conditions.

The overall bioclimate, which can be estimated from local or regional long-term averages, will be considerably modified by local conditions, particularly topography. The effects of slope angle and aspect are outlined in Box 2.13, and other factors such as exposure, summarised in Box 2.14, should be assessed critically on site. As altitude increases, growing seasons are shorter, temperatures lower and rainfall generally higher. Standard altitude adjustments are published for most climatic variables in the UK. Figure 2.18 illustrates a typical average monthly moisture regime for lowland Britain.

Bioclimatic factors can be used to assess the overall site potential for plant growth. A suggested scheme is given in Box 2.15.

Box 2.13 Effect of slope angle and aspect on bioclimate

The effects of aspect, especially at steep slope angles, significantly modify local climate in two important respects:

1) solar radiation input;
2) windspeed and direction, in relation to the local prevailing winds.

These in turn affect the local bioclimate at the ground surface and modify:

1) the beginning, duration and end of the growing season;
2) the potential evapotranspiration and thus soil moisture balance, particularly the intensity of drought;
3) the diurnal temperature fluctuations;
4) exposure.

There are a few empirical studies of some of the effects, but no sufficiently comprehensive models which can be used to predict their likely extent or intensity with respect to the 'normal' data for a horizontal surface. Estimating the effect of local variation of slope is therefore a subjective judgement. Some general guidelines are given below.

Season	Southerly aspects*	Northerly aspects*
Winter	Wide range of diurnal temperature variations with regular freeze-thaw cycles	Narrow range of diurnal temperatures stays frozen/cold. Snow cover protects vegetation from exposure
Spring	Rapid warming of soil, early start to growing season. Early spells with soil moisture deficit (SMD)	Delayed growing season but very rare to experience SMD
Summer	Extreme surface temperatures and very high SMD for extended periods	Moderate surface temperatures, may avoid prolonged SMDs
Autumn	Growing season extends into cooler months. SMD takes longer to be reduced by rainfall	Early end to growing season, early end to SMD

Seasonal prevailing wind conditions should also be taken into account.
The angle of south facing slope receiving maximum solar radiation input:

Winter	75° from horizontal
Spring/autumn	55° from horizontal
Summer	30° from horizontal

* The effect of other aspects will be intermediate between north and south

An important link between the climatic elements of temperature and rainfall and plant performance is provided by transpiration. This is the vital process by which moisture and nutrients are transferred upwards from the soil to the aerial parts of the plant, and its rate is dependent on the rate at which water evaporates from plant surfaces. The pattern of evaporation of water throughout the year is a characteristic of a climate, but plants can to some extent control the rate at which water evaporates from their surfaces, and thus the combination of transpiration and evaporation has an important bearing on plant physiology.

Plant survival depends on an adequate water supply and, where new vegetation is to be established, the expected water requirement may have to be considered in order to assess the water input required to balance the evapotranspiration that will occur. Evapotranspiration is discussed in greater detail in Section 3.4.

Box 2.14 Exposure: local assessment (after Miller, 1985)

The degree of exposure is a relative factor, and can be assessed subjectively on a simple scale (as in the exposure categories of the bioclimatic classification, Box 2.12). A more objective assessment can be based on the TOPEX score, determined as follows.

Topography factor Measure the angle of inclination to the horizon at the eight major compass points. Add together those where inclination is above horizontal, and subtract those below.

Windiness factor Wind zone scores are given for each wind zone in the UK.

Wind zone	A	B	C	D	E	F	G
Score	13	11	9.5	7.5	2.5	0.5	0

Elevation factor

>540 m	score 10	315–360 m	score 6	191–225 m	score 2
466–540	9	286–315	5	141–190	1
406–465	8	256–285	4	61–140	0.5
361–405	7	226–255	3	60	0

Sum the scores for the three factors to give a total TOPEX score from which the exposure category is determined:

	TOPEX
1) Severely exposed	10
2) Very exposed	11–30
3) Moderately exposed	31–60
4) Moderately sheltered	61–100
5) Very sheltered	>100

Wind zones in Britain

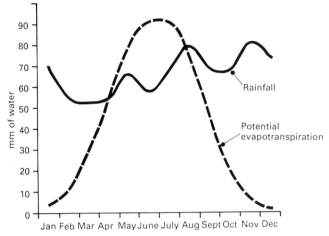

(a) Data for northwest England

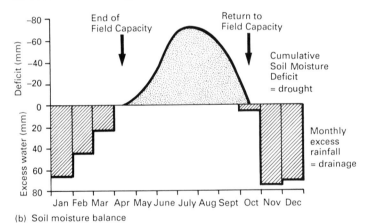

(b) Soil moisture balance

Figure 2.18 Typical average monthly moisture data

Box 2.15 Site assessment of bioclimatic potential for plant growth

	Classes[1]				
Factor	1	2	3	4	5
Thermal region[2]	E	D	C	B	A
Moisture regime[2]	2	2	3	4	5,1.
Growing season[2]	A,B	B	B/C	C	D
Exposure, TOPEX[3]	5	4	3	2	1

1. The classes range from 1 = best, most favourable
        to   5 = worst, least favourable.
    The overall class appropriate to any site should be based on an interpolation/average of the classes for each factor.
2. Classification given in Box 2.12.
3. Classification given in Box 2.14.

2.6 Plant propagation

Plants reproduce by two mechanisms:

1. seed production;
2. vegetatively, for example by runners, suckers or buds.

Many species use both methods to varying extents, depending on their strategies for dealing with stress and disturbance (*see* Section 2.2.4). Man has adapted both reproductive mechanisms to his own use, and has added a few others, including the taking of cuttings, layering and tissue culture. There are three widely used techniques of propagation appropriate for engineering and landscaping: direct sowing, planting nursery-raised plants and planting cuttings. The latter two techniques are generally used for trees and shrubs. In each of these cases the establishment period is critical because the individual plant is at risk from many sources, such as drought, predation and damage.

2.6.1 Seeding

Plants vary in their seed production strategies. Some, such as many grasses, produce a large quantity of very small seeds, each of which has only a small food supply. Small-seeded plants are often susceptible to desiccation early in establishment. Others, for example some trees, produce a smaller quantity of large seeds, each with a fairly large food-store. Establishment of large-seeded plants is often good but the seeds themselves can be subject to predation.

The establishment phase has three stages:

1. A period for the dormancy to break. This may simply involve the seed absorbing sufficient water for metabolism to begin. Many plants have elaborate dormancy mechanisms, however, including a requirement for a cold period and periods of either light or dark.
2. Germination of the seed, where the seed coat splits and the young root emerges and penetrates the soil. Adequate moisture is essential for good germination.
3. Establishment of the young plant in a favourable environment.

Moisture is the most critical factor during these stages. If the seed is unprotected, the chances of its drying out before the root grows to sufficient depth in the soil are quite high. Protection can be provided by covering the seed with a mulch or a thin soil layer, or by preparing a roughened surface so that the seed falls down a crack or crevice where establishment conditions are likely to be favourable.

2.6.2 Planting

A plant which is transplanted will inevitably suffer disruption of its root system. Different types of root systems (*see* Section 2.1.5) respond differently to transplanting. Fine fibrous roots are easily damaged and can quickly dry out when exposed to the atmosphere. Root regeneration can therefore be slow if transplanting is not carried out carefully. Large fleshy roots are more resistant to desiccation and therefore regenerate more readily. If a root system is severely damaged, such as the taproot being severed, it may remain stunted, and the plant suffers accordingly. As a general rule, the younger that a plant is transplanted, the more successful the root system.

The availability of water in the period immediately after planting is critical. The material into which a tree or plant is planted must allow water to move freely and must have sufficient moisture-holding capacity.

2.7 Reliability and variation

Reliability and variation in vegetation growth and persistence are factors which will be of particular interest to engineers considering its use in permanent works. The topics should be considered from two standpoints:

1. reliability and variability in plant material;
2. reliability and variation in site conditions.

Vegetation is a living material and is subject to natural inherent variability and sensitivity to environmental changes. Nevertheless, enough is known about plants and plant behaviour in almost any given set of circumstances to enable reasonably reliable predictions of performance to be made. Furthermore, if these circumstances change as a result of natural events or human interference, it is quite possible to predict in general terms what the consequences of these changes for the vegetation are likely to be.

Individual plants may have a finite life but plant communities can last indefinitely if they are in equilibrium with their environment. This applies both to natural communities, such as ancient woodland, and man-made types, such as coppiced woodland or permanent pasture. Change or unreliability occurs as a result of changing circumstances or very occasional natural catastrophes.

Difficulties can arise when vegetation has to be established, or re-established on bare soil, and it is at this point that experience and knowledge in agricultural systems differs from that in construction. The most important and fundamental requirement in any system based on vegetation is to understand the soil/plant relationships. A farmer achieves this by long experience of working in a particular location and an appreciation of the limitations imposed by external factors such as climate. Failure in this respect was found to be the underlying cause for problems experienced in Wales in establishing vegetation as part of road improvement schemes. The Welsh Office Highways Directorate undertook a study of vegetation failures on highway margins, as summarised in Box 2.16, and concluded that, given the site conditions, the poor performance by the vegetation was predictable, and that the seed mixtures sown had little opportunity of doing any better.

Left to its own devices, the species composition of a plant community will be subject to changes due to natural weather cycles, or to randomly occurring events which cause specific damage. The extent and effect of these changes, which are

Box 2.16 Vegetating unstable and unsightly slopes on highway margins

The Welsh Office Highways Directorate has studied the role and performance of vegetation in providing shallow-seated stability and preventing erosion on highway margins in Wales. The study was prompted by the seemingly poor performance of vegetation in many areas, which contributed to the creation of landscape scars and a maintenance burden due to the continual slippage of material.

The study was in two parts:

1. Characterisation of the physical, chemical and biological attributes of slopes with a history of poor vegetation cover and erosion problems.
2. Investigation of species, seed mixtures and methods of treating these slopes to overcome the problems.

Interim results indicate that:

1. Interaction between geology, climate and design are important in determining the type of vegetation which develops on slopes.
2. Acidity of the soil and altitude of a site are important in determining species survival.
3. Of the seed mixtures sown on the sites surveyed, the only component found some years after sowing was Red Fescue, indicating that a better match is required between site conditions and plant selection.
4. Vegetation cover is directly related to the proportion of material smaller than 2 mm in the soil. Ways of increasing this fraction within the soil or of mimicking its properties, such as water retention, could ensure greater success in establishment. The retention of weathered material would be improved by creating benching or ledges, or by using geotextiles and mulches.
5. Uncontrolled grazing had an adverse effect on vegetation establishment and growth.
6. The active erosion zones which tend to form at the junction between man-made and natural slopes can be removed successfully by reprofiling, as shown in Plate 2.D.

Plate 2D Trial of vegetative slope stabilisation on a highway cutting. Experimental panels in the foreground, with a typical untreated slope in the background. Sheep have been introduced into the lower half of the trial to assess the effect of grazing

discussed below, are bound to influence the performance of vegetation but, with the right vegetation established in the right place and maintained in an appropriate manner, these uncertainties can be reduced in number and degree.

2.7.1 Natural cycles

The performance of vegetation over a number of years and through climatic cycles can be affected by extremes of climate. A sequence of cold winters, or late starts to the growing season, may reduce the frequency of some species in a plant community, allowing others to increase. Similarly a sequence of drought years will affect the rooting pattern and establishment success of some species, as shown in Figure 2.19. Both cold and drought affect growth and this will be important where

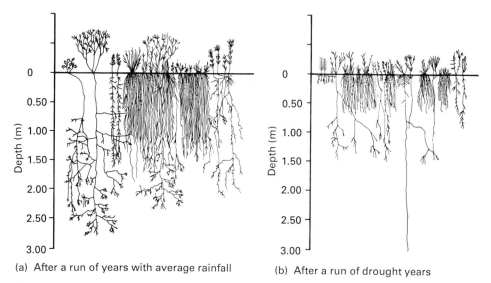

(a) After a run of years with average rainfall   (b) After a run of drought years

Figure 2.19 Root systems of a typical short-grass/herb sward showing variation in depth and density resulting from natural climatic cycles (after Russell, 1973)

tolerance to wear and good repair capacity are important. It is difficult to predict when these cycles will occur and how severe they will be. Meteorological data will give some indication of the spread of climatic variables around the mean values, and an indication of the likely range of conditions to be expected.

2.7.2 Damage

The most common causes of lasting damage to a vegetation cover which may affect its reliability are: extremes of climate, wear, fire, windthrow of larger trees, grazing by stock or wild herbivores, vandalism, pollution, and natural causes (old age, disease). In any application of vegetation, it is prudent to consider the likely impact of its complete removal, whether this is by accident or design. Box 2.17 summarises

Box 2.17 Specific risks of damage to vegetation cover

Cause	Prediction of risk	Protection measures
Windloading	Windthrow hazard assessment, involving consideration of windiness, exposure, soil type and available rooting depth	Deep drainage to lower water table and encourage deeper rooting Avoid exposed plantation edges; dense stands of trees give mutual protection
Fire	Combustibility of vegetation, especially during the dry season. Resinous plants such as evergreens are generally more combustible	Encourage rapid superficial burn in which roots and stumps are left unaffected to regrow and sprout again Limit area which can burn by splitting up with discontinuities, e.g. rides or unvegetated strips Plant proportions of species with green, low combustible foliage Consult the fire brigade
Grazing and browsing (stock or wild herbivores)	Adjacent land used for grazing stock Suitability of habitat for wild animals e.g. rabbits, deer	Protective fencing, regularly maintained Use plants unpalatable to stock Pest control
Natural causes	Life expectancy of plants Disease resistance	Management to encourage natural regeneration Disease control (e.g. fungicides, insecticides) for specific outbreaks Avoid monoculture of species and age classes as far as possible
Climatic extremes (wet, drought)	Meteorological records Specific site factors which modify general climate, e.g. aspect, frost pockets	Avoid sensitive species especially in monocultures, use those with known high tolerance of specific conditions Provide shelter from adjacent structures or planting Mulching
Wear	Type and intensity of use Proximity to heavily trafficked areas	Fencing to exclude use Increase soil fertility to encourage vigorous growth and regeneration Reinforce soil surface Use wear-tolerant species
Vandalism	Proximity to urban areas Accessibility to areas of public access	Secure fencing Vigilance and regular maintenance
Pollution	Testing of soil, water, air for toxic chemicals Proximity to potential sources, e.g. salt water spray at coast and verges on roads subject to salting	Tolerant species

the possible approaches to assessing the risk of damage occurring, and the measures which can be adopted for protection.

Climatic extremes may eliminate species that are at the limit of their tolerance range. The effects are more marked in monocultures and less so in a diverse plant community where a wide range of species gives resilience.

The most common causes of *wear* on vegetation are excessive trampling by humans or animals, and vehicle pressure. Wear affects plant productivity and species composition, and causes the soil to become heavily compacted and nutrient and moisture regimes to change (*see* Section 6.7). This modifies the engineering properties of the vegetation and, in some cases, causes loss of vegetation and initiates erosion.

The extent of damage caused by *fire* depends on its temperature and frequency. Fire temperature is affected by moisture conditions, the extent to which litter has accumulated on the surface, and vegetation type. Hot fires can kill off roots and underground regenerative parts. On the other hand, plants with growing points at or near ground level, or which can regrow from roots, can to some extent withstand fire.

Some types of vegetation are managed by regular burning, to ensure a cycle of regeneration and to maintain a sub-climax by eliminating young shrubs and trees (*see* Section 2.2.3). Specific examples of this are heathland and grassland. Burning is carried out at a time of year when the top growth is fairly dry, but the ground is damp enough to prevent deep burning. It used to be a regular occurrence on railway embankments in the UK during the days of steam trains. Railway engineers favoured a grass vegetation cover with a dense growth which burned very quickly and superficially, allowing the sward to regenerate. Lineside vegetation now has a much greater proportion of woody species.

Wind loading is the pressure applied by the flow of air on the above-ground parts of vegetation. It affects larger trees with shallow root systems and may uproot them. Plantations with new edges exposed by felling, for example to accommodate a road or pipeline, present particular problems, since the trees have not naturally developed a root system comparable with that of the original edge trees to resist the stresses involved. However, a single tree blowing over in an otherwise dense stand is not usually a cause for concern. The destabilising effect of windloading on trees sufficient to trigger slumping of the soil is more important (*see* Section 3.5.5).

Grazing can fundamentally affect the growth and development of a herbaceous sward (*see* Figure 2.7). Whether a particular level of grazing constitutes damage or not depends on what form of vegetation is required. Overgrazing will seriously affect a sward, increasing the amount of bare ground and dramatically reducing root growth, as shown in Plate 2.E. On the other hand, some occasional or regular grazing generally stimulates the ground-level density of a sward. The management of grass swards by grazing is discussed in Section 4.7.2.

Sheep, goats and deer will strip bark from trees, especially young or newly planted ones. Voles, mice, hares and rabbits can also cause extensive damage when present in large numbers. A tree can usually recover from a certain amount of this type of damage, unless the bark has been stripped completely around the main stem.

Vandalism can be a serious problem, especially in urban areas. Physical damage can include breaking stems from trees, pulling up turf and allowing stock to enter by breaking fences.

Plate 2E The effect of overgrazing by sheep on a steep slope; the sward is almost completely denuded

Pollution may affect specific localised areas as a result of spillages or effluent containing toxic materials. Rivers with poor water quality, due to agricultural pollution, storm sewage overflows or industrial effluent, may only be able to support limited bankside vegetation. Salt pollution occurs immediately adjacent to roads, salt-laden water being splashed onto the verges by passing vehicles. Where it is a regular feature of the environment, salt-tolerant plant species need to be selected (Colwill *et al*, 1982).

Natural causes include a whole range of effects such as old age, disease and pests. Old trees are more likely to be windthrown than young ones. Disease and pests can strike unpredictably, though the risk of severe damage is greatest in old age and in monocultures. Most diseases and pests are species specific, such as Dutch elm disease. Fungal diseases can cause significant damage in grassed areas, especially in mixtures with a limited range of species or cultivars. A high diversity will help to overcome the problems. Highly-bred, artificial varieties tend to be much more susceptible to disease than wild types. Disease infection is often a secondary effect following physical damage such as frost or insect attack, or resulting from poor plant health due to nutrient deficiency.

3 Physical effects of vegetation

3.1 Role of vegetation

Vegetation can provide a protective cover or boundary between the atmosphere and the soil, the major effects being hydrological and mechanical, as shown in Figure 3.1. Vegetation influences the way in which water is transferred from the atmosphere to the soil, groundwater and surface drainage systems. In affecting the volume and rate of flow along different routes, vegetation influences the process and the extent of erosion. It also modifies the moisture content of the soil and thus

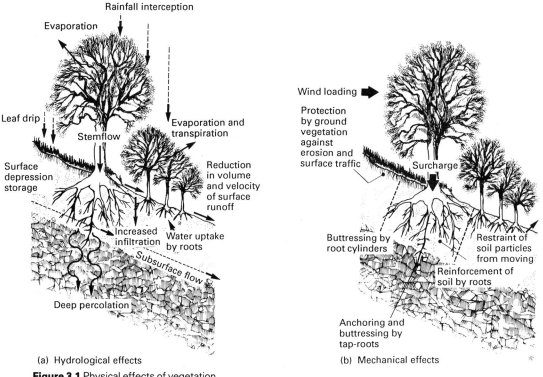

(a) Hydrological effects

(b) Mechanical effects

Figure 3.1 Physical effects of vegetation

its strength. Mechanically, vegetation increases the strength and competence of the soil in which it is growing and therefore contributes to its stability.

The importance of a vegetative cover is demonstrated by the effect of its removal. In the year following clearance of a forest cover for timber or agriculture, soil erosion and landslides increase dramatically because of the removal of the protective layer to the ground surface. Regrowth of the vegetative cover causes erosion rates to decline in subsequent years, but this trend is frequently offset some five to seven years later by a rapid rise in soil loss due to mass failure of the soil as the old roots rot away. Examples such as this illustrate the importance of recognising that existing vegetation may already be playing a major engineering role. Failure to appreciate this can result in unforeseen and often disastrous consequences if the vegetation is removed. The engineering effects of vegetation must be considered not only when proposals are being made for its establishment, but also when policies for the management of vegetated areas or for the clearance of vegetation are being assessed.

In order to explain its engineering effects, it is necessary to understand how vegetation interacts with the soil, the soil/water regime and the flow of water and air over the soil surface. This Section describes the physical principles that are involved and concludes with a summary of the salient vegetation properties which are utilised in the applications described in Section 6.

3.2 Modification of surface water regime

3.2.1 Rainfall interception

Vegetation intercepts a proportion of the incoming rainfall, part of which is stored on the leaves and stems of the plants and is returned to the atmosphere by evaporation. Thus interception decreases the rate and volume of rainfall reaching the ground surface. Interception varies from 100% of light rainfall to only 25% in high intensity storms, as shown in Table 3.1. Expressed over a year, however, interception can amount to 30% of the annual rainfall with tree covers.

Rain reaches the ground underneath a vegetation cover in three forms:

1. direct throughfall, that which passes through gaps in the leaves and between the plants;
2. stemflow, that running down the stems or trunks of the vegetation;
3. leaf-drip.

Leaf drip comprises raindrops that are shattered into small droplets (<1 mm) immediately they strike the vegetation, and drops formed by the temporary storage and coalescence of raindrops on the leaf and stem surfaces, which fall to the ground as large drops (>5 mm).

Concentrations of water from leaf-drip points and from stemflow can result in very high localised rainfall intensities beneath trees and bushes. Intensities may be ten times greater than those of the rainfall received at the canopy (Armstrong and Mitchell, 1987). Grassed surfaces, in contrast, produce a more uniform pattern of rainfall distribution at the ground surface.

Table 3.1 Interception and storage of rainfall by different vegetation types

1) Interception storage capacity for some grass species

Species	Storage (mm)
Big bluestem (*Andropogon gerardi*) dense stand, 0.6 m tall	2.34
Buffalo grass (*Buchloe dactyloides*) 0.3 m high, many stolons	1.65
Meadow grass (*Poa pratensis*) at maximum development	1.02
Annual ryegrass (*Lolium multiflorum*) at various growth stages	0.43–2.81
Tall wheatgrass (*Agropyron elongatum*) at various growth stages	0.25–5.08

(After Branson, Gifford and Owen, 1972)

2) Interception as a percentage of annual rainfall

Forms of vegetation	% interception
Forests: northern hardwood	10–15
temperate broad-leaved	15–25
temperate coniferous	25–35
tropical	25–30
Grass	25–40
Maize	25
Cereals (wheat, oats, barley)	20–25

3.2.2 Surface water runoff

Runoff volume

As a result of a combination of surface roughness, infiltration and interception, surface water runoff from vegetated areas is much less than that from bare soil. Runoff is typically 10–20% of the rainfall received on small watersheds covered with trees or grass, but rises to 30–40% under cultivation and 60–70% for urban development. Changing land use from forest or dense grass to a more open cover results in higher runoff volumes and a more rapid runoff response, giving shorter time to peak and a higher peak flow, as shown in Figure 3.2. The ability of vegetation to reduce runoff volume may be offset, however, by local increases in rainfall volume supplied to the ground surface as stemflow (*see* Section 3.2.1). Where this concentration of supply exceeds the local infiltration capacity of the soil, stemflow may generate runoff. This effect is especially marked with plants where many branches meet at one point on the main stem.

Runoff velocity

Vegetation reduces the velocity of runoff because of roughness presented to the flow by the stems and leaves of the plants. In hydraulic terms, roughness is characterised by a parameter such as Manning's n (average velocity of flow, $v = (R^{2/3} S^{1/2})/n$, where R is the hydraulic radius and S is the slope of the channel or

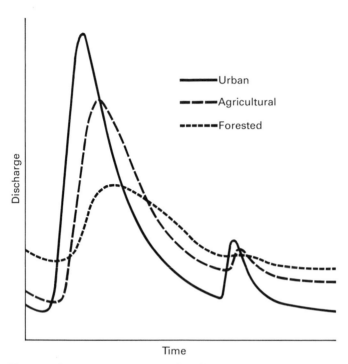

Figure 3.2 Storm runoff hydrographs for different land cover types

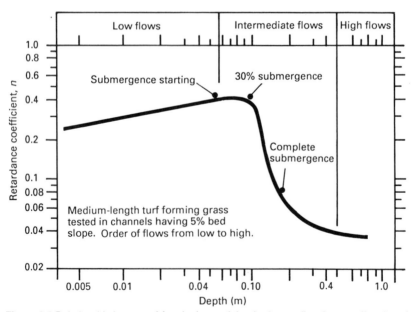

Figure 3.3 Relationship between Manning's *n* and depth of water flow for a medium length grass (after Ree, 1949)

ground). The hydraulic roughness and hence flow retardance depends upon the morphology of the plant and its density of growth, as well as the height of the vegetation in relation to the depth of flow. Plant forms are discussed in Section 2.1.

Considering flow in a grassed waterway, as shown in Figure 3.3, when the flow depth is shallow compared with the height of the vegetation, the vegetation stands relatively rigid and imparts a high degree of roughness (characterised by n values of about 0.25 to 0.30), associated with interference with and internal distortion of the flow by the action of individual plant stems. As flow depth increases, the grass stems begin to oscillate, disturbing the flow so that n values rise to around 0.4 and flow velocity is further retarded. When flow depth begins to submerge the vegetation, Manning's n values decline rapidly by as much as an order of magnitude. This is because the vegetation begins to be laid down by the flow, so that retardance is mainly due to skin resistance rather than interference, and is consequently considerably less.

Theoretically, retardance can be viewed as comprising the effects of both the soil surface and the vegetation cover. In practice, however, the n values for bare soil and for short grass vegetation are rather similar, at about 0.02 to 0.03. This implies that this level of grass cover exerts the same effect on the flow as the soil roughness in an unvegetated channel, and that as the vegetation grows its effect replaces rather than adds to that of the soil. With taller grasses, retardance increases. Grass covers can be classified by their length into retardance categories, for which curves relating Manning's n values to a discharge intensity parameter (i.e. discharge per unit width or the product of velocity and channel hydraulic radius) have been determined, as illustrated in Figure 3.4.

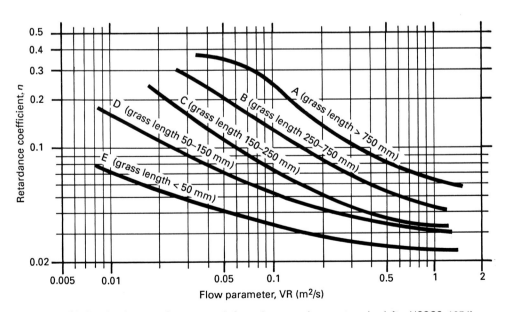

Figure 3.4 Frictional resistance of grass swards for various retardance categories (after USSCS, 1954)

The Manning's n values developed for channels cannot necessarily be applied to overland flow, where discharge intensity is considerably lower. The high magnitude of the roughness in relation to the shallow depths of flow means that the vegetation is rarely submerged. Values of n for shallow overland flows may be an order of magnitude higher than those for channels (Morgan, 1980).

3.2.3 Infiltration

Vegetation increases the permeability and infiltration of the upper soil layers due to:

1. roots;
2. pipes or holes where roots have decayed;
3. increased surface roughness;
4. lower densities and better structure of surface soils.

These effects can give rise to increased rates of infiltration by means of both rainfall and overland flow into a soil, thus potentially increasing the moisture content above that of unvegetated areas. However, the effects are generally offset by increases in interception, transpiration and slope angle. The relations between infiltration rate and ground cover, rainfall intensity and slope gradients are shown in Figure 3.5. Permeability testing within the root zone is necessary to quantify infiltration effects on specific sites, particularly where infiltration may be increased by soil cracking (*see* Section 3.4.5) or decreased by surface crust formation under the action of intense rainfall and surface evaporation.

3.2.4 Subsurface drainage

Subsurface water flow occurs on sloping ground within the superficial litter and upper layers of soil containing a dense mat of roots running parallel to the surface. Subsurface flows can be as much as 80% of the total slope drainage under trees with a thick humus layer. The horizontal permeability of the upper layers of well-vegetated soils is often greater than the vertical permeability. Shallow subsurface flow thus diverts infiltrated water so that, although infiltration on vegetated soils is greater than on unvegetated ones, the depth of infiltration may well be quite shallow.

3.3 Surface protection

3.3.1 Raindrop impact

Vegetation can be extremely effective in preventing the breakdown of soil aggregates and their detachment from the soil mass by raindrop impact. In this way it can help maintain soil infiltration rates (*see* Section 3.2.3) by preventing surface crusting. The extent to which the soil surface is protected depends upon the height, percentage area and characteristics of the vegetation canopy.

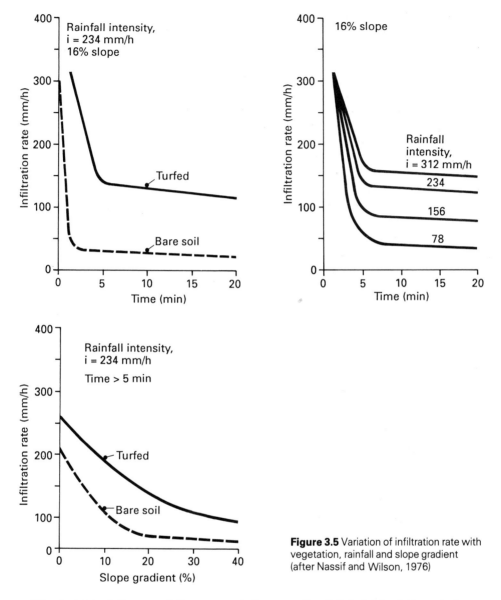

Figure 3.5 Variation of infiltration rate with vegetation, rainfall and slope gradient (after Nassif and Wilson, 1976)

The height of the vegetation cover influences the fall height of the raindrops intercepted and then released by the canopy as leaf drip (*see* Section 3.2.1). This affects their fall velocity at impact and therefore their energy for detaching soil particles. Vegetation on the ground surface or with a low-growing canopy generally results in low impact velocities but, with tall canopies, the drops may regain their terminal velocities before reaching the ground. The proportion of vegetation cover determines the amount of ground shielded by vegetation from direct rainfall impact. Maximum protection is given by covers of 70% or more.

Canopy characteristics affect the role of vegetation in soil protection in two ways. Firstly, large broad leaves allow more storage of rainfall. This decreases the amount of potentially erosive rainfall that reaches the soil during the rain event. Second, interception by the canopy changes the drop size distribution (*see* Section 3.2.1) and energy of the rain. Large broad leaves cause intercepted raindrops to coalesce before they fall to the ground as leaf drips. If these drops fall from canopies less than 0.5 m in height there is no significant increase in soil detachment, as the drops do not gain sufficient velocity in descent. If the drops fall from taller canopies, however, they have been observed to cause more detachment than would occur on the bare soil without a plant canopy. Leaf drips, 5–6 mm in diameter, falling from only 1 m, have greater momentum and are capable of thus detaching more soil than 2–3 mm drops at terminal velocity in natural rainfall (Finney, 1984).

Different vegetation types afford different levels of soil protection against detachment by raindrop impacts. In Figure 3.6, protection is expressed by a soil loss ratio, i.e. the ratio of soil loss under a given vegetation cover to that from bare, loosely-tilled soil. If the vegetation canopy is close to the ground, as with a grass or low shrub cover, the soil loss ratio decreases exponentially with increasing

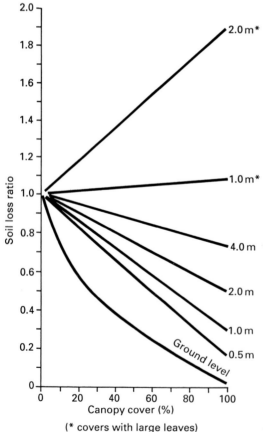

Figure 3.6 Soil loss ratio for soil detatchment by raindrop impact against percentage vegetation cover for different canopy heights (after Rickson and Morgan, 1988)

percentage cover. If the vegetation canopy is about 0.5 m tall, the soil loss ratio decreases linearly with increasing percentage cover. For taller canopies, the soil loss ratio varies linearly with percentage cover, in a manner depending upon canopy height and whether the vegetation generates large leaf drips. If none or only small leaf drips are produced, the soil loss ratio still decreases with increasing vegetation cover. If large erosive leaf drips are formed, the soil loss ratio increases with cover and, for 2 m-tall canopies with 90–100% cover, may be double that on bare ground.

Vegetation litter, i.e. dead plant remains on the soil surface, protects soil from raindrop impact, and the soil loss ratio decreases exponentially with increasing percentage litter cover in the same way as with increasing ground cover. The presence of surface litter may reduce detachment by 93% relative to a bare soil beneath tall tree canopies, which would otherwise be associated with high detachment rates (Wiersum, 1985).

3.3.2 Surface water erosion

The passage of water across a bare soil surface may entrain and transport particles already detached and, particularly if the flow is channelled, may also detach further soil particles. Vegetation can limit the capacity of flowing water to detach soil particles and transport sediment, both through its retardance effects on runoff volume and velocity, and through the physical protection of the soil surface from flowing water. The soil loss ratio (*see* Section 3.3.1) decreases exponentially with increasing percentage vegetation cover as a result of these effects. This can be demonstrated by taking data on runoff coefficients for different land uses, expressing them as a proportion of the value for bare soil, and constructing the curve shown in Figure 3.7, assuming that soil loss varies directly with the volume of

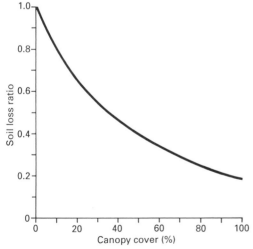

Figure 3.7 Change in soil loss ratio due to reduction in runoff volume as a function of increasing percentage vegetation cover (after Rickson and Morgan, 1988)

runoff. In practice it varies with runoff raised by a power of between 0.67 and 1.7 in value.

The detaching power of flowing water, and its transport capacity, vary exponentially with the mean flow velocity. Reductions in runoff velocity therefore have a considerable effect on erosion. For very shallow flows at low Reynolds numbers such as unchannelled runoff on slopes, the sediment transport capacity can be shown theoretically to vary with Manning's n raised by a power of -0.15 (Morgan, 1980). For bare soil (a soil loss ratio of 1.0), it can be assumed that n is equal to 0.01 which gives $n^{-0.15}$ of 1.99. By calculating $n^{-0.15}$ values for different values of n and expressing these as a proportion of the value for bare soil, it can be shown that the soil loss ratio falls rapidly as roughness, n, is increased from 0.01 to 0.05 but that further increases have little additional effect. This is illustrated in Figure 3.8.

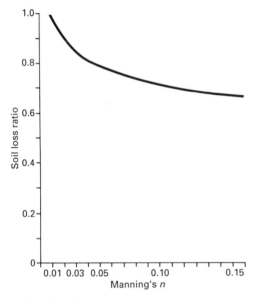

Figure 3.8 Change in soil loss ratio due to reduction in water flow velocity as a function of Manning's n for shallow unchannelled flows (after Rickson and Morgan, 1988)

Local variations in vegetation cover can locally increase the erosive capacity of surface water flow, due both to local increases in velocity and to form drag. When the flow separates around a clump of vegetation, the pressure (normal stress) is larger on the upstream face than it is downstream, as shown in Figure 3.9, and eddying and turbulence occur immediately downstream of the vegetation. This can result in vortex erosion up-slope and down-slope of the vegetation. Where vegetation is patchy, as with tussocky grasses, the erosion potential is increased due to all these effects. The combined effect may be sufficient to match the erosive power of overland flow on an unvegetated surface of the same slope (De Ploey et al, 1976). A dense uniform vegetation cover of grass or shrubs will not only reduce erosion by retarding flow but will also increase the deposition of sediment being carried in the flow. The denser the vegetation, the more sediment can be trapped and removed from the flow.

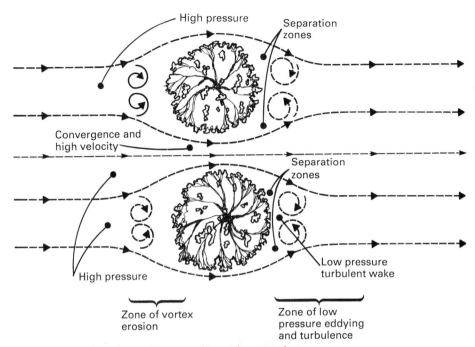

Figure 3.9 Plan view of water flow around tussocky vegetation

For deeper channel flows at turbulent Reynolds numbers, vegetation interacts with the flow processes to protect the soil from erosion in two main ways. Firstly, at low discharge intensity, the high retardance associated with the vegetation standing rigid and unsubmerged (*see* Section 3.2.2; Figure 3.3) reduces velocity below that required for soil particle entrainment. Secondly, at higher discharge intensity, the submerged vegetation bends downstream as a flattened plant layer which, although having low retardance, protects the soil from erosion. While it is common in sediment transport theory to express the soil entrainment relations in terms of shear stress, there are practical disadvantages in doing so due to the significant effects of internal flow patterns and soil cohesion on soil erosion. For vegetated surfaces the present understanding of critical shear stresses for erosion applies only to non-cohesive soil and is not well developed for cohesive soils. Channel design is normally based on the concept of a maximum allowable velocity at which erosion by scour either will not take place or is kept to acceptable levels. Values for maximum allowable velocity are based on flume experiments and engineering experience; they depend on soil, channel slope and vegetation cover, as shown in Table 3.2. Adjustments for varying flow durations are considered in Section 6.4.3.

Maximum allowable velocities are only valid for uniform cover, where the roughness imparted to the flow by the vegetation is due to skin friction or internal distortion resistance. The presence of clumps of vegetation or tufted grasses in a vegetated channel can result in high local flow drag and rapid localised erosion.

Table 3.2 Maximum allowable flow velocities in vegetated channels

Cover expected after two seasons	Maximum flow velocity (m/s)		
	Channel gradient, (%)		
	0.5	5–10	>10
1. Easily eroded soils (sands, sandy loams, silt loams, silts, loamy sands)			
Very good cover (100%) of creeping grasses	1.8	1.5	1.2
Good cover (88%)	1.5	1.2	0.9
Moderate cover (30%)	0.8	NR	NR
2. Erosion resistant soils (clay loams, clays)			
Very good cover (100%)	2.4	2.1	1.8
Good cover (88%)	2.1	1.8	1.5
Moderate cover (30%)	1.1	NR	NR

(After Temple, 1982; Gregory and McCarty, 1986)

NR – not recommended
The maximum allowable velocities are permissible on slopes up to 20% provided the vegetation cover exceeds 70%; otherwise they should not be used on slopes above 10%. For steeper slopes, see Hewlett *et al.* (1987).
Duration effects not stated; for discussion on duration of flow, see Section 6.4.3.

3.3.3 Mechanical role

Vegetation protects the soil mechanically by directly absorbing the impact of human and animal feet and wheels of vehicles. This effect can be demonstrated by considering the ability of the vegetation to withstand damage due to walking. Compression of the vegetation occurs in the early part of each step taken by a walker and results from the action of the heel. Shearing occurs at the end of each step and is associated with the toe. It is the shearing action which creates the most damage. The resistance of vegetation to wear depends on the tensile strength of the stems, leaves and branches above-ground; the strength of the composite soil-root mat below-ground; and the rate of recovery of the individual plants. Species composition and climate are therefore critical factors. Few studies have been made of the strength of vegetation in the sense of an engineering material, however, and therefore knowledge of the extent to which different vegetation types can absorb the impact of humans or machinery before tensile failure is largely empirical.

The long-term ability of vegetation to withstand impacts also depends upon the position of its buds or growth points. Those buds that are on or below the ground surface, as with grasses, have some protection against damage (*see* Section 2.1.3). Shrubby species therefore disappear more rapidly than do grasses under impact from traffic. Fragile mountain plant swards can withstand little traffic and take many years to recover from damage (Liddle, 1973). For this reason, walkers must often be restricted to designated paths in high mountain environments.

3.3.4. Soil insulation

Vegetation cover modifies the ground microclimate, reducing variations in soil temperature and soil moisture. This, in turn, subdues the mechanical weathering processes that lower the cohesiveness of the soil by aggregate breakdown and loosening of the structure. In particular, potentially damaging freeze-thaw cycles are reduced. At present there is no quantitative information published which illustrates the extent of these effects. Nevertheless they are widely accepted as a natural mechanism in geomorphology.

3.3.5 Soil restraint

Roots of 1–12 mm diameter physically restrain soil particles from movement induced by gravity, raindrop impact, surface runoff and wind. Laterally-spreading root systems are more effective in reducing surface erosion than vertically-structured ones with tap roots. Vegetation with substantial laterally spreading surface root systems is commonly used in vegetated channels, in order to utilise its soil restraint effect to restrict erosion. Trees, large bushes and shrubs are able to prop otherwise unstable or loose boulders and stones, preventing them from rolling down slope. The most effective plants for this role are:

1. resilient, to minimise damage from the impact of falling debris, so that their stems and branches bend rather than snap;
2. multi-stemmed, i.e. with more than one leader, so that growth is not stunted if a leader is damaged;
3. tolerant of burial, i.e. able to produce new roots from buried stems and develop a new root system close to the new ground surface.

3.4 Modification of soil water properties

This Section discusses how the presence of vegetation, particularly roots, affects the behaviour of water within the soil mass.

3.4.1 Evapotranspiration

The term evapotranspiration is variously used to describe the removal of moisture from a plant by transpiration, and the evaporation of intercepted rainfall from the plant surface. Strictly, transpiration is the mechanism of interest here, though the empirical relationships used to model it often include an element of evaporation as well.

Potential transpiration losses arising from plant surfaces are assessed in terms of the equivalent transpiration taking place from a well-watered reference vegetated surface, usually a short green sward. Penman (1948) expressed the evapotranspiration (E_t) from short green vegetation as:

$$E_t = f E_o$$

where f is about 0.8 in summer and 0.6 in winter, and E_o is the equivalent evaporation from an open water surface.

Values of E_t based on Penman (1948) are widely available, calculated from measured meteorological data for wind, sunshine and temperature. E_t figures for short grass type vegetation, as long-term averages and for any given current period, are published on a 5-, 10- and 30-day basis by the UK Meteorological Office.

The Penman estimates of evapotranspiration produce significant errors, however, when applied to tall, non-grass, vegetation (Thom and Oliver, 1977; Clarke and Newson, 1978). Monteith (1965) developed the Penman approach by introducing factors to account for the physiological control of transpiration by the plant and the aerodynamic roughness of the transpiring surface. The resulting Penman-Monteith equation represents the present understanding of the evapotranspiration from live plant surfaces of all types. Further details of this equation are given in Bache and MacAskill (1984) and standard irrigation references, such as Doorenbos and Pruitt (1977).

A plant adequately supplied with water will transpire at the potential rate. With progressive depletion of soil moisture, however, the plants find it more difficult to withdraw water by root suction, since the water potential of the roots is similar to that of the soil. To avoid dehydration, transpiration is restricted by reducing the pore openings in the leaves. Actual evapotranspiration (E_a) is therefore often less than potential evapotranspiration (E_t), depending on the accumulated soil moisture deficit (SMD; see Section 2.4.2).

Actual evapotranspiration can be estimated using the root constant model proposed by Penman (1949). This defines the root constant, C, as the amount of soil moisture (expressed in mm equivalent depth) which can be extracted without difficulty by a given vegetation type. Thus the actual evapotranspiration is equal to the potential ($E_a = E_t$) as long as SMD $< C$. When SMD $> C$, a further 25 mm of moisture can be extracted with increasing difficulty. Thereafter extraction becomes minimal ($E_a = 0.1–0.25 \times E_t$) when SMD $> 3C$. Root constants for a range of vegetation types are given in Table 3.3.

An alternative approach, developed as a model for predicting crop water requirements in irrigation planning, is based on the relationship between the reference crop evapotranspiration (E_t) and an empirically determined crop factor K_c:

$$E_a(\text{crop}) = K_c.E_t$$

The crop factor depends on the type of vegetation, the stage of growth, the growing conditions and the prevailing weather conditions (Doorenbos and Pruitt, 1977). The determination of K_c is not a simple formula, and the data available relate mainly to forage and arable crops.

3.4.2 Soil moisture balance

The balance of water in the soil depends on the relative levels of rainfall input, R, actual evapotranspiration, E_a, surface drainage and deep soil percolation. During summer, when E_a exceeds R, then the drainage and percolation factors become negligible and $E_a - R$ accumulates as a soil moisture deficit. During winter the

Table 3.3 Values of the root constant, *C*, for use in estimating actual evapotranspiration (after Grindley, 1969)

Vegetation	Maximum SMD (mm)	Root constant, C, (mm)
Cereals	200	140
Temporary grass	100	56
Permanent grass	125	75
Rough grazing	50	13
Trees (mature stand)	125–250	75–200

The maximum soil moisture deficit (SMD) which can be tolerated by a vegetation type depends partly on the physiological adaptation of the species but mainly on the depth of the roots. Long–rooted vegetation therefore has a much higher *C* than short–rooted types.

excess water, $R - E_a$, results in a waterlogged soil or is removed as surface drainage or percolation through the soil.

Figure 2.18 illustrates an actual soil moisture condition, estimated by analysing the monthly balance between rainfall and potential evapotranspiration. Estimates of soil moisture deficit are published regularly by the UK Meteorological Office for grassed and bare soils of varying water capacity. A more comprehensive method for estimating the soil moisture balance, taking account of rainfall, potential evapotranspiration, deep percolation, surface runoff, subsurface flow and changes in groundwater and soil moisture storage is described by Doorenbos and Pruitt (1977).

3.4.3 Soil moisture depletion

The ability of vegetation to modify soil moisture content is extensive and can reach beyond the physical extent of the roots. Measurement by Ziemer (1978a), for example, showed that the greatest moisture depletion occurred at depths of 2–4 m beneath ground level and extended as far as 6 m from an individual tree. Changes in the soil moisture content beneath young oak and pine plantations in Germany, measured throughout the year, are shown in Figure 3.10 (see also Biddle, 1983 and Ziemer, 1978a). This not only illustrates that the effect of vegetation varies with species and depth but also that the effect may, in some cases, be seasonal only. Highest levels of potential evaporation occur in the summer and lowest levels in winter, when vegetation is dormant. The result of a decreasing soil moisture content is to reduce the pore-water pressure in saturated soils, and to increase soil suction in soils below saturation. This has important consequences for soil strength (*see* Section 3.6).

Few measurements of soil suction induced by plants have been recorded, particularly for non-tree vegetation. In a study in Oregon, Gray (1977) found maximum differences in the order of $60 \, kN/m^2$, between tree-planted and cleared areas, though the difference diminished with increasing rainfall, as shown in Figure 3.11. Soil suction values of $2 \, kN/m^2$ have been measured for trees in Hong Kong by Greenway (1985). The relative potential of various UK trees to induce soil suction may be deduced from their typical water demand.

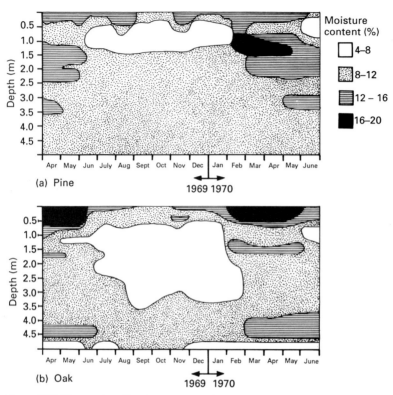

Figure 3.10 Changes in soil moisture content for young stands of pine and oak over an annual cycle (after Brechtel and Hammes, 1985)

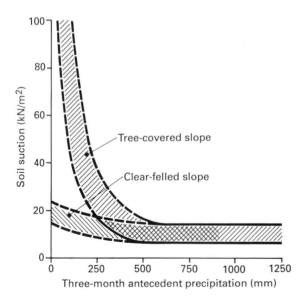

Figure 3.11 Comparison of soil suction between a forested and clear-felled stope (after Gray, 1977)

Many plants, mainly those that live in damp habitats, are characterised by high transpiration rates, and hence have a high capacity to remove water from the soil. Such plants are referred to as *phraetophytes* (Schiechtl 1980) and are potentially useful for relieving areas of high pore-water pressure. Species which might be used for this are included in Appendix 1. Such plants will not be tolerant of drier conditions and cannot be relied upon to increase soil suction.

Although the ability of trees to reduce soil moisture is recognised qualitatively, it has yet to be quantified. The magnitude of their influence on soil strength, however, is likely to be less than that of soil reinforcement by the roots (*see* Section 3.5.1), especially at periods critical for slope stability.

3.4.4. Soil weight reduction

Apart from increasing the strength of soil by reducing its moisture content, evapotranspiration by plants reduces the weight of the soil mass. This weight reduction can be important on vegetated slopes where the soil may be potentially unstable.

3.4.5. Soil cracking

In certain soils, prolonged extraction of moisture by plant roots can lead to desiccation and thus to the formation of shrinkage cracks. Once formed, such cracks may permanently increase the permeability and infiltration capacity of the soil. Crack depths can be as great as 125 mm in clays, sometimes increasing in width with depth below the upper heavily rooted soil layer. There is a compensating action, however, in that the root matrix tends to restrain movement (*see* Section 3.3.5), binding cracks together. Shading by grass and other vegetation can also reduce the incidence of cracking resulting from the exposure of particularly plastic soils to intensive drying or baking in full sun.

In a study of a 12 m by 9 m area of a 7 m high clay embankment on the M4 motorway in southern England, with side slopes of 1 in 2.5, or 26°, Anderson *et al* (1982) found that few cracks developed in the very densely tussock-grass vegetated upper part of the slope, which was thinly topsoiled. On the sparsely vegetated lower slopes, however, where the topsoil layer petered out and clay was exposed, cracking was both extensive and deep. The most vulnerable part of the slope appeared to be the middle, where cracks persisted longest after the onset of wet weather because they were partly shielded by the grass. These open cracks allowed rainwater to enter the slope during the winter long after the larger but exposed cracks on the lower slope had closed. Thus positive pore-water pressures developed in the upper zone of the middle slope, leading to shallow-seated failure. The authors concluded that cracking in clay fills, and the cost of associated remedial works, could possibly be reduced by special soiling and planting measures, incorporation of lime, or the use of geotextiles to restrain lateral shrinkage movements.

3.5 Modification of soil mechanical properties

3.5.1 Root reinforcement of soil

Roots embedded in soil form a composite material consisting of fibres of relatively high tensile strength and adhesion within a matrix of lower tensile strength. This is analogous to the reinforced soil system, where a soil mass is stabilised by the inclusion of metallic, synthetic or natural materials. The shear strength of the rooted soil mass is enhanced due to the presence of a root matrix. This effect can extend, in the case of trees, to several metres both in depth and spread, varying directly with root concentration. The mechanical effect of the roots of vegetation is to enhance the confining stress and resistance to sliding and increase the strength of the soil/root mass through the binding action of roots in the fibre/soil composite; the soil friction angle remains unchanged, as shown in Figure 3.12. Failure occurs either by pull-out, that is slipping due to bond failure, or rupture, that is tension failure.

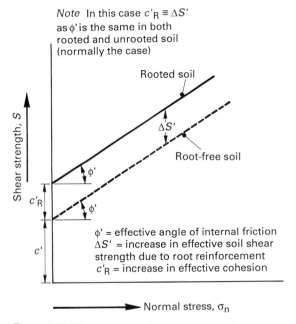

Figure 3.12 Effect of root reinforcement on the shear strength of soil

Another way of regarding root reinforcement of soil is that it provides relief of local over-stress by transferring load to regions of lower stress, through the interaction of semi-continuous root systems. This is the role of all reinforcing inclusions in composite materials.

The magnitude of the mechanical reinforcing effect of vegetation is a function of the following root properties:

density
tensile strength
tensile modulus
length/diameter ratio
surface roughness
alignment i.e. straightness/angularity
orientation to the direction of principal strains.

Measurements of root densities, their strengths in tension and the shear strengths of root reinforced soil have been made by several workers. Some typical values of the increase in soil cohesion due to roots, c_R, are given in Table 3.4. Typical values of root tensile strengths are given in Table 2.1. Both sets of data are intended solely to illustrate the range of values which occur and are not for use in design. There are a number of important points with respect to root tensile strength:

1. Shrubs and trees can have very high strengths for individual roots, e.g. up to $74 \, MN/m^2$ for alder.
2. There is a very large range of strengths in a single species, e.g. 4 to $74 \, MN/m^2$ for alder, depending on size, age, condition of root and season of the year.
3. Tree root thickness and strength respond to asymmetrical loading such as that experienced on slopes.

Table 3.4 Typical values for increases in soil cohesion (c_R), due to roots (after O'Loughlin and Ziemer, 1982)

Investigators	Soil/Vegetation	$c_R(kN/m^2)$
Swanston, 1970[1]	Mountain till soils under conifers, Alaska	3.4–4.4
O'Loughlin, 1974[1]	Mountain till soils under conifers, British Columbia	1.0–3.0
Endo and Tsuruta, 1969[2]	Cultivated loam soils (nursery) under alder	2.0–12.0
Wu et al. 1979[3]	Mountain till soils under conifers, Alaska	5.9
Waldron and Dakessian, 1981[4]	Clay loams in small containers growing pine seedlings	5.0 (approx)
O'Loughlin and Ziemer, 1982[4]	Shallow stony loam till soils under mixed evergreen forests, New Zealand	3.3
Gray and Megahan, 1981[3]	Sandy loam soils under conifers, Idaho	10.3
Riestenberg and Sovonick-Dunford, 1983[4]	Bouldery, silty clay colluvium under mainly sugar maple forest	5.7
Burroughs and Thomas, 1977[4]	Mountain and till soils under conifers, West Oregon and Idaho	3.0–17.5
Barker in Hewlett et al., 1986[2]	Boulder clay fill (dam embankment) under grass in concrete block reinforced cellular spillways	3.0–5.0

1. based on back analysis.
2. based on direct shear tests.
3. based on root density information and vertical root model equations.
4. based on back analysis and root density information.

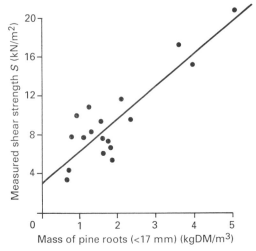

Figure 3.13 Shear strength of root-permeated sand as a function of root density (from Ziemer, 1981)

Herbaceous plant roots can also have a high strength and variability in tension, particularly the perennial roots.

The increase in soil cohesion c_R, due to the presence of roots, varies in proportion to their density or concentration in the soil, measured directly in terms of the mass of roots per unit volume, as shown in Figure 3.13. Usually only roots less than 15 mm to 20 mm in diameter are counted. Field studies have shown that roots over this size do not contribute significantly to the increase in soil shear strength; it is better to treat large roots as individual anchors (*see* Section 3.5.2).

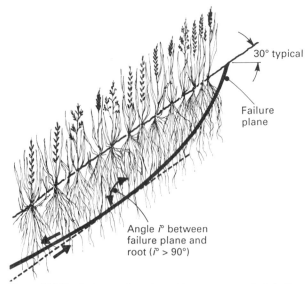

Figure 3.14 Typical root orientation with respect to typical shallow slope failure plane

Another frequently used measure of root density is the root area ratio, RAR (*see* Section 2.1.5).

The interaction between roots and soil can be quantified using a simple perpendicular root model, as shown in Box 3.1. This considers roots as elements initially crossing a slip plane perpendicularly, and utilises the limit equilibrium analysis, whereby ultimate strengths of materials are assumed to be mobilised along a failure plane induced in the soil and are in equilibrium with applied ultimate or limit state loading. The basic assumption made in the simple root model, that plant roots cross the failure plane at right angles, is not, however, always correct. For instance, roots of grasses deeper than about 150–200 mm tend to be vertical, whereas slope failure planes are for the most part inclined quite steeply, as shown in Figure 3.14. Studies of shrub and tree roots on slopes, however, indicate their

Box 3.1 Simplified perpendicular root model

The simplified perpendicular root soil model allows quantification of increased shear strength of soil due to root reinforcement.

The effect of shear displacement on elastic vertical roots crossing the shear zone perpendicularly is to increase the confining stress on and direct shear resistance along the failure plane at the onset of shear. In this model, the force developed in the root as the soil is sheared is resolved with a tangential component resisting shear and a normal component increasing the confining stress and hence frictional resistance along the shear plane.

The mobilisation of the tensile resistance of roots in vegetated soils can be modelled as an increase, ΔS, in the shear strength of the soil as follows:

$$\Delta S = t_R \left(\cos \theta \tan \phi + \sin \theta \right) \qquad (1)$$

where ΔS = shear strength increase from root or fibre reinforcement, kN/m^2
$\quad \theta$ = angle of shear rotation
$\quad \phi$ = friction angle
$\quad t_R$ = average tensile strength of root or fibre per unit area of soil, kN/m^2

The average tensile strength of roots or fibres per unit area of soil (t_R) is given by:

$$t_R = T_R \left(A_R / A \right) \qquad (2)$$

where T_R = average tensile strength of root or fibre, kN/m^2
$\quad A_R / A$ = root area ratio or fraction of soil cross-sectional area occupied by roots

A_R can be determined by counting the number of roots in different size classes (n_i) in a given soil cross-sectional area (A), and determining the mean cross-section area (a_i) for that size class:

i.e. $$t_R = T_R \sum \frac{n_i a_i}{A} \qquad (3)$$

Since for natural root systems, the root tensile strength tends to vary with the size or diameter of the root, the last equation can be re-written:

$$t_R = \sum \frac{T_i n_i a_i}{A} \qquad (4)$$

where T_i = tensile strength of roots of size class (i)

The only unknown in the equations is the angle of shear rotation or distortion (θ). This varies with the thickness of shear zone (Z) and the amount of shear displacement (X).

Results of tests carried out by Waldron (1977) confirm that θ varies between 45°–50°. Field observations by Wu *et al.* (1979) of failures in root permeated masses on slopes indicated that θ varies at most between 45° and 70°. The value of the bracketed term in equation (1) varies between 1.0 to 1.3 for 25° < ϕ < 40° and 40° < θ < 70°.

(Continued overleaf)

Box 3.1 *(Continued)*

Hence, adopting a median value of 1.15 as the most likely value of the bracketed term, equation (1) may be re-written:

$$\Delta S = 1.15 t_R$$

i.e. $\Delta S = 1.15 T_R (A_R/A)$

i.e. $\Delta S = 1.15 \sum \dfrac{T_i n_{ia_L}}{A}$ (5)

This root reinforcement model assumes that the failure mode is a tensile failure of the root fibres, i.e. their tensile strength is fully mobilised. For this assumption to be valid, pullout or bond failure must be prevented. To meet this condition, the roots must have a combination of sufficient length beyond the failure zone and sufficient roughness so that the bond between the root and soil exceeds the tensile strength of the root.

The minimum length (L_{min}, mm) of roots of uniform thickness (d, mm) required to prevent pullout or bond failure is given by the following:

$$L_{min} > \dfrac{T_R d_R}{2 \tau_R}$$ (6)

where T_R = tensile strength of root (kN/m²)
τ_R = maximum bond stress or pullout resistance between root and soil (kN/m²)

As a guide to the order of this effect, typical values of root tensile strengths are given in Table 2.1; typical values of root densities are:
trees: in 5 to 10 mm diameter class: 70-113 roots/m², giving A_R/A ratio of 0.14 to 0.93 (Rocky Mountain douglas fir 0.05 to 0.17)
cereals: barley A_R/A ratio of 0.1 to 0.8

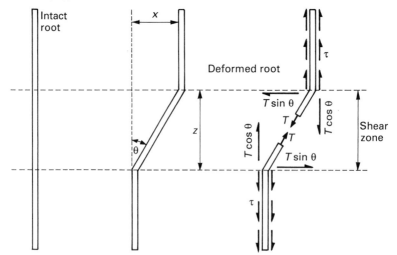

Model of flexible elastic root extending vertically across a horizontal shear zone (after Wu *et al.*, 1979)

tendency to grow preferentially in the up-slope direction, in other words to increase the angle of intersection at the failure plane to approximate more closely to the model.

Although the simple vertical root model often provides a sufficiently accurate prediction of root reinforcement of soil, a more complex inclined root model has been proposed by various workers (Waldron, 1977; Wu, 1976; Brenner and James, 1977), as reported in Gray and Leiser (1982), to cater for the initial inclination of roots. In general, the optimum root inclination is between 40° and 70° for a range of common soil friction angles of 25–40°, but the effective difference between roots orientated between 30° and 90° to the failure plane is relatively small. It should be noted that both root models are based on the full mobilisation of root strength, i.e. tensile as opposed to bond failure.

3.5.2 Anchorage, arching and buttressing

The taproot and sinker roots of many tree species penetrate into the deeper soil layers and anchor them against down-slope movement. The trunks and principal roots can also act in the same manner as toe stabilising piles, further restraining the down-hill movement of soil. Gray (1978) describes slope buttressing in a shallow granitic regolith under pine trees, where tree spacing was too sparse, the unbuttressed part of the slope had failed. The pile action of the tree supports the up-slope soil mass. Where trees are closely spaced the soil layer above may yield and arch between them, as shown in Figure 3.15. The magnitude of the arching effect is influenced by:

1. spacing, diameter and embedment of trees;
2. thickness and inclination of the yielding stratum of slopes;
3. shear strength properties of soil.

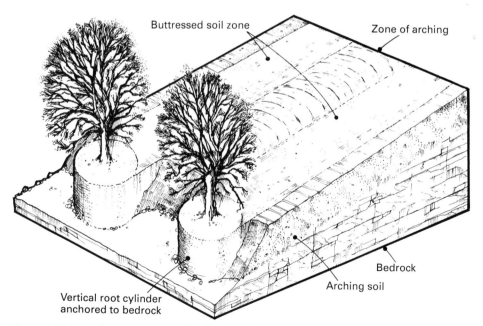

Figure 3.15 Anchoring, buttressing and arching on a slope

Theoretical models for estimating lateral forces acting on a single row or multiple rows of embedded piles as soil tends to 'spill through' them have been proposed by Nakamura (1970), Wang and Yen (1974), Ito and Matsui (1975) and DeBeer and Carpentier (1977). Gray (1978) has adopted Wang and Yen's theory to quantify soil arching based on a semi-infinite slope model and rigid-plastic-solid soil behaviour, as described in Box 3.2. Application of the approach to trees, or more accurately vertical root cylinders, on steep sandy slopes shows that tree spacings commonly observed in the field are of the right order to develop slope stabilisation by arching, as illustrated in Figure 3.16.

Box 3.2 Quantification of soil arching

Based on a theory (Wang and Yen, 1974) developed for a single row of piles or trees (diameter, d) spaced at a distance (B) apart embedded onto a slope, an expression for the load (P_R) generated against a pile by a thickness (H_z) of yielding soil is as follows:

$$P_R = 0.5K_o\, d\gamma H_z^2 + (0.5K_o\gamma H_z - p)BH_z$$

where B = clear spacing between trees/piles
H_z = vertical thickness of yielding soil stratum
d = diameter of the embedded section of the tree
γ = unit weight of soil
K_o = coefficient of lateral pressure at rest
p = average lateral pressure (arching pressure) in openings between piles/trees on a slope

The maximum allowable or critical spacing (B_{crit}) between fixed embedded piles for the existence of arching in a slope is given by the following equation:

$$B_{crit} = \frac{H_z K_o(K_o + 1)\tan\phi' + \dfrac{2c'}{\gamma}}{\cos\beta(\tan\beta - \tan\phi_1') - \dfrac{c_1'}{\gamma H_z\cos\beta}}$$

where

c' = effective cohesion of soil
c_1' = effective cohesion along basal sliding surface
β = effective slope angle
ϕ' and ϕ_1' = effective angle of internal friction of soil and along basal sliding surface respectively

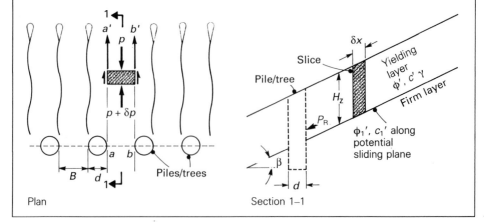

Plan   Section 1–1

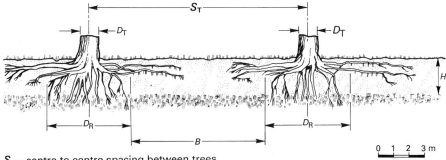

S_T = centre to centre spacing between trees
D_R = diameter of 'vertical root cylinder'
D_T = trunk diameter at breast height
B = spacing between root cylinders

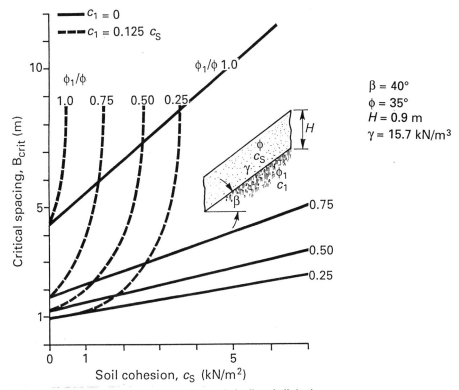

The critical spacing in the shallow soil mantle is directly linked to the value of cohesion along the underside of the supported soil mass. If cohesion is zero and residual friction along the underside sliding surface is half the peak friction, the critical spacing is only 1.2 m. If a cohesion of 2.4 kN/m² is assumed with residual cohesion only 12% of this value, the critical spacing increases to 6.4 m.

Figure 3.16 Critical spacing for arching for trees acting as piles embedded in a steep sandy slope (after Gray and Leiser, 1982)

3.5.3 Surface mat effect

A network of intertwined roots at shallow depth forms a mat or net having continuity, good anchorage and a significant degree of in-plane strength, all of which can make a significant contribution towards reducing soil creep. This role of vegetation has been noted in heavily forested regoliths in New Zealand (O'Loughlin 1984). Grass and shrub roots can act in a similar way but, since 60–80% of the grass root mat is in the top 50 mm of soil (*see* Section 2.1.5; Garwood, 1967b), this effect is restricted to shallow depths. The effect is recognised as contributing to the stability of river banks (*see* Section 6.4.2). No rigorous approach has been developed yet to quantify and predict the root mat effect.

3.5.4 Surcharge

Surcharge is the effect of the additional weight on a slope resulting from the presence of vegetation. Normally this effect is only considered in the case of trees, since the weight of grass and herb swards and most shrub vegetation is comparatively insignificant. Figure 3.17 relates tree height to equivalent uniform surcharge. Though generally considered an adverse effect, surcharge can also be beneficial, depending on slope geometry, the distribution of vegetation over the slope, and the soil properties. On a slope, surcharge increases the down-slope forces; on the other hand the additional vertical load increases the frictional component, i.e. the magnitude of up-slope forces. Surcharge at the top of a slope can lead to reduction in overall stability, whereas it can add to stability when applied at the bottom.

Considering the critical failure surface shown in Figure 3.18, it is possible, though admittedly not usual, for the centre of gravity of the trees to be located such that they provide a restoring moment about the centre of rotation. This occurs if the majority of trees are growing over the bottom portion of a slope. The component of the surcharge acting normally to the slope adds to the frictional resistance or restoring forces against sliding along the failure plane. Even if the first condition is adverse, the beneficial effect of the second may more than compensate for it. Gray and Megahan (1981) show that, for an infinite slope, surcharge is beneficial when cohesion is low, groundwater level is high, soil angle of internal friction is high, and slope angles are small.

3.5.5 Wind loading

Wind loading (*see* Section 2.7.2) is usually only significant when the wind is stronger than 11 m/s (Beaufort wind scale 6). The forces induced in vegetation by wind can be sufficient to disturb upper soil layers and thus directly initiate landslips. Wind loading can have a destabilising effect on a slope whether it is directed up- or down-hill, as shown in Figure 3.19. An up-hill wind, if sufficiently strong, can cause a toppling rotation of a tree and impart a destabilising moment to the slope. A second and possibly greater destabilising effect can result from increased water infiltration through the scar created by an uprooted tree.

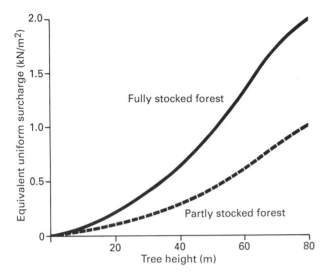

Figure 3.17 Equivalent uniform surcharge of coniferous forest

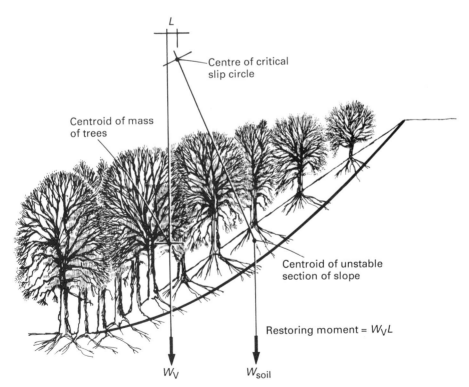

Figure 3.18 Effect of surcharge by trees applied to the bottom of a slip surface

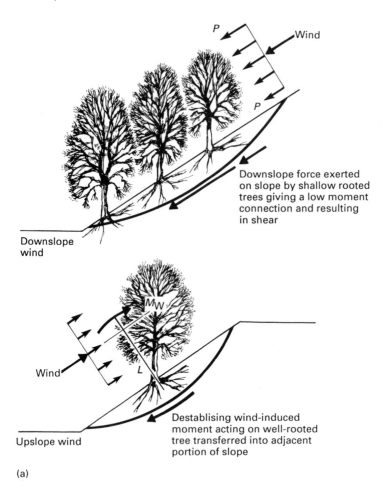

Figure 3.19 Effect of wind loading on trees

The magnitude of the drag force exerted by trees on wind is dependent on the following factors:

1. wind speed
2. tree height
3. extent of crown
4. slope angle.

Wind tunnel tests on a model forest carried out by Hsi and Nath (1970) have led to the following approach for quantifying windthrow. For wind blowing parallel to a level ground surface the wind pressure, p, on the trees is given by:

$$p = 0.5\rho_a V^2 C_D$$

where ρ_a is the air density in kg/m^3 (1.22 kg/m^3 at 20°C and 1013 mb pressure),
V is the wind velocity, m/s.
C_D is the dimensionless drag coefficient; *see* Figure 3.20.

Brown and Sheu (1975) developed equations for predicting shear forces and overturning moments due to wind on the basis that wind acts fully on individual trees, dynamic effects being ignored. For the situation shown in Figure 3.19, where a single tree is exposed to a wind parallel to the slope (slope angle β) the wind pressure (p_s) normal to the tree is given by:

$$p_s = p\cos^2\beta$$

The drag force, D, transmitted by a single tree into the slope is given by:

$$D = \sum_{i=h_1}^{h_1+h_2} (p_s b)i$$

where b is the transverse width of the crown at each height increment, i.

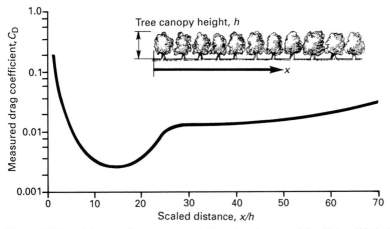

Figure 3.20 Local drag coefficient on a model tree-forest canopy (after Hsi and Nath, 1970)

3.5.6 Root wedging

Root wedging is a potentially destabilising effect whereby fissures and joints in rocks are opened up by the advance and growth of roots in the quest for water. Trees cause the biggest problem, though grass roots can also force open small fissures. Root penetration into joints and fissures also leads to increased water infiltration and weathering of the rock, further contributing to slope instability. The decay of tree roots can also trigger falls of rock as the binding and restraining action fails. Soft slopes are unlikely to be affected by root wedging.

3.6 Soil strength

The presence of vegetation, mainly roots, results in an overall increase in the strength, and thus competence, of a soil mass. This arises from the combined effects of soil reinforcement by a mass of roots and soil moisture depletion by evapotranspiration. It must be emphasised, however, that evapotranspiration is dependent on climatic factors (*see* Section 3.4) and soil moisture levels can build-up in winter to field capacity (Figure 3.10).

As already seen in Section 3.5.1, root reinforcement increases the cohesiveness of the soil by an amount c_R (*see* Figure 3.12) whilst the depletion of soil moisture (*see* Section 3.4.3) reduces pore-water pressure and increases soil suction. A lower pore-water pressure increases the degree of particle-to-particle contact, making the soil more resistant to deformation under a load. Higher suctions increase the attraction of soil particles to one another through residual capillary water effects. Although suction effects could also be considered as a reduction in pore-water pressure, this is only appropriate for saturated soils. On a partially-saturated soil, the effect of a sustained development of soil suction on soil strength may be more conveniently expressed as an increase in cohesion by an amount c_S (Ho and Fredlund, 1982; Walker and Fell, 1987).

The Mohr-Coulomb equations used to describe the strength of a saturated soil can be modified as follows to allow for the effects of vegetation and for partially saturated soils, where indicated. In total stress terms the basic equation

$$S = c + \sigma_n \tan\phi$$

becomes:

$$S = (c + c_R + c_S) + \sigma_n \tan\phi$$

In effective stress terms:

$$S = (c' + c'_R + c'_s) + \sigma'_n \tan\phi'$$

becomes, for partially saturated soils:

$$S = (c' + c'_R) + (u_a - u)\tan\phi^b + (\sigma_n - u_a)\tan\phi'$$

The contribution of vegetation to soil strength during the active growing season is usually most significant in saturated soil conditions. Since u approaches zero as soil saturation is reached, for practical purposes this term may be discarded, yielding:

$$S = (c' + c'_R) + (\sigma_n - u)\tan\phi'$$

where S is the shear strength of the soil

    c is the apparent soil cohesion

    c' is the effective soil cohesion

    c_R is the contribution to soil cohesion from roots

    c_S is the contribution to soil cohesion from soil suction

    σ is the normal stress

    σ'_n is the effective normal stress

    ϕ is the angle of internal friction of the soil material (angle of shearing resistance)

    ϕ' is the effective angle of internal friction of the soil material

    ϕ^b is the angle of internal friction of soil with respect to changes in $(u_a - u)$, with $(\sigma - u_a)$ constant

    u_a is the pore-air pressure

    u is the pore-water pressure

  $(u_a - u)$ is the soil suction

Since soil suction $(u_a - u)$ increases as the size of voids and capillary channels decreases, its contribution to cohesion is greater in finer-grained soils. Plant-induced soil suctions may therefore compensate for gradual loss of soil strength over time due to weathering (*see* Section 6.2.2.). It should be remembered that during winter the effect of vegetation on soil moisture content will probably be minimal.

A particular advantage of vegetation is that it occupies the upper layers of the soil. Surface soils display low shear strengths compared with soils at greater depth. Vegetation can therefore make a contribution to the strength of the soil mass where it is most needed. The shear strength of a surface soil of $1.5\,\mathrm{Mg/m^3}$ density and 0.6–3 m deep is only 25–80% of that of deeper soil materials, when assessed using a normal stress path test (Mitchell, 1983).

As a general point, in soils of low to medium permeability where the rate of replacement of transpired moisture is not large, reduction in pore-water pressure or development of soil suction can result in a lowering of the water table. Taking the amount of this lowering into account in stability computations, and not adjusting the soil strength in the ways indicated above, can be an appropriate way of allowing for the effect of vegetation on soil strength.

3.7 Modification of air flow

3.7.1 Effect of vegetation on wind velocity

In the absence of convective eddies generated by vertical temperature gradients, wind speed over uniform, open, level ground increases logarithmically with height.

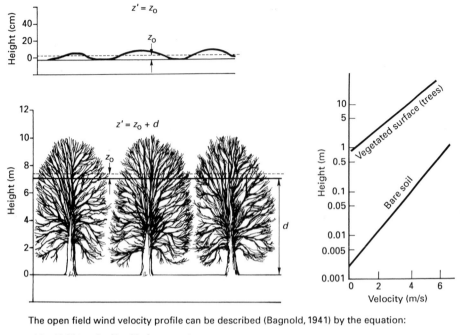

The open field wind velocity profile can be described (Bagnold, 1941) by the equation:

$$u(z) = (2.3/k)\ u_* \log[(z-d)/z_0], \qquad z > d + z_0$$

where u is the mean wind velocity at height z
k is the von Karman universal constant for turbulent flow (0.4 for clear fluids)
u_* is the shear velocity ($=\sqrt{\tau/\rho_a}$, where τ is shear stress and ρ_a is the density of the air)

d is the depth of zero plane displacement
z_0 is the roughness length

Figure 3.21 Wind velocity as a function of height above a bare and vegetated soil surface

The effective height of the plane of zero wind velocity over a bare soil surface is defined by the roughness length (z_0), a measure of ground roughness equal to the difference in height between the actual plane of zero wind velocity and the mean aerodynamic surface. A vegetation cover increases the roughness length and displaces the plane of zero wind velocity upwards by height, d, known as the zero plane displacement, shown in Figure 3.21. As rough guides, z_0 approximates $h/10$ where h is the height of the foliage elements and d is usually between 0.6 and 0.8 h.

The ability of wind to detach soil particles from the soil mass and to transport sediment is related to the square and the cube of the wind velocity respectively. Reductions in wind speed can therefore significantly reduce wind erosion. Vegetation reduces the velocity of the wind by exerting a drag on the air flow close to the ground surface. The drag is a combination of skin friction, associated with the passage of air over the top of the vegetation, and form drag, associated with flow separation around individual vegetation elements, which behave like blunt objects within the flow. Various attempts have been made to express the drag on wind velocity due to vegetation using roughness or drag coefficients, as described in Box 3.3. The terms z_0 and C_D can be used to describe the effect of vegetation on

Box 3.3 Roughness length and drag coefficients for vegetation in air flow

1. Roughness length (z_o)
Increases in roughness length (defined in text) brought about by, for example, a vegetation cover reduce wind velocity. Roughness length can be determined by plotting a linear relation between wind velocities (u) measured at heights (z) and values of log ($z-d$), where d is zero plane displacement, and extrapolating to the point where $u = 0$ at $(z-d) = z_o$. Its ease of determination means that roughness length is a commonly-used indicator of the effect of vegetation on wind velocity above plant canopy level.

2. Bulk drag coefficient (C_D)
The bulk aerodynamic resistance of vegetation on air flow above the plant canopy can be described by a drag coefficient (C_D) derived from a simplified expression of the total drag force (τ) exerted on a unit area of the plant cover (Skidmore and Hagen, 1977):

$$\tau = 0.5 \, \rho_a \, C_D \, u(z)^2$$
$$\text{since} \quad \tau = \rho_a \, u_*^2$$
$$C_D = 2u_*^2/u(z)^2$$

(3) Vegetation drag coefficient (C_d)
The drag exerted by the vegetation during the transfer of momentum from the wind to the plant elements is expressed by the drag coefficient (C_d). This can be calculated by balancing the drag force of the wind profile exerted at height (h) with the extraction of momentum due to the frictional surface area of the individual foliage elements (Wright and Brown, 1967).

$$\tau(h) = 0.5 \int_o^h C_D \, A \, (z) \, u(z)^2 dz$$

where A is the leaf area per unit volume. Assuming that C_d is independent of wind speed and therefore of height, rearrangement of the above with $\tau = \rho_a u_*^2$ leads to:

$$C_d = \frac{2u_*^2}{\int_o^h u(z)^2 \, A(z)dz}$$

Notes
1. *Typical values of z_o, C_D and C_d are given in the Table below.*
2. The roughness coefficient z_o has dimensions of length whereas C_D and C_d are dimensionless.
3. Despite their similarity of notation, the coefficients C_D and C_d do not have comparable values. They cannot be substituted one for the other because they refer to different properties.

Typical values for roughness length and drag coefficients

Vegetation	z_o (m)	C_D	C_d
Grass	0.01–0.02	0.005–0.009	
Wheat	0.12–0.30		0.001–0.08
Planted straw strips	0.20		0.001–0.08
Apple orchard (winter)		0.02–0.03	
Apple orchard (summer)		0.06–0.07	
Coniferous forest	0.10–1.0	0.03–0.10	
Deciduous forest	0.20–3.0	0.01–0.03	
Barley strips			0.001

C_d data are for crop biomass in the lower 50 mm of the atmosphere above a datum height equal to an estimated value of roughness length for the soil surface and for a wind velocity at 50 mm height of 1 m/s (after Morgan and Finney, 1987).

Values of z_o, C_D and C_d are not independent of wind speed but can both increase and decrease with increases in wind velocity (see Monteith, 1973; Wright and Brown, 1967; Bache, 1986; Morgan and Finney, 1987).

airflow above the canopy, whereas C_d describes effects within the canopy. Thus C_D is useful for quantifying effects such as wind loading (*see* Section 3.5.5), while C_d is helpful for analysing the effect of the foliage on wind speed in the vegetative layer close to the soil surface and, therefore, on wind erosion.

Although values of the drag coefficients have been determined for vegetation stands and barriers, in practice they cannot be defined precisely from simple plant measurements. Since vegetation is not a rigid material, drag coefficients vary with wind velocity as against those for solid barriers, which are independent of velocity.

Studies of the drag coefficient (C_d) for the effect of low-growing vegetative barriers on the lowest 50 mm of the atmosphere show that, under most atmospheric conditions, the coefficient falls in value with increasing wind speed as a result of streamlining. With a reasonably continuous wind speed, however, the drag coefficient is also found to increase with increasing wind velocity, particularly over low vegetation in its early stage of growth (Morgan and Finney, 1987). This is attributed to the constant movement of the leaves, which disturbs the atmosphere surrounding the plant and sets up a wall-effect so that the barrier behaves more like a solid. Wind speed increases over the top of the vegetation, however, so that velocity rises more rapidly with height and shear velocity is increased. Under these conditions, the presence of a plant cover increases the likelihood of wind erosion. Leaf shape has a significant influence on these effects (Morgan *et al*, 1988).

The drag exerted by a stand of vegetation depends upon its height, its openness and its biomass. Laboratory experiments by Marshall (1971) show that the drag decreases as the diameter, D, to height, H, ratio of the plant elements increases until the D/H ratio equals 2.0, beyond which the drag remains constant. The drag increases as the projected plant area facing the wind increases. These relations imply that a dense cover of slender cylinders will be the most effective in reducing wind velocities, which in turn means that dense grass covers are more effective than scattered low bushes or shrubs. Indeed, the latter may result in localised increases in wind velocity due to funnelling of the wind between the plants.

The drag exerted by a windbreak, such as a live vegetation barrier or shelterbelt, modifies the pattern of air flow. Flow around a barrier can be divided into a number of zones, as shown in Figure 3.22. An understanding of these basic flow patterns is utilised in the design of vegetative barriers to provide shelter (*see* Section 6.6.1) and to control wind erosion (*see* Sections 6.5.4 and 6.5.5).

3.7.2 Noise attenuation

Vegetation affects the rate at which sound diminishes with distance, depending on the amount of foliage and the sound frequency (Robinette, 1972). Attenuation results from a combination of deflection, refraction (producing dispersal) and absorption of sound energy. Foliage absorbs sound most effectively at high frequencies to which the human ear is more sensitive, as shown in Table 3.5. The reduction in sound level of middle to low frequencies appears to be relatively small except over wide belts of trees. The attenuation of high frequencies may account for the general impression that tree screens reduce the perceived volume of sound.

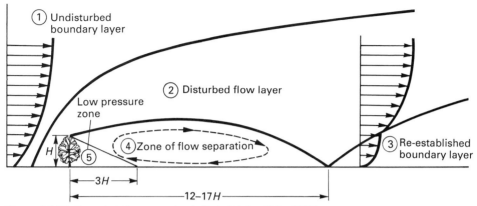

Figure 3.22 Pattern of air flow around a shelterbelt (after Plate, 1971)

Table 3.5 Attenuation of sound by vegetation (after Moore, 1966)

Frequency (Hz)	125	250	500	1000	2000	4000
Reduction (dB) per 30 m of dense tree foliage	0.8	1.5	1.8	2.0	3.0	5.0
Reduction (dB) per 30 m over rough grass	0.5	1.5	3.0	2.5	1.0	1.0

The review by Zulfacar and Clark (1974) showed that noise attenuation rates with vegetative barriers vary considerably from 1.5 dB to 30 dB per 100 m. OECD (1971) quotes the muffling effect of thick leafy vegetation as 2–3 dB(A) per 100 m and that of thick plantations of coniferous trees as 5–10 dB(A) (*see* Section 6.6.2).

In principle, the most effective plants will have many thick fleshy leaves with thin stalks, allowing for a high degree of flexibility and vibration, which in turn causes deflection and refraction. In practice, however, different tree species do not appear to differ greatly in their ability to reduce traffic noise, though evergreens are best when year-round screening is required (Cook and van Haverbeke, 1970).

3.8 Structural combinations

Combinations of live vegetation with other materials provide a composite system whereby the performance of one component can make good any shortcomings in the other. Vegetation can also of course improve the visual appearance of inert structures.

3.8.1 Geotextiles

Geotextiles, including geowebs, geogrids and mats, interact as a composite with soil and vegetation in two ways, depending on whether they are laid on the surface of the soil or buried within the upper soil layer.

Surface-laid geotextiles enhance the role of vegetation in reducing erosion and serve as a temporary aid to vegetation establishment by:

1. protecting against the effects of raindrops and surface flow at ground level, thus preventing or minimising the soil aggregate breakdown and detachment by raindrop impact and the erosive effect of surface water flow;
2. reducing the volume of runoff generated, by creating depression storage within the cells of the geotextile mesh and retaining moisture on or within the material; this effect in turn increases infiltration and makes more water available in the soil for plant growth. Some natural-fibred geotextiles can retain water to up to 500% of their dry weight;
3. reducing the velocity of runoff and wind by retarding the flow;
4. modifying the microclimate of the soil.

The extent of these effects depends a great deal upon the ground cover afforded by the geotextile.

Buried geotextiles, including geowebs, can improve the performance of vegetation by:

1. reinforcing the soil in a similar way to plant roots;
2. creating preferential root-growth paths, and thereby contributing to soil reinforcement through lateral continuity of the root network;
3. forming a soil-root-geotextile composite which acts as a surface mat, reducing soil creep in the less compacted upper soil layer;
4. increasing infiltration along the root-growth paths when the roots decay;
5. absorbing part of the impact of foot and wheeled traffic and thereby reducing compaction in areas of heavy traffic;
6. transferring load to an unloaded area, thereby reducing its local intensity.

When combined with a buried geotextile, vegetation performs the additional roles of:

1. anchoring and binding the geotextile into the soil through the network of roots.
2. protecting the geotextile from ultra-violet degradation and surface damage.

3.8.2 Other structural materials

Vegetation can be combined with other structural materials such as timber, stone, concrete and steel to form a composite material (*see* Section 6.2.9). The functions of vegetation when used in this way are:

1. to provide additional long-term reinforcement of the soil;
2. to reduce soil moisture content, thereby reducing pore-water pressure and the weight component of water to soil loading on the structure;
3. to anchor structural elements to the ground surface;
4. to shield the structure from the effects of solar radiation, wind, frost and surface water erosion.

Effectively, vegetation can have an indefinite life, while inert structures have a finite life span. Combining the two may considerably extend the life of a structure compared with inert structures on their own. Vegetation can also have a disruptive effect on an inert structure, however, and this must always be borne in mind when a combination of live and inert materials is being considered. Possible effects include:

1. enhanced rates of corrosion or deterioration due to higher moisture contents and root penetration;
2. distortion of a structure as stems and roots develop and increase in girth;
3. toppling and wind-loading effects.

3.9 Summary of salient properties and functions of vegetation

The overall function of vegetation is the result of a balance between a range of beneficial and adverse effects, summarised in Box 3.4. The properties of vegetation

Box 3.4 Summary of the beneficial and adverse effects of vegetation

Hydrological effects		Mechanical effects	
Foliage intercepts rainfall causing:		Roots bind soil particles and permeate the soil, resulting in:	
1. absorptive and evaporative losses, reducing rainfall available for infiltration	B	1. restraint of soil movement reducing erodibility	B
2. reduction in kinetic energy of raindrops and thus erosivity	B	2. increase in shear strength through a matrix of tensile fibres	B
3. increase in drop size through leaf drip, thus increasing localised rainfall intensity	A	3. network of surface fibres creates a tensile mat effect, restraining underlying strata	B
Stems and leaves interact with flow at the ground surface, resulting in:		Roots penetrate deep strata, giving:	
1. higher depression storage and higher volume of water for infiltration	A/B	1. anchorage into firm strata, bonding soil mantle to stable subsoil or bedrock	B
2. greater roughness on the flow of air and water, reducing its velocity, but	B	2. support to up-slope soil mantle through buttressing and arching	B
3. tussocky vegetation may give high localised drag, concentrating flow and increasing velocity	A	Tall growth of trees, so that:	
Roots permeate the soil, leading to:		1. weight may surcharge the slope, increasing normal and down-slope force components	A/B
1. opening up of the surface and increasing infiltration	A	2. when exposed to wind, dynamic forces are transmitted into the ground	A
2. extraction of moisture which is lost to the atmosphere in transpiration, lowering pore-water pressure and increasing soil suction, both increasing soil strength	B	Stems and leaves cover the ground surface, so that:	
		1. impact of traffic is absorbed, protecting soil surface from damage	B
3. accentuation of dessication cracks, resulting in higher infiltration	A	2. foliage is flattened in high velocity flows, covering the soil surface and providing protection against erosive flows	B

A = adverse effect
B = beneficial effect

which define its role as an engineering material are summarised in Box 3.5. Many of these properties are seasonal in character and change with the stage of growth, and at different rates, for each vegetation type. The way that these effects and functions are utilised in the applications is discussed in Section 6, and summarised in Box 6.1.

Box 3.5 Summary of salient vegetation properties and their significance for engineering functions

Effect on	Influence	Ground cover (%)	Height	Leaf shape and length	Stem/leaf density	Stem/leaf robustness	Stem/leaf flexibility	Root depth	Root density	Root strength	Annual growth cycle	Weight
Surface competence	Soil detachment	●	●	●	●						●	
	Mechanical strength	●	●		●	●			●	●	●	
	Insulation	●			●						●	
	Retarding/arresting		●		●	●	●					
	Erosion	●			●						●	
Surface water regime	Rainfall interception	●		●	●							
	Overland flow/runoff	●			●							
	Infiltration				●			●	●			
	Subsurface drainage							●	●			
	Surface drag	●	●	●	●		●				●	
Soil water	Evapotranspiration			●	●				●		●	
	Soil moisture depletion leading to increased soil suction, reduced pore-water and soil weight							●			●	
Properties of soil mass	Root reinforcement							●	●	●	●	
	Anchorage/restraint							●	●	●		
	Arching/buttressing							●		●		
	Surface mat/net								●	●	●	
	Surcharge		●									●
	Windthrow		●		●	●		●		●	●	●
	Root wedging							●	●			
Air flow	Surface drag		●	●	●		●				●	
	Flow deflection		●		●	●	●				●	
	Noise attenuation		●	●	●						●	
	Suspended particulates		●		●						●	

Vegetation properties

4 Vegetation selection, establishment and management

In order to use vegetation for an engineering purpose, proper procedures and techniques for its selection, establishment and maintenance should be followed. The engineer will generally need to seek advice on these topics from a vegetation specialist. This Section does not therefore give a complete account of the techniques for vegetation establishment and management, but aims to provide engineers with:

1. sufficient information to obtain the appropriate specialist advice;
2. an understanding of the operations involved, how they are used and what can go wrong;
3. guidance on supervision, quality control and troubleshooting (Section 4.6);
4. guidance with setting up appropriate management and maintenance programmes (Section 4.7);
5. guidance on the timing of operations (Section 4.8);
6. safe working methods on slopes (Section 4.9).

The procedures and techniques are described here in relation to the UK but the principles apply anywhere in the world, with appropriate allowances for climate, local materials and technology.

4.1 Plant selection

There are five interrelated criteria for plant selection:

1. bioengineering properties or function
2. ecological or site conditions
3. the plant community
4. method of propagation
5. management.

Information on plants suitable for different sites and soils, with varying growth forms and habits, can be found in many published lists. Some guidance on plants with good bioengineering potential and suitable for use in the UK is given in Appendix 1. Selection criteria and their application are discussed here.

Box 4.1 Plant selection criteria for bioengineering properties

Plant growth form, habit and growth cycle

Roots	Structure	fine and fibrous	
		tap–rooted	
		branched systems	
	Depth	shallow (80% within 150 mm)	
		deep	
	Density		
Shoots	Height		
	Stems	single	spreading
		multiple	upright
		branched	
	Leaf	narrow/long	
		small	
		large/broad	
	Flexibility		
	Density of foliage		
	Ability to coppice		
Growth cycle	Annual		
	Perennial	evergreen	dieback to ground level
		deciduous	dieback completely
Habit	Single stems		
	Clumped		
	Spreading	rhizomes	
		stolons	
		suckers	
Growth rate	Quick establishment for erosion control		
	Low maintenance		

Resistance to mechanical damage:

High flow of air or water	Elasticity of stems and leaves, which easily deform under force; in doing so they also protect the ground beneath
Scour and abrasion	High tensile strength and toughness of root and shoot tissues
	Capacity to regenerate rapidly and regrow
	Dense surface mat of roots and rhizomes
Partial burial of stems	Formation of adventitious roots on the buried portion of trunk or stem
Partial exposure of roots	Ability to form bark on root tissue when exposed to air

4.1.1 Bioengineering properties and function

The engineering function that plants are required to fulfil determines the type of vegetation that is needed. For example soil stabilisation requires plants with an appropriate root system structure whereas, for surface erosion control and shelter, top growth is more significant. The growth form, structure and habit of the plants are the principal determinants of choice, as detailed in Box 4.1. How these can be applied to different situations is discussed fully in Section 6.

4.1.2 Site conditions and environment

The specific tolerances and preferences of individual plant species are widely covered in the literature (e.g. Coppin and Bradshaw, 1982, Hillier, 1974, Hubbard, 1968).

Soil fertility (*see* Section 2.4.3), particularly long-term fertility, can be manipulated with fertilisers. 'Leguminous' species such as clovers, vetches and lupins fix their own nitrogen and so are invaluable for sites with soils of low fertility.

The bioclimate (*see* Section 2.5) cannot be modified, though design and management can moderate its effects. Species selection for tolerance of factors such as cold, drought, exposure and short growing season is therefore important.

Soil water regimes cover a very broad range, from drought to waterlogging (*see* Section 2.4.2). The range and seasonality of a moisture regime are important (*see* Sections 2.5 and 3.4.2). Since the moisture regime reflects the physical characteristics of a soil, a plant species which thrives on a heavy soil, for example, may only be expressing an intolerance of the drier conditions of a light soil.

4.1.3 Plant communities and mixtures

For any specific engineering purpose, it is unlikely that one species alone will fulfil all requirements, and it is anyway undesirable to rely on one species, i.e. monoculture (*see* Section 2.7.2). Mixtures of species with complementary characteristics will allow vegetation to fulfil the desired functions, and at the same time will allow adjustment of the species balance in response to changing environmental conditions. Appropriately selected mixtures will also be more viable ecologically. Mixtures therefore need to be designed with the plant community and its natural dynamics in mind. Other factors to take into account are cost and availability.

The proportions of each species will depend on the role each has to play, its competitive ability and successional status (*see* Section 2.2.3). Long-term species composition is not always predictable but, in a bioengineering context, management will be specified to maintain a desired species composition.

Mixtures can be designed to include species with a range of establishment rates, so that fast-establishing 'pioneers' stabilise the surface and protect more slowly establishing ones. Pioneer or 'nurse' species will die out as others develop and take over. For trees and shrubs, pioneer or nurse species are mixed with longer term climax species. A high proportion of nurse plants will require more frequent management to thin them out as they grow, in order to maintain the required vegetation structure. The design should take account of both vertical and horizontal structure within the mixture.

Grasses are usually selected as the main component of groundcover, often mixed with 10–50% of legume and/or other herbaceous species. The use of grass-dominated swards is based on agricultural and sports-turf experience, where grasses are the best plants for the purpose. Mixtures based on a majority of herbs or shrubby species could be more suitable for situations where deeper rooting is required.

A diverse mixture of herbs and/or grasses with a range of 6–10 species will allow for variability and flexibility in site conditions. Nurse species should be kept to a low proportion, say 10%, so that they do not dominate the sward and suppress more slowly growing species. Legumes will usually be a significant component of mixtures, particularly on soils with low fertility.

Low-maintenance mixtures are frequently used for areas not in intensive use. Many cultivars of grasses have been bred specifically for shortness of growth, requiring less maintenance. These low-maintenance types are less vigorous and will be slower to establish and to recover from damage. They will also have correspondingly less root growth, so may not always be suitable for bioengineering purposes.

4.1.4 Methods of propagation

Seeds

The most widely used form of propagation is from seeds, particularly for herbaceous plants. Seeding is also, however, becoming more widely used for trees and shrubs. Seeds are cheap and very versatile but during the establishment phase they are very vulnerable to desiccation and predation (*see* Section 2.6.1).

Sprigs

Herbaceous plants and grasses which spread by creeping rhizomes can be propagated by planting, or even broadcasting, chopped sections of rhizome which then take root and grow. Some trees and shrubs will also propagate in this way. This technique is not widely used in the UK.

Bare-rooted plants

Bare-rooted planting is widely used for trees and shrubs on large-scale schemes. There is a wide variety of choice in sizes and types. Herbaceous plants, reeds, sedges and some grasses, such as Marram Grass, will also propagate best by means of bare-rooted transplants.

Container-grown plants

A plant grown in a container can be planted with minimal disturbance to the roots at almost any time of the year. The use of container-grown stock can extend the planting season but is costly. There can be difficulties in encouraging the roots to grow out into the surrounding ground (*see* Section 4.5.3).

Tubed seedlings

Tubed seedlings have the merit of cheapness and ease of handling. They consist of seedlings or cuttings, up to one year old, grown in a small tube or container. Several types are available, in particular root trainers, which are thermoformed plastic folding pots with longitudinal grooves down the side which help to control root orientation, guiding roots downwards and discouraging spiralling around the pot.

Cuttings

Cuttings can be taken from plants, notably willows and poplars, which root easily from live wood. The size of cuttings depends on the planting technique, and varies from short stems for nursery rooting (300 mm) to long poles for fascines (2 m). Cuttings also include live brushwood used for slope work.

Turves

Grass and herbaceous vegetation can be pre-grown as turves for transplanting.

Plant-rich soil

Topsoil may contain a substantial 'seed bank' and many plant fragments, rhizomes and rootstocks. Techniques have been developed to utilise this for establishing vegetation where the range of species it contains would not be available commercially. The techniques include:

1. stripping and respreading the surface soil;
2. collecting 'hay-bales' when the plants are just seeding;
3. collecting seed and plant litter from the ground surface;
4. removing and transplanting small turves.

This approach might be used where restoration of a semi-natural 'wild' community is important. It has been applied to heather and grass moorland, woodland and grassland. The composition of the seed bank will not necessarily reflect that of the existing vegetation, and so advice should always be sought when using this technique.

4.1.5 Ecotypes and cultivars

Within any species of plant, there is a natural genetically-controlled variation in characteristics between different 'populations', usually forming distinct ecotypes with specific growth characteristics and site preferences. It has long been recognised that two plants of the same species but from differing habitats differ genetically and may not grow successfully in each other's habitats. This natural variation is exploited by man in selecting and crossing plants to produce cultivated varieties, i.e. cultivars with particular characteristics. This technique is the basis of plant breeding. It is not sufficient, therefore, to rely simply on a species specification to obtain the desired plant; it is also necessary to select the appropriate cultivars. Certification of approved cultivars is discussed in Section 4.3.9.

For plants such as trees, where wild sources are often used for propagation, some attention to the provenance or locality of origin is needed. When buying nursery tree stock provenance is rarely controlled, except for plants for forestry use which are mainly conifers. Much of the stock used in the UK is imported from Europe, especially the Netherlands, or is based on imported seed sources.

If the opportunity arises, however, it is preferable to obtain planting material from a suitable source or provenance. This may involve collecting local seed or cutting material; in some cases, particularly willows, this is the only way to obtain plant material adapted to the right conditions. Some nurseries are beginning to respond to the need for planting stock from native or otherwise suitable sources for use in special situations.

4.2 Site preparation

Careful preparation will enhance vegetation growth and help to overcome the establishment problems which often arise on construction sites. Much of the work can be incorporated into normal engineering operations, but specially modified equipment is sometimes required. A summary of the methods available to ameliorate adverse site conditions is given in Box 4.2.

4.2.1 Selection of soil materials

The simple system for assessing soil potential described in Box 2.10 can be used as a general guide to classify all material which the engineer intends to use as soil, regardless of origin, according to its potential for plant growth. Classes are allocated as follows.

Soil type

Class A   Highest growth potential, important when it is necessary for soil to have minimal restrictions on plant growth. Suitable for final soil covering or topsoil.
Class B   Where growth potential is not critical, but reasonable growth is still required. Also suitable for subsoil layers beneath Class A.
Class C   Will still support good growth if managed properly, but susceptible to handling problems which may restrict growth. Can also be used as subsoil layers.
   Suitability cannot be based on soil texture alone and the classes proposed in Box 2.10 have only general application. For some uses special soil characteristics may be required; examples are given in Box 4.3.

Soil fertility
Class A   Highly fertile, will produce dense vigorous growth, requiring higher maintenance and leading more quickly to successional changes. This is not always necessary nor desirable, however, and the group is best used for intensively managed areas and for grazing.
Class B   Moderate fertility; fertilisers may be required to support very productive growth.
Class C   Minimal fertility, suitable for low-maintenance vegetation but fertilisers will be necessary. Swards should have good legume component.
   Soil physical properties and fertility are defined separately so that different classes can be selected for each, depending on the situation.

Box 4.2 Methods available to ameliorate adverse site conditions (after Coppin and Bradshaw, 1982)

Ameliorants	Texture		Water retention		Excessive temperatures	Unstable surface	Compaction	Acidity	Alkalinity	Salinity	Toxicity
	Too fine	Too coarse	Too high	Too low							
Natural weathering, time	(+)						−	(+)	−	−	(−)
Reducing slope		+		(+)	+	+					
Compaction	−	+	−	(+)		+					
Ripping/scarification	+			+		(+/−)	+				
Liming (CaCO₃, Ca(OH)₂)						(−)		+	(−)		+
Inorganic chemical fertilisers										(−)	(−)
Bulk additions											
inorganic e.g. soil, inert waste	+	+	(+)	+	+	(+/−)	+	+	+	(−)	(−)
organic e.g. peat, manures	+	+		+			+		+	+	+
Drainage			+			+				+	
Irrigation				+							(−)

(− deleterious effect, + improvement, ( ) depends on site and material)

Box 4.3 Soil suitability for specific purposes based on texture

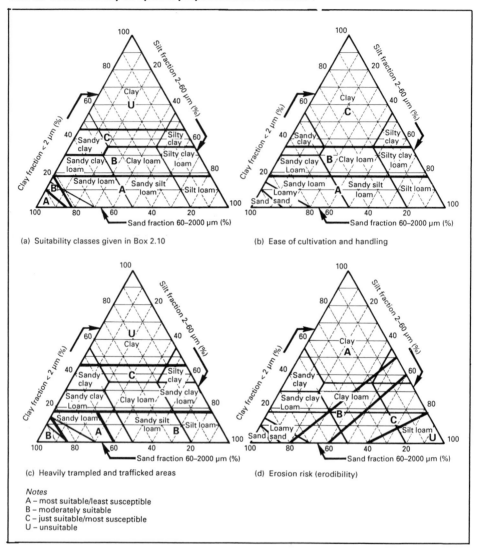

(a) Suitability classes given in Box 2.10

(b) Ease of cultivation and handling

(c) Heavily trampled and trafficked areas

(d) Erosion risk (erodibility)

Notes
A – most suitable/least susceptible
B – moderately suitable
C – just suitable/most susceptible
U – unsuitable

In specifying soil moving operations the engineer should be aware of the significance of soil horizons (*see* Section 2.4.4). In many cases it will be necessary to strip and replace more than one soil horizon in the proper sequence if full reinstatement of the original site conditions is required.

When importing topsoil, care in selection is needed to ensure that it is compatible with its new location and purpose. When used unwisely, topsoil can give rise to many problems, as described in Box 4.4, for example, when the pH or textural

Box 4.4 Use of topsoil

Before using topsoil the following points should be considered carefully

1. Is it really necessary for the purpose intended?
2. Can the right quality be obtained at reasonable cost?
3. Can it be handled and spread in a way that will not destroy any advantages which its use might provide?
4. Is it compatible with the underlying subsoil?
5. No amount of careful handling will re-create quickly a completely stable soil profile, this takes time to develop.
6. The addition of topsoil is not a universal panacea for revegetation problems

Advantages of topsoil	Disadvantages
Has existing fertility and organic matter content	May be too fertile for the intended purpose, especially if deep root penetration is to be encouraged
Vegetation should immediately grow very well	Can contain many weed seeds
	Costly to import, especially from any distance
May be already available on site	Can be of dubious quality unless source is well monitored
	May be difficult to integrate with underlying layers
	Fragile and difficult to handle without causing irreparable damage
	May be difficult to match geotechnical requirements (e.g. levels of compaction) with requirements for plant growth

characteristics of the topsoil do not suit the underlying subsoil on which it is laid. In particular, root penetration into the subsoil can be affected, leading to poor drought tolerance and inadequate root reinforcement. When topsoil is available on site, it usually makes good sense to conserve and re-use it. If the soil is obtained from an arable field, however, it may be too fertile for its new purpose, especially if the site is intended to require only a low level of maintenance.

Despite their inherent infertility, many mineral subsoils, spoils, overburden or other strata make good soil substitutes and can support vegetation.

4.2.2 Soil handling and spreading

The selection, handling and treatment of soils which are to be used within the potential root zone of the vegetation, say within 1 m of the final ground surface, should take account of:

1. their potential as a medium for plant growth;
2. continuity between soil layers.

Irreparable damage can be done, in terms of potential for plant growth, if a soil is handled incorrectly. The problems to avoid are:

1. stockpiling topsoil in such a way that the natural aerobic soil organisms are killed;
2. destroying the existing soil structure;
3. compacting soil to excessive densities that reduce water infiltration and inhibit root growth.

When moving large quantities of soil it is usual to employ the most cost-effective, and sometimes the largest, machinery available. For engineering purposees, the compaction effects of large machinery are beneficial, but tracking over surface soils with machinery which imposes a high ground pressure destroys soil structure and produces conditions which are very inhospitable to plant growth. The cost of precautions to avoid damage to soil may be offset against the benefits of improved plant establishment and growth. However the conflict between soil compaction for stability and looseness to permit plant growth is one which has to be considered carefully in each situation.

The risk of damage to a soil is related to its clay and moisture contents and hence to soil strength and bearing capacity. Clay soils are most at risk because they lose strength rapidly when they are wet and rely on their structure for natural permeability. Sandy soils are least susceptible and can be moved with little damage

Box 4.5 Soil handling restrictions and moisture content

The following are guidelines suggested for restricting the handling of soil materials to be used within 1 m of the final surface. Application of these will impose restrictions on a contractor's freedom of operation, so the contractual implications should be considered before using it.

Based on rainfall records kept on site

	Rainfall (mm) in last 24 hours		Rainfall (mm) in last 3 days	
Recommence soil handling	Risk*		Risk*	
	high	moderate	high	moderate
Straight away	<7	<10	<12	<5
Next day	7–15	10–20	12–20	15–25
After 2 days	>15	>20	>20	>25

* risk class of soil damage: high   = clay content >30%
                 moderate = clay content   18–30%

If there is heavy or persistent rain during the current day, then all soil handling and tracking over soil should be suspended.

Allowance should also be made for the depth of groundwater table or other sources of moisture.

Based on soil moisture deficit (SMD)

Avoid soil handling during periods when the SMD is:

<20 mm for high risk soils
<10 mm for moderate risk soils

SMD can be measured directly using soil tensiometers, or estimates are published for all areas of the UK on a weekly basis (*see* Section 2.5, Box 2.11)

Note: Procedure (a) is suitable for day to day site operations.
       Procedure (b) is better for longer–term planning, for the periods during which soil damage is least likely to occur.

at almost any moisture content up to field capacity. Soil strength is the governing factor, and an indication of susceptibility of a soil to damage at various moisture contents can be assessed by determining standard shear strengths and Atterberg limits. These can be compared to the likely compression and traction forces which may be exerted by the machinery used on site.

Damaged soil can never be fully restored by cultivation, however intensive, but there are a number of practices which, if followed, will reduce the extent of soil damage.

- Where possible, excavators and dumpers rather than scrapers should be used to move soil.
- Double handling should be avoided as much as possible.
- Stockpiles, where they are necessary, should be shallow and not heavily compacted but graded to shed rainfall. Long-term stockpiles should be seeded to avoid erosion.
- Handling of soil should be strictly controlled according to soil moisture conditions. A suggested guide is given in Box 4.5. Similar restrictions should apply to tracking over existing or re-spread soils, when wheel damage can be extensive. In addition to these, a useful rule of thumb is only to allow tracking over a soil the strength of which, as measured with a pocket penetrometer, is greater than the ground pressure of the machinery involved. Soil trafficability is discussed further in Section 6.7.1; *see* Box 6.21 for trafficability classes.
- Indiscriminate tracking by heavy earthmoving machinery over surfaces of existing or spread soil should be avoided. Vehicles should keep to the same wheeltracks as much as possible, so confining the damage. These wheel tracks can be specially treated later by deep cultivation.
- The temptation to travel repeatedly over an area of spread soil to grade off the surface should be resisted, since this will only produce a smooth, compacted soil surface which will make vegetation establishment difficult.

A range of techniques for soil spreading using heavy machinery but avoiding excessive surface compaction is illustrated in Figure 4.1.

Stability and vegetation performance will be improved by scarification to a depth of about 150 mm of the surface of each layer within the potential root zone (0.5–1.0 m). Scarification helps to ensure continuity of water movement, good root growth, integration of one layer with the next and, of particular importance, deep root penetration. Scarification also helps to improve soil stability when topsoil is spread loose over completed slopes. If the topsoil is placed over a compacted and smoothed surface, it is likely to slump, creep or slough off entirely, especially when wet, and carry away the vegetation. If any layer within the potential root zone has been heavily compacted during placement, it should be loosened to greater depth by deep cultivation or ripping (*see* Section 4.2.4).

Problems can arise because of a conflict between geotechnical requirements to meet particular shear strengths for slope stability and economy of earthwork construction and the need to maintain a suitable environment for plant growth.

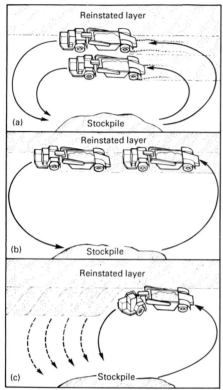

Soil surface reinstatement with earth scrapers:
(a) indiscriminate running over the site;
(b) improved method keeping to wheeltracks;
(c) improved method with no running over the
reinstated surface. Subsoiling of intermediate
layers will be necessary to relieve heavy
compaction caused by earth scraper

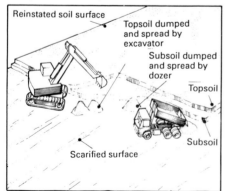

Reinstatement of topsoil and subsoil layers by
dumper and excavator. Soil material is dumped
on the fill surface and moved to its final position
by excavator or dozer. There is no running over
the reinstated surface.

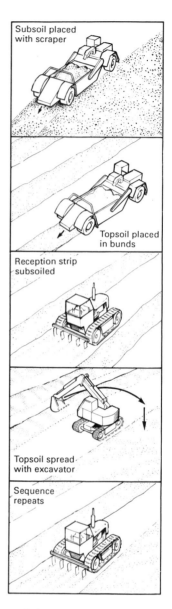

These techniques are appropriate for the final stages of an
earth moving operation for spreading any soil materials
which will form the top 1 m growing layer. They apply
equally to topsoils, subsoils and soil substitutes.

Figure 4.1 Techniques for soil spreading
with heavy machinery

Generally, vegetation needs a minimum of 12% air voids in order to thrive. For soils placed in the potential root zone, within 0.5–1 m of the final surface, a compromise is often necessary.

In most cases, quick-growing vegetation will compensate for early deficiencies in soil strength. Alternatively additional temporary safeguards against instability may be adopted, such as geotextiles, geowebs or live wood planting (*see* Sections 4.2.7 and 6.2.9).

4.2.3 Slope contouring and grading

The gradient of a slope has an important bearing on its management, since it is its accessibility to machinery, for example, which determines the kind of management operations which are carried out. Section 4.9 discusses safe working methods on slopes. Turning movements on slopes are particularly dangerous and all areas which are to be prepared and maintained mechanically should be provided with safe areas for turning at the top and the bottom of the slope.

Slopes require some special measures at the time of construction in order to improve their capacity to support vegetation. With excavated slopes, completion leaves a surface of undisturbed soil and rock strata. There is little opportunity for surface or soil modifications on steep slopes, except those which can be achieved by the machinery as the slope is formed. For good plant growth on embankment slopes, machine-laid layers should be uncompacted towards the sides (*see* Section 4.2.2). On steep slopes, surface or soil modification has to be carried out as the slope is formed, as access will be limited once the slope is completed.

On long slopes surface water flows can increase in volume, to the extent that rill and gully erosion occurs. Where rainfall erosion risks are high and infiltration rates are low, effective slope lengths should be restricted (*see* Section 6.3.3). Reducing slope lengths involves constructing a series of berms or terraces to intercept runoff, as shown in Figure 4.2. To allow machinery access for seeding and maintenance, these berms should be wide enough to accommodate a turning movement, otherwise they need only be terraces 1 m or so wide. All terraces should be angled back into the slope, with a ditch, drain or grassed channel on the inside. Terraces should have a gradient across the slope to remove water, which is discharged into down-slope drains consisting of stone-lined gullies, pipes or flumes. The gradient of the terrace should be determined by the velocity of flow permitted in the drain/channel.

The crest of a slope and any sharp changes of gradient are the most difficult to vegetate and usually the places where erosion begins. They also suffer most from drought, exposure and wind erosion. Rounding off sharp edges reduces these problems (*see* Figure 4.2) and is a standard practice with some authorities. Plate 2.D shows a typical over steepened roadside cut where an overhang has developed at the junction between the man-made and natural slopes. In the foreground are trials, established by the Welsh Office Highways Directorate at the Welsh Office, to examine the effectiveness of different methods of controlling erosion.

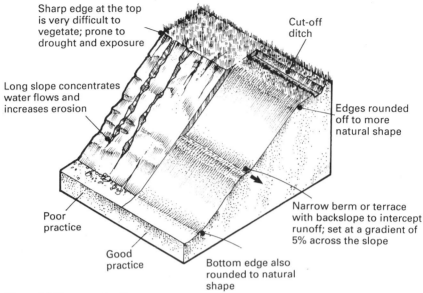

Figure 4.2 Slope construction

4.2.4 Deep cultivation

Deep cultivation helps to solve problems posed by excessive soil compaction in a number of ways:

1. increasing infiltration of water into the soil, and thus reducing surface runoff;
2. reducing soil density, and thus increasing available water capacity and rooting potential;
3. providing drainage pathways through the soil, if the ripping is carried out along a gradient.

The ideal implement for deep cultivation is a winged tine (Figure 4.3), working to 0.6–0.8 m depth with the tines spaced 1.0–1.2 m apart. This can be directly mounted on a crawler or towed as a separate implement, as shown in Plate 4A. The wings greatly increase the degree of disturbance and non-winged tines would have to be spaced 0.5 m or so apart to achieve a similar effect.

If the site is flat, with restricted downward permeability, ripping will tend to increase waterlogging unless drainage is installed to remove water. Overall drainage on level sites can be improved by forming a series of parallel ridges 30 m apart and 1.5 m high. These are then cross-ripped and water is removed by drains laid in the valleys between the ridges (Wilson, 1985).

On slopes, the direction of ripping relative to the contour will influence the balance between drainage and soil water storage. In most of the UK, some drainage is desirable. A balance has to be achieved between increasing the soil water storage for good vegetation growth and providing drainage to prevent the build-up of soil water, with subsequent reduction in slope stability. Ripping at too

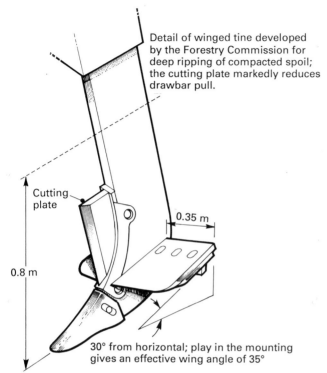

Detail of winged tine developed
by the Forestry Commission for
deep ripping of compacted spoil;
the cutting plate markedly reduces
drawbar pull.

Cutting
plate

0.35 m

0.8 m

30° from horizontal; play in the mounting
gives an effective wing angle of 35°

Figure 4.3 Winged tine implement for deep ripping of compacted soil (after Wilson, 1985)

(a) Typical implement showing winged tines

(b) Problems can occur getting deep
penetration of the soil; here the tines are
only churning up the surface

Plate 4A Three-tine ripper mounted on a large crawler

steep an angle will encourage rapid surface runoff and may also dramatically increase slope erosion. As a guide, the gradient of any rip lines should be about 1 in 20 in lighter soils and 1 in 15 in clay soils. Gradients of rip lines should never exceed 1 in 10. If waterlogging persists, additional drainage measures, such as a piped system, may be required.

The effectiveness of any deep cultivation depends on the moisture content of the soil. If the soil is too dry, cultivation is difficult and increased resistance tends to force the tine out of the ground. When clay soils are wet ripping is usually ineffective. No cultivation should be carried out if the soil moisture content is above the plastic limit. As a general rule, heavy soils should have a soil moisture deficit of at least 50 mm before deep cultivation is attempted.

4.2.5 Final surface preparation

To a large extent, the method of vegetation establishment will dictate surface preparation (*see* Section 4.9). A smooth finish is only required where the vegetation will need to be close mown, or in water channels to reduce surface roughness. The following types of surfaces are appropriate to various seeding methods.

1. Drilling: a reasonably level surface and a loose tilth are necessary for the seed-drill machine, but machines are available for use on rough terrain.
2. Broadcast and harrowing: a reasonably fine tilth is needed to allow the harrows to bury the seed to the correct depth.
3. Broadcast without harrowing (includes hydroseeding): a rough surface texture will result in the best seedling establishment.

Box 4.6 Surface cultivation prior to seeding or planting

1. When accessibility is not a problem (slopes up to 1 in 3)
   - Initial cultivation up to 300 mm or so depth with tined cultivator to loosen compacted soil and incorporate any fertilisers or ameliorants (*see* Sections 4.2.6 and 4.2.7).
   - Removal of any large boulders, stones or surface obstructions.
   - Disc harrow to produce a reasonable tilth on heavy soils; rolling with a Cambridge roller may be sufficient on lighter soils.
   - Stonepicking and removal of obstructions which are upstanding. The specification should take account of site conditions and after–use.
   - Seed, harrow and roll.
2. Limited accessibility (such as on slopes of 1 in 2.5)
   - The above operations can be carried out using tracked machinery or specially adapted wheeled tractors.
   - Limited cultivation with, say, just the tined cultivator, making two or more passes in different directions, leaving the tilth in a coarser condition.
   - Using a long-armed excavator to spread and level the soil in loose and friable condition.
   - Use heavy harrows or a 'clodbuster' dragged along the slope on a chain from the top.
3. No direct access (slopes more than 1 in 2)
   - Long-armed excavator to trim the surface and leave a suitable surface texture
   - Special cultivators consisting of long arms, booms or chains mounted on a tractor working from the top or bottom of the slope (*see* Figure 4.4).

   Note: The direction of cultivation on slopes is important (*see* Section 4.2.5).

Surface preparation should achieve a texture suitable to promote vegetation growth, particularly on slopes where erosion control is important. The soil surface should be loosened, fractured, grooved or stepped, according to the situation. A rough surface texture provides a better microclimate at the soil surface; seeds can fall down into cracks and crevices, where moisture levels are higher and drought effects less severe. A smoothed surface will not have such protected microsites and, unless the seed is properly buried in a loose tilth, it will be at the mercy of hostile surface conditions (*see* Section 4.3).

Cultivation techniques are summarised in Box 4.6. The extent of surface cultivation employed will depend on accessibility, gradient, moisture content, establishment methods and type of soil.

Normal cultivation techniques can be carried out on slopes as steep as 1 in 3, while at steeper gradients safety becomes an important factor. Tracked or double-wheeled machinery can operate on slopes up to 1 in 2.5. Working up and down the slope is usually preferred for safety reasons, but this will leave vertical striations which can dramatically increase erosion, so that working across a slope should be undertaken where possible, as shown in Figure 4.4.

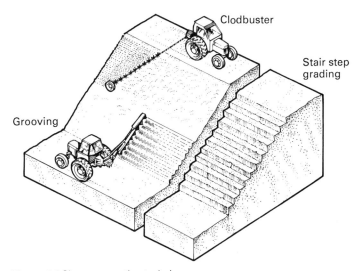

Figure 4.4 Slope preparation techniques

4.2.6 Soil improvement

Soil used as a growing medium will often benefit from improvement. Soil ameliorants fall into three classes.

1. Bulk organic matter (manures, composts, etc), which improve the structure, fertility and water-holding capacity of the soil.
2. Inorganic fertilisers and lime, which improve soil fertility.

3. 'Special' soil conditioners which improve soil structure and water holding capacity.

The use of bulk organic manures, composts or waste products to improve soil depends to a large extent on local availability and price. Those with a high nutrient content, especially nitrogen, are obviously desirable, as the nutrients are largely in a slow-release form and become available as the organic matter decomposes. Organic ameliorants should be used with care because those with a carbon:nitrogen ratio greater than 25:1, such as straw, will consume available nitrogen in the soil as the organic matter decomposes. Inorganic nitrogen fertiliser may need to be increased to compensate for this condition.

Inorganic chemicals are a cheap and readily available source of plant nutrients. Their nutrient content is given as the percentage content of nitrogen, phosphate and potash ($N:P_2O_5:K_2O$) (*see* Box 2.9), plus any other constituents such as magnesium. Although they are more expensive, slow-release fertilisers are often preferable for low maintenance areas, because the nutrient supply is spread over a longer period than is the case with conventional fertiliser.

The most widely applied liming material is ground limestone, though slaked lime is sometimes used. Ground agricultural limestone typically has a particle size such that 80% will pass through a BS 100 mesh sieve (0.15 mm). For low-maintenance areas where control of acidity over a long period is desirable, coarser grades of ground limestone should be used.

The factors to take into account in determining fertiliser and lime applications are:

1. existing fertility levels in the soil;
2. the demands of the intended vegetation and level of productivity required;
3. the soil type, its ability to store and release soluble nutrients;
4. the amount of rainfall likely to leach out soluble nutrients;
5. any nutrients contained in bulk organic ameliorants.

Special soil ameliorants such as soil conditioners should be used cautiously and only on the advice of a specialist. Materials of particular benefit are those which improve the structure of heavy soils and absorb water and help to retain it in dry soils. Such materials include:

1. alginates: natural seaweed extracts which provide nutrients, improve soil structure and absorb water;
2. polymers: manufactured compounds which absorb many times their own volume of water and release it slowly;
3. polysaccharides: natural and artificial products which help to improve heavy soils.

Added materials should be worked well into the soil during cultivation. Deep placement may encourage deeper rooting, so incorporation into successive soil layers is often advantageous. Bulky organic materials can also be used as a surface mulch to good effect (*see* Sections 4.3.3 and 4.3.4).

4.2.7 Establishment aids and erosion control

The period between completion of the ground surface and establishment of vegetation cover is critical since this is when the risk of erosion, surface slippage and surface drought is greatest. A number of measures can be taken to reduce this risk. For example, the surface layers of loose soil can be restrained with a plastic or degradable geoweb (*see* Section 6.2.9) which is installed at the time of soil spreading, as shown in Plate 4.B. This will hold the soil in place during the time

(*a*) During installation and soil spreading

(*b*) After seeding and establishment of grass

Plate 4B Use of a cellular geoweb to hold soil in place on a steep slope

Box 4.7 Surface treatment of slopes to reduce erosion and aid vegetation establishment

Surface cultivation
  Slopes <18° (1:3) should be left roughened and undulating.
  Slopes >18° but <27° can be stair-step graded, grooved or roughened.
  Slopes >27° (1:2) can be stair-step graded.

Roughening is done across the slope using cultivation implements such as harrows or tines (*see* Figure 4.4).
  Grooving of a slope creates a series of parallel serrations of loosened soil, the grooves being 80–150 mm deep, 400–800 mm apart. This can be undertaken with a simple scarifying blade, on a boom or arm mounted on a machine operating from the top or bottom of the slope.
  Stair-step grading involves cutting the slope into a series of steps, up to 1 m wide (but usually less) with the ratio of vertical:horizontal faces being less than 1:1. Rapid establishment of vegetation soon hides the appearance. Soil which sloughs off the corners and vertical faces is caught on the ledges and provides an ideal medium for growth of plants.

Geotextiles (*see* Section 3.8.1)
  Where erosion prior to vegetation establishment is expected to be especially severe.
  Where some additional erosion resistance is necessary, e.g. spillways.
  When erosion may also be due to other agencies such as soil creep, and additional surface reinforcement is necessary.

There are three types (*see* Appendix 2):

● Two-dimensional netting or mesh, fixed to the soil surface. Often biodegradable, such as jute netting.
● Three-dimensional plastic mesh embedded in the soil surface.
● Three-dimensional mulch mat (biodegradable) laid on the soil surface.
● Glassfibre matrix tacked with binder, acting as reinforcement and mulch.

To be fully effective, geotextiles must be very firmly fixed to the soil surface and must have a good intimate contact with the underlying surface over their whole area. Installation details are given in Figure 4.5.

Soil binders or stabilisers
Liquid plastic, rubber or natural emulsions sprayed onto the soil surface in water solution. When dry, they form a protective film or crust, restraining soil particles. For details, *see* hydroseeding, Section 4.3.3. Binders or stabilisers are a good, cheap, temporary solution but they do not, on their own, enhance the establishment of vegetation and can reduce water infiltration, thereby increasing runoff. They are not effective under conditions of intense runoff or overland water flow.

Mulches
Long-fibred mulches such as chopped straw and natural wood or cotton fibres, often tacked down with a binder or rolled out as a pre-prepared mat. Application of mulches is discussed under hydroseeding (Section 4.3.3) and mulchseeding (Section 4.3.4). Mulches are a good short-term establishment aid, reducing erosion and surface drought.

required for root growth to develop sufficiently to anchor and reinforce the soil. Control of surface erosion on slopes can be achieved by several methods, which are described in Box 4.7 and Section 6.3.3. These include the use of geotextiles (*see* Section 3.8.1) as surface protection, as illustrated in Figure 4.5 and Plate 4.C.

Wind erosion protection also involves increasing surface roughness, but with the direction of cultivation across that of the prevailing airflow. Some short-term protection of the surface using soil binders (*see* Section 4.3.3) may be necessary where the soil is very dry and fine grained or the site is exposed.

Plate 4C Installation of geotextiles on steep slopes; trial panels with three-dimensional synthetic mat (left) and jute netting (right)

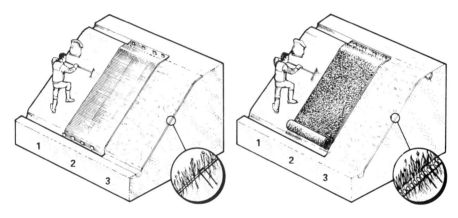

1 Surface smoothed, raked and fertilised.
2 Geotextile rolled down slope and pinned, securely fastened at top and bottom of slope in trench[2].
3 Seed broadcast dry over netting so it falls into interslices.

(a) Two-dimensional erosion control net (biodegradable) or seedmat

1 Surface smoothed, raked, fertilised.
2 Mat rolled down slope and pinned, securely fastened in trench at top and bottom of slope[2]. Overlap 100 mm.
3 Seed broadcast and soil brushed over netting to cover. Seed should be broadcast over top of soil and lightly tamped if necessary.

(b) Three-dimensional synthetic erosion control and surface reinforcement mat

Note
[1] It is important to ensure that the geotextile is in intimate contact with the ground surface over its whole area.
[2] Care should be taken not to create a potential weakness at the top of the slope with the trench. This should be some distance back from the crest.
[3] Geotextile types are described further in Appendix 2.

Figure 4.5 Installation of geotextiles for erosion control and surface protection

4.3 Seeding

There are five principal methods of applying seeds:

1. drilling: direct placement of seeds in the soil;
2. broadcasting: dry-spreading seeds over the soil surface;
3. hydroseeding: spreading seeds in a water slurry;
4. mulchseeding: wet or dry constituents with a heavy mulch layer applied dry;
5. hand seeding: includes hand broadcasting, spot seeding and similar techniques.

The first three techniques are the most widely used; their relative advantages and limitations are compared in Box 4.8. The use of broadcasting, hydroseeding or mulchseeding depends partly on access but mainly on other site conditions, such as the severity of the climate and the risk of surface erosion. A seed lying on the soil surface is at the mercy of drought and cold at a critical time. Extremes of dessication and temperature which occur at the soil surface can dramatically reduce the chances of seedling establishment (*see* Section 2.6.1). Seeds can be protected in several ways:

- burial, either by placement (drilling) or incorporation (harrowing or rolling);
- a rough soil surface: seeds will fall into cracks and crevices which have a better microclimate;
- mulching, in lieu of burial, to cover the seed.

Too deep a burial by soil or mulch will prevent growth.

4.3.1 Drilling

When topography, terrain and soil characteristics permit, seeding can be carried out with conventional agricultural seed drills but these are rarely rugged enough for use on construction sites. Rough terrain drills are more suitable in these circumstances.

4.3.2 Broadcasting

Broadcasting is a cheap and convenient method of seeding on most terrain accessible to wheeled tractors. Light harrowing or rolling with a Cambridge roller will assist seed burial, though this may not be necessary on rough-textured soils. Seed can be broadcast by hand on difficult terrain. Pneumatic broadcasters are available, where seed is fed into an air stream and then blown out through a nozzle. These are useful as a backpack model in areas inaccessible to machines.

4.3.3 Hydroseeding (hydraulic seeding)

Hydroseeding is a technique for the rapid application of seeds and fertilisers onto an area where, for reasons of access, speed of application or ground conditions, conventional techniques cannot be used. It is not an alternative to topsoiling or

Plate 4D Hydroseeding a steep slope. Note the rough surface texture
which will hold seeds well

proper surface preparation, though some standard construction specifications may
unwittingly give this impression, leading to frequent misuse of the hydroseeding
process and disappointment with the results. Surface preparation and soil
amelioration are as important for hydroseeding as for any other technique,
notwithstanding that on slopes and difficult terrain, where hydroseeding is most
widely and properly used, preparation can be difficult (*see* Section 4.2.5).

Specialised hydroseeding machinery usually consists of a tank of 700–14,000
litres capacity, fitted with a slurry pump, paddles for stirring and a moveable
monitor jet and hoses. This is mounted on a lorry or trailer to form a highly mobile
unit as illustrated in Plate 4.D.

Hydroseeding consists of mixing the constituents into a slurry with water, which
is then sprayed onto the ground. Typical constituents of the slurry are:

1. seeds
2. legume inoculum – *Rhizobium* bacteria (*see* Section 4.3.9)
3. soluble fertiliser
4. slow release fertiliser
5. mulch–bulk material to act as a carrier for other constituents, to protect seeds,
   reduce soil moisture loss and provide initial erosion protection
6. stabiliser/binder – to protect soil surface from erosion and tack down seeds and
   mulch.

Most of the materials are insoluble and therefore have to be kept in suspension with
paddles. Liquid application rates vary, a rate of 2 litres/m^2 being the minimum for a
fairly even application on open sites, with up to 4 litres/m^2 for heterogeneous sites
or where a very even application is important. The slurry pump can usually deliver
about 10–15% solids, so if mulch material has to be applied the work should be
done in two passes, the bulk of the mulch material always being applied in the
second pass.

Box 4.8 Advantages and limitations of various seeding methods

	Drilling	Broadcasting	Hydroseeding	Dry mulchseeding
Topography and terrain	Slopes <15°, good terrain necessary	Slopes <20°, unless by hand; can cope with rough terrain	Any terrain, up to 40 m reach with spray (depends on wind), up to 200 m reach with hose	Any terrain, slopes <45° but reach only 20 m or so
Obstructions	Limited; seed drill needs a clean site	Few limits	Few limits	Few limits
Season and rainfall	Limited by high soil moisture	Limited to warm moist season; incorporation or mulch extends season	Limited to warm moist seasons; mulch extends season	The heavy mulch extends season and protects seeds in hostile environments
Soil texture	Not stony soil, difficult on heavy soils	Rough surface allows seeds to fall into cracks with better microclimate	Rough surface improves microclimate, but any soil if mulched	Any
Seed rates	Low rates are sufficient	Higher rates to allow for losses during establishment	High rates on poor quality soils to allow for losses during establishment	High rates on poor quality soils
Seed sizes	Can only cope with uniform, small seeds; mixtures well mixed beforehand	A variety of small seed sizes can be spread, mixtures well mixed beforehand	Any seed size can be accommodated: grasses, herbs and trees; no pre-mixing necessary	Depends on seeding machinery

Box 4.8 (Continued)

	Drilling	Broadcasting	Hydroseeding	Dry mulchseeding
Seed distribution	Uniform, in rows; bare ground between rows is unprotected	Variable, random	Random, can be very difficult to control with inexperienced operators	Random, can be variable, difficult to control with inexperienced operators
Seed establishment	Most effective method	Variable, improved with incorporation	Variable, improved with a mulch	Good under right conditions
Fertilising	Usually a separate operation	Separate operation; incorporation mixes in	Can be done in same operation, but surface application can be antagonistic to germinating seeds	Separate operation
Mulching or incorporation	Not required, seed placed at correct depth	Desirable; separate operation except where surface is very rough, e.g. harrowing	Mulch required, can be done in the same operation	Usually high mulch rates used
Equipment	Seed drills available in most locations	Easily available: hand, tractor and helicopter mounting	Specialised hydroseeding equipment	Broadcaster or hydroseeder, mulchblower
Relative cost	Usually inexpensive on easy terrain	Cheapest on suitable areas	Expensive but cost-effective on rough terrain	Expensive but cost-effective on hostile sites
Difficulty and logistics	Straightforward; normal agricultural machinery	Very easy; normal agricultural machinery	Specialist machinery and experienced operators; quick to undertake	Specialist machinery and experienced operators; complex process

Hydroseeding is carried out by specialist firms who may have developed specific techniques. The specification should be clear about the finish that the ground will receive before seeding, the erosion risk, and the degree of protection required for the seeds. Within these parameters, however, firms should be free to include their own preferred prescriptions and constituents.

Application can be very variable when hydroseeding, especially on difficult terrain. On very uneven terrain, where there are many obstructions, or where an even cover is very important, the application should be split into two passes, each made from a different direction. This will also help to avoid 'shadows' behind obstructions.

Mulches, binders and stabilisers are vital constituents of the hydroseeding mixture as aids to establishment. How they are used depends on the site conditions and season of seeding. Typical mulch materials include straw, woodfibre, peat or proprietary cotton/cellulose fibre. Mulches are often applied at far too low a rate; to be effective, they should cover the ground surface and the seeds, usually achieved by applying 1.5–3.0 tonnes/ha. Low mulch levels are rarely effective and only help to act as a 'marker' during hydroseeding application.

Box 4.9 Mulch requirements for hydroseeding and mulchseeding

Season[1] (climate)	Site Conditions			Requirements for	
	Surface state[2]	Soil moisture[3]	Erosion risk[4]	Mulch rate[5,6]	Binder
Spring	Smooth	Good	Low	Low	No
		Poor		High	Yes
	Rough	Good		Low/none	No
		Poor	Low	Low	No
			High	High	No
Summer	Smooth			– Do not seed –	
	Rough	Poor		Very high	Yes
		Good	Low	High	Yes
Autumn	Smooth	Good	Low	Low	No
			High	Low	Yes
		Poor		High	Yes
	Rough	Good	Low	Low/none	No
			High	Low	Yes
		Poor		Low	Yes
Winter				Very high	Yes

[1] Aspect, altitude and latitude will modify this considerably; requirements for spring and autumn might apply on north-facing slopes or, at high altitude, during summer. Conversely summer requirements might apply during spring or autumn on south-facing slopes.
[2] Surface state depends on the surface finish, cultivation and tilth of the soil.
[3] Soil moisture depends on a combination of the available water capacity and recent rainfall.
[4] Erosion risk during the establishment period resulting from rainsplash runoff.
[5] Mulch rates depend on the material being used but, generally, low rates would be about 1.5 tonnes dry solids per hectare, high rates up to 3 tonnes and very high rates up to 5 tonnes per hectare.
[6] Where no mulch is required, broadcast seeding is appropriate. For high and very high rates, dry mulchseeding is used.

A mulch improves seedling establishment in two important ways:

1. by reducing water evaporation, thereby retaining soil moisture;
2. by preventing erosion due to raindrop impact and runoff.

Stabilisers are chemical products which bind soil particles together, reducing soil erosion. Binders are similar products used to bind mulch and seed materials to the soil surface. Both materials may reduce surface permeability, reducing water infiltration but also reducing evaporation. The use of mulches and binders for different situations is summarized in Box 4.9.

Further discussion of the hydroseeding process, including details of all the constituents and how they can be used, is given in Coppin and Bradshaw (1982) and Roberts and Bradshaw (1985).

4.3.4 Mulchseeding

The foregoing discussion of mulches in relation to hydroseeding applies also to mulchseeding. The main difference between the two techniques is that the mulch is applied dry, using for example a special mulch-blowing machine, as shown in Plate 4.E. Such machines may not be able to apply seeds, fertilisers and binders at the

Plate 4E A mulch-blower applying chopped wheat straw tacked with bitumen emulsion

same time. If this is the case, these elements can be spread by broadcasting, hand seeding or hydroseeding. The main advantage of dry mulching is that larger quantities of bulk mulches, such as chopped straw or glassfibre 'rovings', can be applied to sites where the soil and climate are hostile or the surface erosion risk is very high, as illustrated in Plate 4.F. The method is also used for seeding with species that are particularly sensitive to drought during establishment.

Chopped wheat straw or hay are the most widely used materials for mulching. Rates of 4.5–6.0 tonnes/ha are usually appropriate, much higher than normal hydroseeding equipment can apply. A binder is also necessary to fix the mulch to the soil surface. The very heavy mulches often used to protect a slope and conserve

Plate 4F Fibreglass rovings applied to a channel to reduce scour. This mulch would be tacked down with a bitumen binder to keep it in place while a grass sward grows

Plate 4G Steep slope protected with a pre-seeded mulch mat, showing initial growth of the grass

soil moisture may be so thick as to smother smaller seeded species. In this case the finer seeds are best broadcast over the top of the mulch, so that they fall down into it for protection.

4.3.5 Seed mats

Seed mats are a variation on mulching, where a pre-prepared mat of seeds and mulch, usually straw, coir or paper, is sewn into a light mesh or geotextile, which can be rolled out and pegged directly onto the ground surface. Fertilisers and soil amendments are raked into the soil before the mat is laid. For these methods to be successful the ground surface has to be smooth and friable, with no major undulations or obstructions. It is very important that the mat is installed and fixed in good contact with the ground over all its area. Installation and fixing procedures are much the same as for surface geotextiles; *see* Figure 4.5 and Plate 4.G.

Provision and installation of seed matting is labour intensive and expensive, but the method is particularly useful for situations where:

1. the site is accessible only to labour;
2. the site is too small or remote for hydroseeding;
3. extremely hostile or erosive conditions are expected.

4.3.6 Spot seeding

Spot seeding, as illustrated in Figure 4.6, is a hand seeding technique used where:

1. there is an existing groundcover and it is desired to introduce different species such as trees and shrubs into a grass sward;
2. where continuous ground cover is not needed in the short term and seeding in spots or patches is a more cost-effective use of seed material.

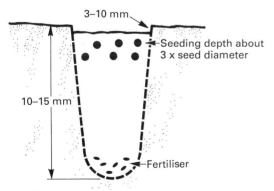

Fertiliser placed deeper to encourage rooting downwards. Depression helps to accumulate moisture.

(a) Spot seeding hole on level ground

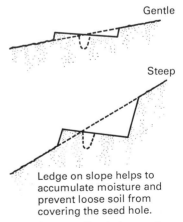

Ledge on slope helps to accumulate moisture and prevent loose soil from covering the seed hole.

(b) Spot seeding ledge on slope

Figure 4.6 Spot seeding

Seeding spots can vary in size from 100–150 mm diameter containing a few seeds only, to 1–2 m² patches containing many species. The density of seed spots depends on the species being used and the density of vegetation cover required. Any existing groundcover should be killed or removed from around the spot before seeding, in order to reduce competition for moisture and nutrients.

4.3.7 Modifying existing swards

An existing sward not fulfilling its required engineering function should not necessarily be completely removed, because the temporary protection it may be providing could still be important. Instead a non-destructive modification of the sward is necessary. Sometimes an adjustment in management practices alone may be sufficient to bring about the necessary changes, but, if this is not the case, other species must be introduced. Spot seeding is one way of doing this. Although appropriate for trees and shrubs, it is not practicable for introducing herbaceous species on a large scale.

Overseeding an existing sward with fresh seed is often unsatisfactory. To improve germination, measures must be taken to:

1. reduce competition from existing vegetation;
2. ensure the new seed is in close contact with the soil.

Agricultural machinery has been developed which can spray a strip of turf with a contact herbicide such as paraquat and then place fresh seed in a drill in the centre of the strip. The spacing of the strips is usually around 200–450 mm. Rough terrain machines are available, such as the rotary stripseeder, which has independently-mounted drill heads, each with a rotovator blade, and can cultivate and seed a narrow strip in one operation, as shown in Plate 4.H.

Plate 4H Rotary strip seeder for rough terrain

Alternatively on rough terrain or slopes, the sward should be first cut if necessary, then scarified with heavy harrows or a light cultivator. The seed is then sown, and finally the surface is given a light harrowing or rolling to incorporate the seeds.

4.3.8 Seeding trees and shrubs

Mulching, drilling, broadcasting and spot seeding techniques are also appropriate for most seeds of trees and shrubs. Because the seeds are more expensive or less abundant, however, greater care will be needed to ensure their successful establishment. Trees and shrubs also tend to be more sensitive than grass seedlings to drought stress at the critical establishment stage. The following are the most important considerations for successful tree and shrub seeding.

1. Good ground preparation is necessary.
2. Competition from existing vegetation or nurse species should be kept to a minimum. Chemical or manual weed control should be used where necessary.
3. A higher degree of seed protection (mulching or incorporation) than for herbaceous species is required.
4. Seeds vary greatly in size, so where a mixture is being used sowing should be done separately for each size class. For example, larger seeds should be incorporated to the correct depth and smaller seeds broadcast and mulched on top.
5. Very large seeds such as acorns should be spot seeded after any main seeding.
6. Many tree and shrub seeds are easily damaged by passing through a hydroseeder pump, so recirculation of the mixture through the pump should be avoided.
7. Seed may need to be pre-treated to break dormancy.

These points apart, techniques for direct seeding of trees and shrubs are the same as for grasses and herbs.

4.3.9 Specifying and buying seeds

The production and marketing of many seeds is covered by regulations designed to protect the user and guarantee standards of purity and viability. The EC Plant Varieties and Seeds Regime covers amenity turf grasses, and the Fodder Plants Seeds Regulations, 1980, cover agricultural varieties. There are also EC regulations covering seeds used in forestry, governing registered approved sources of parent stock. Therefore seeds of recognised amenity and agricultural grasses, legumes, crops and some forest trees bought in the UK should be of a guaranteed minimum standard of purity, germination, freedom from weed seeds, and consistency of type. Such seed is known as Certified Seed, and each bag of pure seed carries a blue label, confirming that the batch has been tested and meets with the minimum standards.

In the UK there are a number of species, particularly infrequently used amenity grasses, that are not covered by certification regulations, referred to as commercial seed. Each bag of seed carries a brown label. Regulations governing commercial strains are under review at present and may in future have standards of purity and germination, though lower than for certified strains. Seeds of wildflowers and many trees and shrubs, especially if collected from the wild, are not covered by any regulations, so will have absolutely no guarantee of quality, purity or viability.

Seed testing of certified and commercial strains is undertaken as a matter of course by an official seed testing laboratory (in the UK through the Ministry of Agriculture, Fisheries and Food and the Forestry Commission). It is possible to have any seed lot tested by such a laboratory to check its viability.

The seed supplier should be asked to provide copies of seed test certificates for all seeds sown, including any seed lots not automatically covered by the regulations. Minimum levels of purity and germination can be specified, but the contract should be so arranged that any constituent which is lower than specified will have to be increased in quantity to attain the required pure live seed content.

The mixing of seed for sale is strictly controlled. Once seed is mixed, an official green label must be stitched on each bag on which the following information must be stated:

1. 'seed mixture for . . . . . ';
2. the type of mixture: amenity, agricultural or ley;
3. certifying authority;
4. reference number (which can be cross referenced with the original seed lot and thus the Seed Certificate);
5. month and year when sealed;
6. nett or gross weight;
7. Details of any additives, e.g. bird repellent, inoculum.

Contractors obtain their seed mixtures from a seed merchant. In the UK, blue and brown labels from seed bags would not normally be seen on site. However the green label from a mixture of such strains should be inspected by site supervision staff. The serial numbers can be compared with the official seed test certificates provided on request by the seed supplier. If there is any doubt about the authenticity of the seed, a copy of the original invoice supplied to the seed merchant should be requested. This will give details of the year of harvest, purity and germination rate and certificate number of the batch of seed which has been supplied.

Specifications for seed mixtures should state clearly the percentage by weight of each constituent listed by species, acceptable certified cultivars or commercial strain as appropriate, or otherwise the source or provenance, together with the total quantity required. Any special treatment of the seed should be included in the specification, for example:

1. inoculation or pelleting of legumes with the appropriate strain of *Rhizobium* bacteria;
2. pre-treatment of tree and shrub seed to break dormancy. The seed supplier will be able to determine the precise pre-treatment requirements for each species present.

In order to 'fix' nitrogen, legumes need to be infected with the correct strain of a bacterium (*Rhizobium*), and this should be supplied at the time of seeding. The 'inoculum' can be either coated onto the seed or spread along with it.

4.4 Turfing

Turfing, or sodding, involves the transplanting of pre-grown swards, usually grass-based, along with the roots and a thin layer of soil, onto a prepared site. A complete turf cover gives an instant, stable sward, but usually at much greater cost than other techniques. Turf can be used cost-effectively in appropriate situations:

1. in critical areas, where an instant, stable cover is necessary, such as on verges and around a waterline where erosion or disturbance is concentrated;
2. on large areas of slope in grids or rows, to provide some initial erosion protection and act as nuclei from which surrounding areas are colonised.

Turfing is not a good way of introducing deep or tap-rooted species, as the roots of these are severed during transplanting.

Poor root penetration, as a result of inadequate subsoil preparation and drought, is a frequent cause of turf failure. A temporary restraint to prevent movement and lifting of the turf is necessary in some applications, such as grassed spillways, until good root anchorage is achieved.

4.4.1 Sources of turf

Commercial turf nurseries produce large quantities of consistent product but have little flexibility to produce special types for particular purposes. Turves are usually produced as small slabs or strips, 0.3–0.4 m wide and 0.5–1.0 m long, which are easy to handle, as illustrated in Figure 4.7. Alternatively, local turf can be stripped from areas being disturbed, near to where it is needed. The sward is not pre-prepared for stripping, however, so turf quality is often poor, especially if the ground is uneven or stony. An advantage is that the plants will be adapted to local conditions. Pre-grown turf mats often incorporate netting or a reinforcing

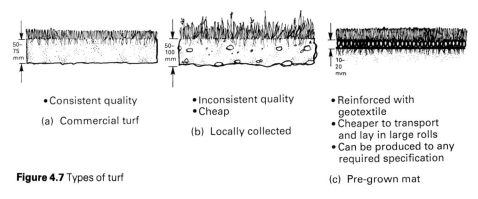

50–75 mm	50–100 mm	10–20 mm
• Consistent quality	• Inconsistent quality	• Reinforced with geotextile
(a) Commercial turf	• Cheap	• Cheaper to transport and lay in large rolls
	(b) Locally collected	• Can be produced to any required specification

Figure 4.7 Types of turf   (c) Pre-grown mat

geotextile and can be produced to suit many purposes with any seed mix. Large mats which can be handled as a roll, often 2 m wide and 10 m long, are most cost-effective in situations where instant surface protection is required. Being reinforced with geotextile, such mats are strong and can resist considerable erosive and disturbing forces, especially as there are few edges which can give rise to weak points.

4.4.2 Installation procedure

The soil must be spread and cultivated to permit proper root penetration, otherwise the turf will not be anchored properly to the ground and will also suffer from drought (*see* Sections 4.2.2 and 4.2.3). The receiving ground is prepared by levelling and raking and any fertiliser or ameliorant, such as alginate or polymer (Section 4.2.6), is incorporated. It is important to remove all undulations and obstructions so that the turf or mat can sit easily on the ground without bridging low spots. The surface should be loose, to give a good contact with the turf roots, and preferably moist. The turf or mat is then laid out, ensuring good contact with the underlying ground over all its area. On steep areas, the turf should be well pegged down along the laps. Edges of large mats should be overlapped slightly, the up-slope mat over the lower one.

Where slipping or lifting of the turf on a steep slope after laying is a problem, it can be overlaid with a geotextile grid to help anchorage and maintain lateral continuity. The grid can also help to reduce damage by pests or vandalism. Irrigation may be necessary if the ground is dry or if rainfall is not imminent, and watering may be necessary if there is a prolonged dry spell.

When used in grid patterns, turves are usually laid about 1 m apart, with the rows aligned diagonally across the slope. The interstices should be seeded with an appropriate seed mix and mulched. On soils of low fertility, the growth out from the turf into the surrounding soil can be very slow.

If turf requires storage, this should be for as short a time as possible and in stacks no more than 0.6 m high and 1 m wide. In summer, turves can be left stored for up to 4 weeks, provided the stacks are watered occasionally, though some deterioration will result if the period is longer than one week or so.

4.5 Planting

4.5.1 Site preparation

Areas for planting need not be graded perfectly smooth, as no machinery is involved in the planting operation. Proper attention to soil conditions such as compaction and drainage, however, is vital. On sites with poor drainage, the ground should be ploughed with a forestry plough to create ridges and furrows for planting and drainage respectively. The existing vegetation should be removed using hand tools or cleared with herbicide, either from the whole planting area or from a circle of 1 m diameter around the planting position. The choice of method depends on the density or spacing of plants and whether a ground cover is necessary for erosion control.

Where damage is likely from animals such as sheep, rabbits or deer, planting areas should be protected with fencing. On small areas it may be more cost-effective to protect the individual trees with guards. Very large fenced areas should be subdivided into smaller ones so that, in the event of a break occurring in the fence, limited damage is done before repairs are made.

4.5.2 Specifying and buying plants

In the UK, the types of commercial planting stock available are covered by BS 3936 (*see* Appendix 3).

A specification for plants should include:

- species and cultivar
- type of stock required (its age and dimension)
- origin or provenance
- nursery preparation prior to delivery
- handling and delivery procedure.

The handling of plant material between lifting in the nursery and eventual planting on site is critical. All too frequently, plants are dead by the time they reach the planting site. Exposed root systems are fragile and can very easily be damaged by desiccation and exposure, and a problem may only become apparent when the plant fails to grow properly. This is often wrongly attributed to poor site conditions. The main problems to be watched for are discussed in Section 4.6. The Code of Practice for Plant Handling, published by The Committee for Plant Supply and Establishment (CPSE, 1985), is a detailed guide which provides much good advice. A specification can require adherence to the Code by direct reference to it.

Damage to root systems by drying out during handling can be reduced, and root regeneration after planting thus enhanced, by using root dips. These dips can be either proprietary products, based on natural alginates, or suspensions of clay, and should be applied in the nursery before despatch to the site. The root systems of treated plants are coated with a protective layer which reduces evaporation losses. Root dips are not an alternative to proper plant handling and protection, which should always be carried out.

4.5.3 Planting methods

Saplings can be planted directly into soil which has a good moisture holding capacity. Transplants and seedlings can be 'notch' planted, whilst for whips and larger trees a hole is excavated, the tree placed in the hole with roots spread out, and the hole backfilled with the original soil. The damage to root systems during planting is usually much less for younger plants such as transplants and seedlings. They are also much more likely to recover quickly and develop a better root system than larger plants.

In poorer soils, some additional work is needed to improve the soil in the immediate vicinity of the plant. Most techniques are variations on pit planting, whereby the excavated soil is mixed with some ameliorant such as compost, manure, alginate, water-retaining polymer or slow-release fertiliser, before being backfilled around the roots. As a general rule, the transition between the pit backfill and the surrounding soil should not be too abrupt, otherwise the roots will become 'pit-bound'.

A method of pit planting sometimes employed involves complete removal of the excavated spoil and its replacement with topsoil. This technique should only be used in extremely poor soils or spoils, and in situations where root development outside the pit, which can be very restricted, is not a critical factor.

A successful method of planting many species which should have a wide application in bioengineering is the use of tubed young seedlings or cuttings (*see* Section 4.1.4). This method is ideal for planting large areas. The tubed seedlings can be planted directly into the ground, or into small pits. Plants should be removed from their containers, because both the plastic and paper varieties have been found to restrict root development.

The establishment of planted trees and shrubs can be improved by increasing the moisture available to the root system during the crucial early stages. This can be done by:

1. incorporating a water-holding ameliorant (such as alginate or polymer) into the planting pit.
2. removing ground-cover vegetation, and keeping the area free of growth for a year or so;
3. mulching with a granular material such as coarse bark (>25 mm size fragments), gravel, or a sheet material such as polythene, felt, etc., in a 1 m diameter area around each plant; this will suppress weed growth and conserve soil moisture.

If soils have a low water holding capacity, or are dry at the time of planting, newly planted trees should be well watered in with 5–10 litres of water around each tree, repeated on a regular basis if periods of drought occur in the first few months after planting. Applying insufficient water will encourage shallow rooting.

After planting, it may be necessary to prune whips and larger stock to improve the ratio between root and shoot (*see* Section 2.1.5; Box 2.1) and to remove any dead or diseased wood.

4.5.4 Planting techniques for special situations

Steep slopes

On steep slopes, the main problem is soil creep and slippage, which can bury the plants. Even walking over the slopes during planting can move material down-slope. It may be necessary therefore to sow a stabilising ground cover first, but this should be a non-competitive sward (*see* Section 4.1.3) which should be controlled around the planting spot.

Planting on steep slopes of loose material can be undertaken successfully if work starts at the top of the slope, progressing downhill and across, and traffic on the already planted slope is avoided. If soil creep is likely to be a problem after planting, species such as willow, which root adventitiously from the stems and will thus tolerate some degree of burial, should be used. On the steepest slopes, planting may have to be confined to benches on the slope, where some access for maintenance is possible, and the benches intercept runoff for use by the roots.

Exposed sites

On exposed sites, as illustrated in Figure 4.8, trees may be protected by:

1. installation of artificial windbreaks of brushwood or netting across the direction of the prevailing wind, with planting on the lee side;
2. initial planting of exposure-tolerant species, followed by planting of less tolerant ones in the resulting shelter;
3. staking and/or pruning to prevent windrock;
4. using small planting stock;
5. using plastic tubes 1–1.5 m high to shelter and support the plants.

Very dry soils

Cultivation of very dry soils should aim to maximise infiltration of the available rainfall and soil water storage. Mulches will help to conserve moisture and prevent unnecessary evaporation from the soil surface. Competing surface vegetation

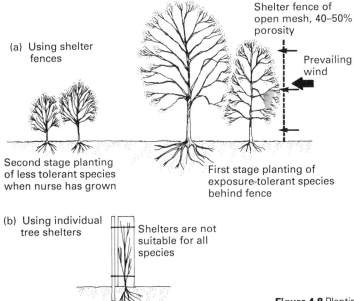

(a) Using shelter fences

Shelter fence of open mesh, 40–50% porosity

Prevailing wind

Second stage planting of less tolerant species when nurse has grown

First stage planting of exposure-tolerant species behind fence

(b) Using individual tree shelters

Shelters are not suitable for all species

Figure 4.8 Planting trees on exposed sites

should also be removed and irrigation may be necessary during establishment. Generally, the more sandy the soil and the greater the potential soil moisture deficit, the more likely the need for irrigation.

On slopes, small planting ledges can be made, with a slight backslope to divert runoff water into the slope, where it will be available for use by the roots. Water-holding ameliorants can be worked into the immediate rooting zone. If there is insufficient rain to moisten the ameliorant, watering will be required. On very coarse materials, such as shale or rock wastes, pocket planting is appropriate. This technique was developed for afforesting slate waste tips in North Wales, but has applications elsewhere. A hole or pit formed in the spoil, is filled with moist peat, soil and fertilisers. Alternatively, placement can be effected by mixing the peat and soil into a slurry with water and injecting the mixture into the voids. Saplings are planted after a few days when the slurry has drained.

4.5.5 Plant spacing

Plant spacing will depend on the type of vegetation required. For quick tree and shrub cover, spacing may be in staggered rows with about 1.5 m between plants. Such close spacings will need thinning at an early stage. A more usual spacing for planting wooded areas is with individuals 2–2.5 m apart, depending on species. Shrubs are planted more closely than trees, between 0.5 and 1.5 m apart, again depending on species. On slopes where stability of the surface soil layers is critical, a row of planting pits across the slope may introduce a weakened zone, allowing water infiltration. Plant spacings and pattern should be carefully considered so as to avoid creating such potential failure zones.

4.5.6 Willow cuttings

In bioengineering work, many techniques have evolved using live cuttings of willows or other easily rooting species. These are used for slope planting and for bank protection works. The application of these techniques is described in Sections 6.2, 6.3 and 6.4, and the methods of installation are illustrated in Figures 4.9 and 4.10.

Cuttings, brushwood or poles should be of dormant, fresh, green wood. Storage of more than a few hours between cutting and replanting should be in plastic bags, and in cold store for longer periods. On slopes, cuttings should always be placed with the cut end down and at a minimum angle of 10° to the horizontal, otherwise rooting will be restricted. Up to three quarters of the cutting should be buried and new leafy shoots will grow from the exposed remainder.

On channel banks it is important that some part of the live wood is inserted in the ground below the groundwater level. The fact that willows will sprout roots below the water and quickly develop a strong root system is an important characteristic which makes them invaluable for bank support. It is important to select cuttings from parent plants that are adapted to the soil conditions on site; for example, riverbank types will not survive on exposed dry slopes.

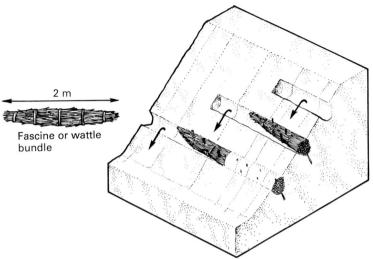

2 m

Fascine or wattle
bundle

1 Prepare fascine bundles, (or
  wattles): cigar-shaped bundles
  of live brush with butts
  alternating; 200–250 mm
  diameter bundles, tied firmly
  every 375–450 mm.
2 Use species which root readily,
  such as willow.

3 Stake firmly through and below
  the bundle, stakes 300–450 mm
  apart
4 Fascines should be buried to leave
  50 mm above ground surface,
  covered with soil and tamped
  firmly. Bundles should be
  overlapped in the trench.

Figure 4.9 Planting slope fascines

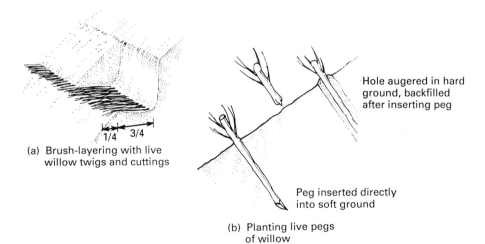

1/4   3/4

(a) Brush-layering with live
    willow twigs and cuttings

Hole augered in hard
ground, backfilled
after inserting peg

Peg inserted directly
into soft ground

(b) Planting live pegs
    of willow

Figure 4.10 Planting live willow cuttings

4.5.7 Sprigs and grass shoots

Techniques for planting sprigs and shoots of grasses, herbs or small shrubs are much the same in principle as those for planting tree saplings. The most frequent use of sprig or shoot planting in the UK is for sand dune stabilisation with Marram Grass (Section 6.5.6). Techniques for dune planting are given in Boorman (1977) and Ranwell and Boar (1986).

4.5.8 Reeds and sedges

Commercially available plants for wet areas are mainly produced for domestic and amenity use. For most bioengineering purposes, wild plant material will have to be collected. Collection should not damage the donor site; ideally plants should come from a site that is being unavoidably disturbed or destroyed.

Plants which inhabit channels, banksides and shorelines usually have specific water regime requirements and care must be taken in their selection. Transplanting most waterside plants is usually straightforward. It is vital that the plants do not dry out, and are transplanted as soon after lifting as possible. Amelioration of the planting pit is rarely appropriate, though anchoring or restraint will prevent the plants being dislodged before they become established. Techniques for vegetative protection of river and canal banks (*see* Section 6.4) are discussed further in Hemphill and Bramley (1989).

4.5.9 Aftercare

Aftercare is the term used to describe work carried out to ensure that plants establish themselves after being placed in their final position. Lack of proper aftercare probably kills as many trees as does inadequate planting in the first place. An aftercare programme should include the following:

1. re-firming plants loosened by windrock or frost every two weeks or so during winter, and particularly after windy periods;
2. top-dressing with fertiliser as necessary, usually in the spring;
3. pruning any plants with dead or diseased parts, say once a year, though this should not be in lieu of replacement if the dieback is due to the plants having damaged root systems;
4. maintaining mulches and protection, 2–3 times a year;
5. checking and maintaining fences regularly throughout the year;
6. weed control, either by mulching or herbicides (for detailed information see Sale *et al*, 1983);
7. replacing dead or severely retarded plants during the planting season.

The aftercare programme should extend over at least two years and preferably three, with appropriate contractual arrangements where necessary (*see* Section 5.5). Provided that the appropriate procedures are set up and integrated with other contractor or owner-related maintenance, aftercare is not a major expense. However, it is a vital part of vegetation establishment and must not be neglected.

4.6 Quality control and troubleshooting

Good workmanship and informed supervision are as important in the establishment of vegetation as in other specialist elements of construction, particularly if the vegetation is to have an engineering function or purpose and if its failure or poor performance can have important consequences. Box 4.10 summarises the problems that commonly occur after vegetation establishment and gives guidance on remedial actions. Some simple tests to assist the engineer in gauging vegetation performance are described below.

4.6.1 Seeding

It may be prudent to take a few random samples of seed delivered to site, for testing for purity and germination at a later date, to compare with the official seed test certificate in the event of any dispute (*see* Section 4.3.9). A useful way of checking on the overall seeding process, especially hydroseeding or broadcasting, is to bury a series of rigid seed trays in the ground within the area being seeded, placing the tops of the trays level with the ground surface filled with the site soil. The trays are then removed after seeding and kept in moist, sheltered conditions where germination should be ideal. After germination the trays are examined to assess the purity of the seed and the success or otherwise of the work.

4.6.2 Planting

Inspections carried out during the establishment period provide the opportunity to note early failures and arrange for their replacement. Reasons for failure are not always apparent. If the wrong species is planted in a poorly prepared site using careless techniques, failure is likely to be immediate. In other circumstances, failure can be progressive and is indicated by a range of symptoms such as yellowing of leaves, fungal attack or stunted growth.

A few simple measures can be adopted during supervision of planting and aftercare to test performance.

1. Part of the site should be prepared as a testing bed with good soil in a sheltered position. Sample plants from a consignment should be planted in the test bed following delivery and after any other phase in the planting programme in which damage could occur.
2. Delivery and storage should be carried out in accordance with the Code of Practice for Plant Handling (CPSE, 1985). If any consignment of plants arrives in an unsheeted lorry with the plants, especially roots, exposed and unprotected, for example, it should be rejected immediately. Similarly, plants in temporary storage which have been not 'heeled in' with the roots well protected are almost certain to suffer damage and should be removed from site.
3. The delivery, storage and planting work should be monitored to ensure that plant roots are not exposed to drying winds and sun. Even a few minutes exposure can cause severe damage.

Box 4.10 Common problems of vegetation establishment, their diagnosis and remedies

Symptoms	Cause	Diagnosis[1]	Remedies[2]
Swards			
Legumes disappear	Acidity Low phosphorus Grass competition	pH <5.5 Extractable P test Sward height >300 mm	Liming P-fertiliser Graze or cut
Poor growth, prone to drought in Summer, shallow rooting, pale colour	Soil compaction Waterlogging	Packing density >1.75 Water table <0.4 m from surface	Cultivation Drainage, use of tolerant species
Poor growth, moribund	Nutrient deficiency Acidity Drought	Extractable nutrients low Low cation exchange capacity pH <5.5 Low AWC, coarse soil texture	Add fertiliser, use legumes Add organic ameliorants Add lime, use tolerant species Add organic ameliorant
Thick matted grass, moribund, no decomposition	Nutrient deficiency Acidity Low N in vegetation	as above as above C/N ratio >25	as above as above Add N-fertiliser, grazing
Growth too dense and vigorous	Soil too fertile	Presence of aggressive weed species	Cut regularly and remove herbage to reduce soil fertility

Box 4.10 *(Continued)*

Trees and shrubs

Symptoms	Cause	Diagnosis[1]	Remedies[2]
Failure to establish	Poor stock or bad handling and planting	All site factors are satisfactory	Replant
Dieback or death, poor root growth, foliage coloured or sickly	Excessive soil compaction	Packing density >1.75	Cultivate: aeration with compressed air
		Planting pit impermeable	Aeration with compressed air; replant.
	Waterlogging	High water table <0.7 m deep	Drainage
Poor growth rates	Nutrient deficiency	Foliar and/or soil analysis	Fertiliser
	Acidity	pH outside preferred range	Lime
	Drought	Low rainfall	Mulches; Watering
		Low AWC, coarse soil texture	Amelioration with organic matter
	Competition from groundcover	Dense vegetation around tree	Mulch or herbicide to surpress
Damaged, disfigured or discoloured foliage, buds and stems	Disease	Symptoms of fungi or insect attack	Pest control; prune or fell affected trees

[1] See Section 2 for details
[2] See Section 4 for procedures
AWC = Available water capacity

4. The planting pits should be examined before they are backfilled to ensure that the sides are not smeared and compacted, especially if an auger is used to excavate the pits. The pit must be dry with the bottom and sides well loosened, and large enough to take the spread roots of the plant.
5. Survival should be assessed by examining plants in the middle of the first growing season after planting, and again during each growing season for 2–3 years. Satisfactory establishment is indicated by healthy shoot growth. The effect of transplanting on shoot growth is often not evident until three years after transplanting; growth in the first year after transplanting may be greater than in the second and third year. Therefore trees with very poor shoot growth over the first three years should be replaced.
6. Die-back may indicate that roots are restricted within the planting pit, or damaged, or too small in relation to the size of the plant. Waterlogging is a common problem with planting pits in engineered earthworks. Trees suspected of being in difficulty should be examined by excavating trial holes to inspect both roots and soils. Healthy trees will show signs of new root growth.
7. Site conditions should be monitored and aftercare carried out when it is required, as indicated by the conditions of the soil or plants.

4.6.3 Growth and performance

Many factors produce similar symptoms in vegetation and so the following should only be used as a guide. Vegetation should look healthy, but this should not be confused with tidiness. For example, long unkempt grassland may result from minimal management, but it may nevertheless be functioning perfectly.

Colour is a widely used indicator but must be interpreted with care. Yellowing leaves indicate nutrient deficiency, particularly of nitrogen, which may be due to infertility in the soil. It can also be due to impaired functioning of the roots in absorbing nutrients, however, resulting from low or high pH, waterlogging, soil compaction or disease. Brown and papery leaf edges indicate that the plant is suffering from drought, either directly through lack of soil moisture or indirectly through the inability of the roots to exploit a sufficiently large volume of soil. Competition from surrounding dense vegetation is also a frequent cause of drought stress. Dark green, or sometimes reddish, leaves associated with poor growth may indicate phosphate deficiency. In unseasonably cold weather many plants take on a bluish or reddish tinge, which disappears when normal conditions return.

Poor growth is caused by many factors but is usually associated with poor soil and root development. Trees that put on very little shoot growth in the first year after planting will probably never grow well, as the root system may be permanently damaged. Pruning back the top growth to reduce the demands on the faltering root system can sometimes help.

Waterlogging leads to many problems and has a direct effect on root growth. It can be due to several factors, each of which needs treatment in a different way.

1. High groundwater level, leading to very shallow rooting; drainage will be needed to lower the groundwater if tolerant species cannot be used.

2. Compaction of the surface or subsurface soil layers, impeding drainage of surface water; deep cultivation will be necessary to alleviate this.
3. Pit binding, inability of the water, or the roots, to escape from the planting pit due to impermeability of the sides or bottom; cultivation and proper replanting is the only cure for this.

4.7 Vegetation management

Despite the emphasis given so far to methods of establishment, it is the subsequent management which really determines the long-term well-being of a vegetation cover.

4.7.1 Management programmes

A planned management programme must be designed to take account of the desired functions of the vegetation, the soil and climatological conditions of the site, and the management capability of the owner or maintaining authority. Box 4.11 summarises the main management activities for different vegetation types. In circumstances where vegetation is performing a bioengineering role, management for visual appearance or 'tidiness' will be secondary and may not even be necessary. Management should not interfere with the function of the vegetation to the extent that it is temporarily impaired. Where the design function allows for changes in vegetation composition and structure with time, management may be required to restrict the development of vegetation within desired limits.

A management programme must include the following.

1. Aftercare (*see* Section 4.5.9; Box 4.11), the work necessary to ensure that plants become properly established. It is a form of intensive short-term management which should be considered as part of the establishment process. In planning for aftercare, problems such as those summarised in Box 4.10, should, as far as practicable, be anticipated.
2. Management, the long-term work needed in order to maintain, or promote through further development, the form and function of the required vegetation, once it is is established.
3. Maintenance, part of both aftercare and management covering the work necessary to maintain plants, drainage, fencing, etc in proper condition. This will include remedial seeding and planting where failures have occurred. In this sense the term is consistent with its contractual meaning in the 'maintenance period' of a construction contract, during which defects are made good.

The extent of all three of these aspects overlaps considerably, the distinction often being a logistical or contractual one as much as a difference in the actual work carried out. Aftercare and maintenance carried out for new works will have to dovetail neatly into the ongoing management and maintenance programme of the site owner or maintaining authority.

Box 4.11 Vegetation management

Vegetation type	Establishment method	Aftercare	Management
Grass or grass-legume swards	Seeding	Fertilising; mowing to encourage tillering	Soil fertility management. Cutting or grazing to maintain desired height and prevent scrub invasion. Removal of noxious or undesirable weeds.
Diverse herbaceous swards	Seeding, maybe some planting	Mowing to control nurse species, fertilising	Cutting, grazing or burning to prevent succession to scrub; timing is important to allow desired species to flower and set seed. Removal of noxious or undesirable weeds.
Short shrubs	Seeding, maybe some planting	Fertilising, weed control maybe necessary on fertile soils	Depends on whether succession to trees is necessary. If not, then occasional cutting or burning, the regime depends on the species.
Trees and shrubs	Seeding	Little, maybe fertilising and weed control	Maybe some selective weeding and fertilising around individual plants. Selective thinning of seedlings to obtain desired balance of species.
	Planting	Weed control, replacement, pruning, fertilising, maintaining protection	Fertilising as necessary, thinning to encourage proper stand structure, removal of nurse species. Coppicing of some species for dense shrubby cover.

4.7.2 Managing grass and herbaceous swards

Management of grass swards is undertaken for two reasons:

1. to control the height and density of the sward, and thus its functional characteristics;
2. to manipulate the species composition, preventing invasion and successional development of undesirable species.

Cutting

Cutting is a common way of managing grass and herb swards. Frequency can vary from several times a year, to maintain short turf, to very occasional cutting, every 1–3 years, to prevent scrub invasion. Low-maintenance swards will need less cutting, but will be less vigorous in other respects (*see* Section 4.1.3). Regular cutting stimulates tillering in grasses (*see* Section 2.1.3) and results in a sward which is thicker and better able to withstand surface abrasion. However, it also reduces the depth and density of rooting (*see* Section 2.1.5) and the leaf area for transpiration. The frequency and height of cutting should be matched to the purpose and function required of the vegetation. Cutting regimes in relation to sward function are outlined in Box 4.12, and timing is discussed in Section 4.8.4.

Controlled burning is an alternative to cutting when very infrequent control is required (*see* Section 2.7.2). Regeneration from a lightly-burnt sward can be expected in a few weeks, its rapidity being due to the nutrients released by the burning.

Grazing

Grazing is a cost-effective way of controlling swards and is ideal where grassed engineering structures, such as flood banks and earth dams, have to be integrated into the local agricultural landscape. It is also useful for steeper slopes and difficult terrain, where cutting machinery cannot be used. Grazing is usually only practical, however, when there is a suitable farming unit nearby, which can undertake the grazing by agreement.

Sheep are the preferred grazing animal because they are light and have small feet which do not damage the sward. They graze the grass short, stimulating tillering. Cattle, being large and heavy, damage the sward by trampling (poaching). They graze by pulling on the grass, which can also be damaging. Horses cause a great deal of damage to soil and sward. They are very selective in their grazing, so that less palatable species spread into large clumps, which may not be desirable. Rabbits are often endemic and graze extensively, producing a fine, short sward. However, their grazing patterns are uneven and they are uncontrollable, so that serious overgrazing can occur when their population becomes too big.

The functional requirements of the sward and soil fertility should be matched to the grazing regime. Stocking density is an important factor. A low density for a long period keeps the grass shorter for longer and the condition of the sward is easy to control, but selective grazing will mean the sward can become very uneven. A high density for a short period gives a similar effect to cutting, but its effect is more

Box 4.12 Cutting regimes for swards appropriate to different functions

Function of sward	Height of sward	Frequency of cutting
Surface traffic protection, wear resistance	Short, <100 mm	2–6 times a year depending on soil fertility and vigour of species used.
Surface erosion control	Medium, 150–300 mm	Probably impractical on steep slopes, but every 1–3 years if possible, more often if tussock grasses develop. Burning may also be used to control scrub if necessary.
Deep rooting, water removal and/or root reinforcement	Medium–tall, 150–400 mm	As above, but grazing preferable to burning.
Wet environments, high water flows	Medium, 150–300 mm (so that shoots lie flat)	Once a year, to keep sward the right length. Maybe twice a year if tussock grasses develop.

Cutting machinery	Application	
Tractor-mounted flail or rotary mower	Good terrain, slopes up to 1:3. Very cost-effective for large, open areas. Cannot work close to obstructions.	
Flail mounted on hydraulic arm	Slopes, hedges, banks, ditches, etc with adjacent access track for tractor. Reach limited to 3–5 m. Cannot work close to or around obstructions.	
Pedestrian flail or rotary mower	Poor terrain but with even surface, slopes up to 1:2.5. Suitable for small localised areas and working around/between obstructions.	
Pedestrian 'hover' rotary mower	As above but more uneven surface and steeper slopes, especially using ropes to manoeuvre machine.	
Hand-held strimmer or scythe	Poor terrain, uneven surfaces, steep slopes up to 1:2 providing there is safe footing for operator. Best for working around obstructions and small areas, also for long grass which would choke a mower. Expensive for large areas, so only suitable if there is no other way.	

Notes:

1) If clippings are removed, the fertility of the soil will gradually decline. If clippings are left *in situ*, they will rot down and recycle nutrients but they may also smother many species in the sward. If the sward is cut infrequently, or is very long through high soil fertility, clippings should be removed and nutrients replaced as fertilisers if necessary.

2) Frequency of cutting will also depend on growth rates of the varieties comprising the grass mix and on year-to-year variations in climate. Frequency must be judged on what is required to maintain the desired height of sward.

difficult to control and overgrazing or trampling damage can occur, with resulting reductions in root growth, changes in composition of the vegetation to favour the less palatable species, and increases in the area of bare ground.

Overgrazing and 'poaching' are the main disadvantages of using grazing, especially during the winter. Swards benefit from being rested during the winter months, with grazing recommencing when the growing season starts in the spring.

Chemicals

Chemicals are frequently used to manage and manipulate herbaceous vegetation. There are three basic forms of chemical control: total herbicides, selective herbicides and growth retardants.

Total herbicides kill all the vegetation either by:

1. contact, only killing the tissues it touches;
2. systemic action being translocated within the plant to all the parts including roots;
3. residual soil action, killing roots or germinating seedlings.

Many chemicals or proprietary formulations combine two or all of these modes of action. Contact herbicides can be used to remove certain types of vegetation by employing special application techniques, such as stump painting and 'weed wiping'.

Selective herbicides kill certain groups of plants. The mode of action is similar to that described for total herbicides. Most formulations are designed for eradicating broad-leaved weeds in grass or cereal crops, though there are some selective grass-killers. In the bioengineering context, broad-leaved plants would not necessarily be considered weeds, except where vigorous undesirable species are dominating the sward and suppressing desirable ones.

Growth retardants are used to control the height of a sward with reduced frequency of mowing, in situations such as road verges. It should be remembered that a reduction in above-ground growth is usually matched by a reduction in root growth. Maleic hydrazide is a widely used chemical, though many proprietary formulations are available. Growth suppressants or retardants can act selectively, affecting the species balance of a sward; broad-leaved species are usually more affected than grasses.

Fertilisers

Fertilisers are important in the management of soil fertility but advice on their use should always be sought, as it is not possible to prescribe levels without assessing each situation individually (Section 4.2.6). Aftercare and early management will aim to build up soil fertility progressively in soils which are very infertile. This can take 5–10 years, depending on the intensity of management available. Nitrogen is particularly important, though adequate phosphorus and potassium are also necessary for good root growth and healthy plant development.

Grazed swards will have nutrients in the leaves recycled through dung, and will maintain a healthy appearance. However, grazing progressively removes a great deal of nutrient, so that fertilisers need to be applied periodically to maintain long-term soil fertility. Ungrazed swards may have little need for fertilisers once the soil fertility has been built up through aftercare and early management. A high proportion of legumes in the sward will rapidly build up nitrogen. Many legumes, especially clovers, will only persist when there is a sufficient level of lime and phosphorus in the soil.

4.7.3 Managing seeded trees and shrubs

Schemes involving tree and shrub seedings usually require very little management. Ideally components of the mixture will develop at their own rate to give a succession from initial groundcover, through shrubs and pioneer trees, to climax trees. Should it be necessary, the balance of species can be altered either by introducing more seed or by the selective removal of established plants. This might be done if, say, a nurse species was too dense and was shading out slower growing later species, or if some species had failed to establish properly.

Soil fertility is a major controlling influence in the development of seeded trees and shrubs. Fertilisers and legumes should be used in much the same way as for herbaceous vegetation, though perhaps the typical communities are less demanding of nutrients than are grass swards.

4.7.4 Managing planted trees

Trees planted in a herbaceous sward will be competing with that sward for water and nutrients until they begin to shade it out. Initially, therefore, it is desirable to give the trees a competitive advantage over the sward, while at the same time maintaining any temporary function that the sward may be performing, such as erosion control. Methods of doing this include:

1. suppressing the grass swards immediately around the trees with herbicide or mulch;
2. keeping the soil fertility low, except for selective placement of fertilisers around the trees themselves.

As a tree plantation develops, quicker growing species planted as nurses will need to be thinned out to allow slower growing climax species to develop. The balance of species can be partially controlled in this way and further species can be introduced into the gaps if necessary. Thinning will be required on a 5–10 year cycle, depending on the density and rate of growth of the trees. Apart from thinning, little management is necessary. There should be no need to tidy up the plantation by removing lower branches or undergrowth.

Many deciduous tree species will respond well to coppicing. This management technique produces denser vegetation than a normal stand, and is suitable for:

1. areas where windthrow or surcharge is a hazard and tall trees have to be avoided;
2. where dense shelter or screening is required near ground level;
3. banks of fast flowing channels, so that the branches will bend and lie flat during flood conditions, and not obstruct the flow.

Coppicing is undertaken on a 5–15 year cycle, depending on the species and the thickness of stem growth required. Until wood was overtaken by iron as the main structural material in building, the management of woodland was a widely practised skill. Healthy stools in some coppiced woodlands are known to be over 1000 years old which confirms that coppicing is an effective means of management long-term.

Most tree species are not high nutrient demanders, though growth check due to low soil fertility is a common problem in young plantations. Periodic fertilising with slow-release fertilisers around individual trees may therefore be necessary for a few years after planting. Proprietary fertiliser pellets or tablets are available which are placed directly in the ground in the root zone. Deep placement (0.5–1.0 m) of fertilisers or tablets can be used to encourage deep rooting and to influence the distribution of the root system.

4.8 Timing of operations

The optimum time for carrying out soiling, seeding and planting operations is determined by climate and local soil conditions. For any single location, long-term averages of climate can be used to estimate the most likely timing for planning purposes. Such information can be obtained from the UK Meteorological Office or from published climatic data for agriculture, such as Smith (1976).

4.8.1 Soil handling and cultivation

Since soils are easily damaged if moved or cultivated when wet (*see* Section 4.2.2) the guide recommended in Box 4.5 should be compared with local climate patterns, to determine the likely periods when soil movement will give rise to least problems. In general this will be between the end of field capacity in spring and the beginning of field capacity in autumn (Figure 2.18). On clay soils a positive soil moisture deficit should be allowed to build up before handling or cultivation, particularly for deep cultivation. Optimum periods for soil handling and cultivation for several locations in England and Wales are illustrated in Figure 4.11.

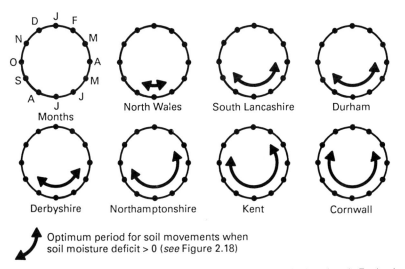

Figure 4.11 Optimum periods for soil handling and cultivation for locations in England and Wales

4.8.2 Seeding and turfing

The timing of seeding is crucial to the success of establishment. The optimum time for seeding and turfing is during a period of warm, moist conditions, sufficient for plants to become well established. This can be conveniently estimated from climatic data as the period when potential evapotranspiration is less than rainfall ($E_t < R$) and at the same time the average temperature exceeds 5°C (*see* Sections 2.5 and 3.4; Box 2.12). This is illustrated for selected locations in England and Wales in Figure 4.12. It can be seen that for most locations the dry summer spell should be avoided. Local modifications due to aspect should be taken into account; on south-facing slopes, for example, the summer drought is likely to be longer and more intense than on north-facing slopes, where a longer sowing season may be available.

Sowing time for trees and shrubs is different from that for grass and herbaceous species. Seed that has been treated to overcome dormancy should be sown in the early spring, when it will germinate fairly readily. Untreated seed should be sown in late autumn or early winter, so that it experiences the natural processes which break dormancy. Young legume seedlings, clovers, etc, are particularly susceptible to frost damage and are best seeded in the spring or late summer/early autumn. The survival of autumn sown legumes through the winter is usually quite low.

At high altitudes or in alpine areas, the shortness of the growing season is a constraint on seeding success. Early spring seeding is favoured, giving the maximum growing period for establishment before the onset of hostile winter conditions. In mountainous regions, seeding is often carried out onto frozen ground and snow, when the ground is still sufficiently hard to support machinery. The seed will germinate as the ground warms up soon after seeding.

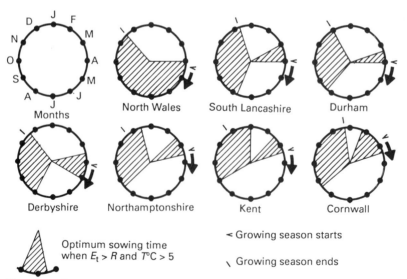

Figure 4.12 Optimum seeding times for locations in England and Wales (from Humphries, 1979, after Smith, 1976)

4.8.3 Planting

Deciduous species are usually planted when they are dormant. This period can be considerably extended by using container-grown plants. The planting season is usually defined as the period when average temperatures are below 5°C but above freezing. Generally in the UK, it is considered to be from October until the end of March, but excluding much of January and February. Planting during the first part of this season (autumn and early winter) is usually much more successful than in early spring. Planting should not be carried out when the ground is frozen. Evergreen species usually establish more readily if they are planted in early autumn or late spring.

Root activity can persist for longer periods than the normal growing season. Root systems can begin to regenerate during the early spring, before the accepted start of the growing season when leaves appear. Trees planted at the very end of the planting season therefore have less chance of good root establishment before the shoots grow, and usually suffer a higher failure rate.

Cuttings and live wood plantings rely on rapid root development at a time when the rest of the plant is completely dormant. For this reason the planting season is shorter than that for bare-rooted plants, generally November to March, though with considerable variation according to location. Cuttings should not be used too soon after the end of the growing season, to allow the shoots to become completely dormant. Planting in the spring should be sufficiently early to enable root development to take place before shoot activity begins.

4.8.4 Aftercare and management

For grass and herbaceous vegetation, fertilisers with a high nitrogen content should be used at the beginning of the growing season in spring, at the time when nutrient demand is greatest. Fertilising during autumn will stimulate late growth, especially roots, though a high phosphate content at this time is preferable to a high nitrogen content. Fertilising trees and shrubs should be as for grass and herbaceous vegetation, except that earlier and later applications will stimulate root activity. Mowing and grazing are mainly carried out during periods of active growth, throughout the spring and summer. To encourage and maintain broad-leaved plants in the sward, cutting should take place in the spring before flowering, or in late summer after most flowering species have set seed. Pruning and coppicing should be carried out during the dormant season.

4.9 Safe working methods on slopes

4.9.1 Methods, management and vegetation type

Steep slopes are more dangerous than gentle ones and safety in working should be the main determinant of the kind of cultivation and maintenance operations which are carried out on a slope. In turn, the kind of operations which can be carried out in respect of both preparation and maintenance must be taken into account in deciding what kind of vegetation is appropriate for an area. There is therefore a very strong interdependence between slope angle, management programme and vegetation type, which ultimately determines the potential role for vegetation in any situation.

4.9.2 Agricultural experience

The Scottish Centre of Agricultural Engineering (SCAE) has a continuing programme of research into vehicle safety on slopes. For example, they have investigated the reasons behind the large number of accidents involving tractors working on slopes on UK farms. A short booklet (SCAE, 1979) summarises the results of the investigation and makes recommendations which are equally applicable to working methods in the construction industry. Further work at SCAE on the preparation of a British Standard for Safety of Machines on Slopes should also be of interest to engineers.

Grass covered slopes should be regarded as intrinsically dangerous, much more so than bare soil; the danger increases in proportion to the steepness of the slope. Safe working methods are dependent on ground conditions, weather, the direction of travel, and the type of tractor and equipment. An analysis of accident records indicates that:

1. grass is particularly dangerous to work on when it is growing vigorously and is fresh and lush;
2. a tractor is most likely to slide out of control when it is working downhill and may then overturn;
3. a four-wheel drive tractor with positive drive to the front wheels is safer with a trailed roller than a two-wheel drive type. For example, a four-wheel drive tractor may be able to descend a 1:2 slope in safety, whilst a similarly loaded two-wheel drive type would slide on a 1:7 slope in the same conditions.

Box 4.13 is based on the SCAE booklet. The maximum and minimum slope angles shown for the equipment are merely indications of how safety on a particular slope can vary under different conditions. *They are NOT necessarily recommended safe slopes for any tractor used on any slope.* Familiarity with equipment, assessment of site conditions and operator experience must determine whether a particular operation is safe or not.

4.9.3 Construction equipment

The main danger in working with wheeled vehicles on slopes covered with vegetation is that they slide out of control when working downhill. This is less of a problem with tracked vehicles. Even though wheeled machines are much safer on bare soil than on grassed surfaces, engineers should consider using tracked machines for surface cultivation and seeding, since these are commonplace in the industry. For maintenance work on large grassed areas, advantage should be taken of the availability of tracked machines, since they will be very much safer and they are likely to do less damage to the surface except in turning areas, which could be hardened for this purpose. Tracked machines are of course slower than the wheeled variety, and standard machines will require modification to operate attachments required for maintenance work.

Box 4.13 Safe working on slopes for two-wheel drive and four-wheel drive tractors with an implement attached (after SCAE, 1979)

Tractor	Maximum safe slope (degrees)[3]	Mean safe slope (degrees)	Minimum safe slope (degrees)[4]	Tractor and plough weight (tonnes)	Axle load ratio
Small 2-wheel drive	20	16	13	2.45	22/78
Medium 2-wheel drive	19	17	14	3.09	22/78
Medium 4-wheel drive[1]	19	17	17	4.16	27/73
Medium 4-wheel drive[2]	30	25	20	4.16	27/73

[1] Front wheel drive disengaged
[2] Front wheel drive engaged
[3] Good site conditions
[4] Poor site conditions

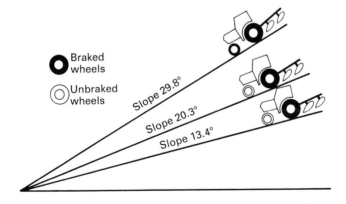

For tractor with implement (e.g. plough) attached

5 Method of approach and implementation

Full consideration of the potential role of vegetation should be an integral part of the whole construction process, no matter whether the vegetation is intended to fulfil an engineering, landscape or other environmental function. To neglect the potential role of vegetation at any stage of a project will usually mean a lost opportunity to utilise its engineering functions in a meaningful way. To this end a 'team' approach should be adopted from the outset.

Some factors that influence the selection, performance and management of vegetation will influence the design and construction process. The engineer may have control over some, such as soil density, surface finish and manpower, but others, such as climate, will act as constraints. This Section provides guidance on how to incorporate bioengineering into civil engineering works. Sources of expertise and advice are discussed in Section 5.2, together with the merits of using contractors or a direct labour organisation (DLO).

5.1 Strategy

In general terms, the strategy for bioengineering works, whether new or remedial, involves the following elements, as illustrated in Figure 5.1.

Inception and initial planning
- incorporate environmental considerations in design brief;
- consider whether inert structural solutions may be too costly or environmentally unsatisfactory;
- consider a vegetation option and whether vegetation can play a useful role or function and be cost-effective;
- conduct preliminary investigations to determine site constraints and potentials;
- develop preliminary design criteria and examine the need for special site studies;
- consider the management regime compatible with the level of long-term maintenance that the maintaining authority is able to adopt.

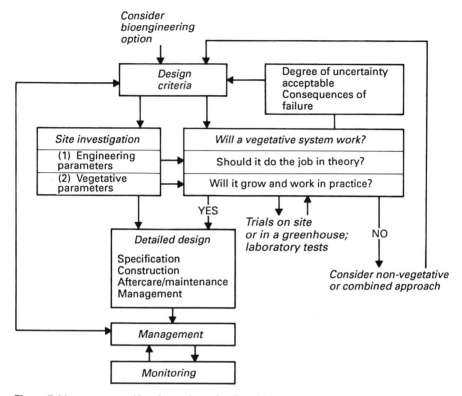

Figure 5.1 Important considerations when adopting a bioengineering approach

Site investigation
- carry out an engineering site investigation;
- conduct site investigations to determine plant growth potential and design properties associated with use of vegetation;
- consider environmental constraints and those factors which can be modified by design or construction to optimise plant potential.

Design and specification
- define roles and functions of vegetation;
- determine the properties required of the vegetation and thus the types which will be needed: herbaceous, shrubby, woody, etc.;
- consider ecological and plant community factors for long-term stability;
- develop long-term management objectives and review requirements, such as revenue and manpower implications, from the viewpoint of the maintaining authority;
- carry out trials or pilot schemes to develop a methodology for main works. These are especially valuable to a DLO as training grounds for personnel, as well as for testing materials and methods;

- design the bioengineering system, bearing in mind the construction methods, to give the required site characteristics, the mixture of plant species and the appropriate management regime;
- where appropriate, specify materials and methods, making special reference to the role of vegetation, the importance of site conditions and timing of operations;
- where appropriate, specify particular performance requirements for vegetation establishment;
- if necessary, make appropriate contractual arrangements to accommodate the special requirements and aftercare of vegetation;
- take advice on the level of specialist supervision which will be required.

Specification and contractual arrangements will be required where construction and management are not undertaken by the same organisation. Large organisations may find it worthwhile to produce manuals for the guidance of their own personnel.

Construction

- monitor climate and soil conditions;
- pay particular regard to the timing of operations, especially in relation to seeding and planting seasons;
- provide appropriate specialist supervision;
- include aftercare in the construction programme to ensure proper establishment;
- attend to defects.

Management.   The strategy for management will require a slightly different approach from that adopted for inert engineering work. The maintaining authority must be fully aware of the role that the vegetation is expected to perform. Regular management will involve the following tasks:

- periodic reviews of management objectives and performance of vegetation;
- monitoring vegetation development, soil fertility and the integrity of the bioengineering system;
- regular management and maintenance operations such as mowing, grazing, coppicing, thinning, weeding, fertilising and repair.

Where failure occurs in a situation in which vegetation was not originally a significant functional element, the maintaining authority should consider whether vegetation could play a functional role and form the basis of a cost-effective remedy. This may require modification of the complete vegetation cover over a large area.

5.2 Sources of expertise and advice

Integration of vegetation and engineering demands the establishment of a design team comprising engineers and vegetation specialists; ecologists will frequently have a key role to play. It also requires a greater appreciation by the engineer of the requirements for good vegetation growth and the opportunities it presents, the questions that should be asked, and how to make the best use of the advice given; and a greater understanding by the vegetation specialist of the engineering requirements, the constraints of the construction process and the advice which the engineer really needs.

Sources of specialist advice, materials and skilled labour in respect of the use of vegetation are diverse and somewhat variable in quality. There is no term in common usage which encompasses all the sources available throughout the landscape, ecological, horticultural, forestry and agricultural fields of interest. Sources are considered briefly below in relation to their advisory/design role or contractor/implementation role.

5.2.1 Professional advice

Vegetation specialists can be drawn from a variety of professions. The nature of the project is likely to dictate the most suitable qualification or experience required of the specialist. Organisations to contact in order to find a suitable specialist are given in Appendix 5. Specialists are listed below with brief descriptions of their areas of expertise.

- Agriculturalist: principal interest is in plant production for food, but with a broad background in soils, drainage, grass production and land management. Some limitation in outlook due to the emphasis on crops, highly productive grassland and fertile soils, which are not often appropriate to bioengineering.
- Arboriculturalist: deals especially with individual trees (cf. forester), their growth, condition and safety; tree surgery.
- Forester: deals with forest management and production; growth of trees, mainly as a crop but also for amenity purposes. The main emphasis is on coniferous species, but increasingly on broad-leaved hardwood species in non-cropped but nevertheless managed situations.
- Horticulturalist: mainly concerned with the production and use of plants for food or ornamental purposes. Specialists in 'amenity horticulture' may have expertise of relevance to bioengineering.
- Botanist: a plant scientist. There are many specialisations in botany, some of which are required in bioengineering from time to time for specific problems or detailed research.
- Ecologist: a scientist, often with a practical approach, concerned with the inter-relations between plants, animals and their environment. Branches of 'plant ecology' include the study of the structure and functioning of plant communities and the effect of environmental factors on species composition and plant growth.
- Soil scientist: a scientist engaged in a practical discipline, dealing with soils, their properties, development, functioning and classification, particularly in relation to drainage, plant requirements and land management.
- Landscape architect: a designer familiar with the use of plants and their manipulation for different purposes. The emphasis is usually, but not exclusively, on visual/aesthetic considerations rather than functional ones.

- Landscape manager: encompasses many forms of land and vegetation management with a similar outlook to landscape architects, though functional considerations are more prominent.
- Landscape scientist: a scientist concerned with the natural environment, particularly an ecologist or soil scientist with expertise in landscape-related matters. Many landscape scientists have special expertise in land reclamation, mineral workings and difficult sites, where the approach and problems are similar to those encountered in bioengineering applications.

It is mainly to the landscape industry that engineers will turn for specialist vegetation advice. This is quite appropriate, given its similar professional framework and its close association with the construction industry. However care should still be exercised by both professions to ensure that the functional requirements of vegetation are fully understood, and that normal landscape requirements are not inadvertently substituted.

5.2.2 Implementation

In the UK, engineering and landscape construction works are often implemented and usually managed by a DLO. Engineers with responsibility for new construction and thus for bioengineering will therefore be found throughout the industry, but it is likely that the responsibility for maintenance work generally lies with engineers in DLOs.

One of the key attributes of bioengineering is that it does not necessarily require the services of an external contractor. Indeed where labour is already available and skills can be learned, it is generally advantageous for the owner or management authority to undertake the work itself. Much design and practice relies at present on pragmatism and local knowledge, and the use of 'in-house' skills and knowledge during construction guarantees that these will continue to be available for the management of the works. In many circumstances the potential application for bioengineering is both extensive and seasonal, for example along river banks and highway margins, and these factors also tend to favour involvement by DLOs.

Specialist bioengineering contractors do not yet exist in the UK, though contractors with expertise in difficult sites, such as those encountered in the reclamation of derelict land and mineral workings, are likely to have the most relevant experience. In some cases where the main works or management is undertaken by direct labour, there may be some elements, such as hydroseeding, that have to be contracted out to specialists in horticultural or landscape work. Some contractors specialise in particular vegetation establishment techniques, often associated with a proprietary product or inert construction material.

General landscape contractors vary greatly in size and experience, though all should be familiar with basic seeding, plant handling and vegetation establishment procedures. Firms who specialise in landscape gardening and urban amenity landscaping are unlikely to be suitable for bioengineering work. Hydroseeding contractors offer a specialist service, though often linked to a general or other specialist landscaping service. They can undertake most forms of seeding of grass, herbaceous plants, trees and shrubs. Forestry contractors generally undertake large-scale tree planting and management, sometimes exclusively in commercial timber forests, but usually for all forms of tree planting. They rarely deal with tree seeding. Agricultural contractors are widely used for normal ground preparation and seeding work and associated ancillary works, such as fencing and drainage. They are quite capable of coping with most situations, where special techniques or difficult terrain are not involved. Nurseries provide a specialised plant propagation and production service, covering most container-grown or bare-rooted plants available as tubed seedlings, transplants, whips and larger trees as required. Some are also able to undertake special pre-conditioning or preparation of the plants for use on particular sites (*see* Section 4.4).

5.3 Site appraisal

The purpose of the site appraisal is to identify the conditions and environmental factors, which are discussed in Section 4.1.2, as well as geotechnical ones. This is best achieved by carrying out a preliminary assessment of climate, soils and geology with reference to published sources, followed by an inspection of the site by the

Box 5.1 Main factors for site appraisal

Climatic	
Rainfall	Quantity, maximum intensity, duration, seasonality and yearly variation
Temperature	Daily averages, seasonal maximum and minimum, dates of first and last frost
Potential evapotranspiration	Monthly averages, yearly variation, soil moisture deficits
Exposure	Relative elevation and aspect; windiness
Aspect	Local modification of all these factors
Soil, physical	
Particle grading	Soil texture class, especially content of clay, coarse material and stones
Density	*In-situ* dry density, potential compaction under load
Water regime	Available water for plants; mainly derived from other measured parameters
Soil, chemical	
pH	Soil reaction, lime requirement
Conductivity	Potential toxicity from soluble salts
Pyrite	Potential toxicity from acid production
Nutrients	⎫ Soil fertility and plant growth potential
Organic matter	⎭
Exchange capacity	Potential to resist leaching of nutrients
Erosion risk	
Rain erosivity	⎫
Soil erodibility	⎪ Mainly derived from other measured parameters, but can be measured
Overland flow	⎬ directly
Channel discharge	⎭
Wind erosivity	Frequency of wind direction and strength
Geotechnical	Normal site investigation parameters appropriate to the situation

engineer with his specialist adviser. The design team should then be able to decide on the extent of the detailed site investigation required. This will include the appropriate tests for engineering purposes and whatever is considered necessary in respect of vegetation, topsoil and subsoil so far as plant growth and design factors are concerned.

In the case of ground in its natural condition, the site investigation report will include more detail about the topsoil and subsoil than appears in a conventional engineering report, as well as a description of the existing vegetation. For disturbed sites, such as mineral workings, where topsoil and subsoil may not be present, much of the normal engineering site investigation for a construction project is also relevant to the needs of vegetation. The information will be interpreted by the soil

Box 5.2 The functional requirements of vegetation

Function	Qualities required	Principal considerations
Soil reinforcement and enhancement of soil strength	Maximum root development to the required depth	Deep rooting species Anchorage Suitable soil profile conditions
Soil water removal	Vigorous root development throughout soil volume Large transpiration area	Vigorous rooting species Substantial top growth which transpires throughout year Soil water balance
Surface protection against traffic	Vigorous development at soil surface of both roots and shoots Ability to self–repair quickly	Species selection, short growth habit Management Soil fertility Inherent soil trafficability Use of reinforcement
Surface protection against erosion by wind and water	Vigorous development at soil surface of both roots and shoots Resistance to damage under high flow conditions Rapid establishment	Erosion risk Behaviour of vegetation under high flow conditions Soil surface conditions Species selection Use of reinforcement with geotextiles
Bank and channel reinforcement	Ability to grow in wet conditions perhaps with variable water levels Rapid effectiveness Root reinforcement Top growth absorbs wave impact Low hydraulic roughness under high flow conditions Ability to self–repair	Species selection with respect to ecological preference Growth habit Management Reinforcement with geotextiles
Shelter or screening	Top growth of suitable height and/or density Rapid development	Species selection Density of foliage Structural arrangement

Note These functions should be considered along with the vegetation effects and salient vegetation properties described in Boxes 3.4 and 3.5.

specialist using different criteria. There may be additional factors which have to be considered, and the normal investigation can be extended to include these.

The interpretation of the results will discuss, as appropriate, the factors summarised in Box 5.1 and the anticipated degree of difficulty in establishing and managing vegetation, the consequences of partial or complete failure, and an assessment of the performance of vegetation. These are matters on which the engineer will be seeking specialist guidance and they mirror the advice provided by geotechnical specialists in respect of the engineering qualities and performances of soil.

5.4 Design and specification

5.4.1 Design

The designer, whether of new or remedial works, will first identify specific roles for vegetation and decide on the functions it will have to perform. These are described fully in Section 6, and are summarised in Box 5.2. Relevant site parameters are summarised in Box 5.3. Their influence on design, specification and remedial work has been considered in detail elsewhere in the Guide under the following headings:

Box 5.3 Site parameters for design, specification and remedial work involving vegetation

Factors	Parameters	Principal considerations for design and specification
Bioclimate	Growing season Exposure	Select suitable plants Limits performance of vegetation
Soil, physical	Density and rootability Permeability	Modify during construction Select suitable soil materials
Soil water	Profile available water Droughtiness Water table/wetness regime	Modify soil profile during construction Select suitable soil materials Select suitable plants Ameliorate soil Limits performance of vegetation
Soil, chemical	pH Fertility Cation exchange capacity	Select suitable plants Add lime and fertilisers Ameliorate soil Select suitable soil materials Limits performance of vegetation
Erosion risk	Soil erodibility Rainfall erosivity Channel discharge Slope	Select suitable soil materials Select suitable plants Management Additional reinforcement with geotextile
Geotechnical	Shear strength Slope Factor of safety	Select suitable soil materials Root enhancement Soil density and moisture Reinforcement with geotextiles

Note This Table should be considered along with Box 5.1. The site appraisal factors are used to derive the design parameters given here (*see* Sections 2 and 6).

- plant selection (Section 4.1)
- soil requirements (Section 4.2.1)
- surface preparation (Section 4.2.5)
- vegetation establishment (Sections 4.3 and 4.5)
- long-term management (Section 4.7).

The major plant groups which can be used for revegetation and bioengineering work are outlined in Box 5.4. Information regarding particular species, their site requirements and growth characteristics is given in Appendix 1. Section 2.4 discusses the important relations between plants and the soil. It is vital that plants are provided with appropriate soil conditions in order to reach their required potential.

In designing a soil profile the objective is to optimise root growth, and thus the whole performance of a plant, by encouraging the roots to exploit the required volume of soil for both water and nutrients. Principles for the design of a soil profile are given in Box 5.5. Designs should specify detailed requirements for soils in respect of those characteristics which determine the success or otherwise of germination and establishment. These were discussed fully in Sections 2.4 and 4.2.

Box 5.4 Plant types for revegetation and bioengineering

Type	Advantages	Disadvantages
1. *Grasses*	Versatile and cheap Wide range of tolerances Quick to establish Good dense surface cover	Shallow rooting Regular maintenance required
Reeds and sedges	Establish well on riverbanks, etc. Quick growing	Hand planting expensive Difficult to obtain
2. *Herbs*	Deeper rooting Attractive in grass sward	Seed expensive Sometimes difficult to establish Many species die back in winter
Legumes	Cheap to establish Fix nitrogen Mix well with grass	Not tolerant of difficult sites
3. *Shrubs*	Robust and fairly cheap Many species can be seeded Substantial groundcover Many evergreen species Deeper rooting Low maintenance	More expensive to plant Sometimes difficult to establish
4. *Trees*	Substantial rooting Some can be seeded No maintenance once established	Long time to establish Slow growing Expensive
Willows and poplars	Root easily from cuttings Versatile – many planting techniques Quick to establish	Care in selecting correct type Planting can be expensive Cannot be grown from seed

The types of work involved and the need for a programme of management to ensure that the newly established vegetation will perform its intended role, are discussed in Sections 4.7 and 4.8. Where applicable, the designer should prepare and agree management objectives with the owner or maintaining authority. Without this dialogue, the purpose and specific objectives of management will not be carried forward and the functional requirements of the vegetation may not be maintained.

Monitoring of the site conditions and assessment of the development of vegetation will be required. This will enable problems to be identified at an early stage and any consequential changes in the management regime to be initiated. Many maintenance organisations are unfamiliar with this type of regular management and monitoring of vegetation, which differs from the usual engineering and ground maintenance. Proper management of vegetation to optimise its function must not be neglected.

5.4.2 Specifications

The designer must, where applicable, make appropriate use of both the drawings and the specification to instruct those implementing the work. Where they may be unfamiliar with the nature or objectives of bioengineering works, the clarity of the specification is even more important than usual. It will usually be worthwhile mentioning in the specification the role of vegetation in the design, and the importance attached to its successful establishment. As for all engineering work the specifications should identify:

1. the materials to be used;
2. the performance to be achieved, or alternatively the methods to be used;

Box 5.5 Soil profile design

Soil profile design involves a number of considerations:
1. Selection of soil material
   - on site soils
   - imported soils
   - topsoils as well as other potential growing media.
2. Handling soil material
   - manipulating the soil density by compaction or cultivation
   - retaining any existing soil structure by careful soil handling
   - integrating successive soil layers by scarification.

The selection of soil material for vegetative potential, and suitable soil types for a range of uses, is discussed further in Section 4.2.1 and handling of soil materials in Section 4.2.2.

From measurements of soil properties and by estimating factors such as Available Water Capacity, it is possible to design a soil profile with an appropriate Profile Available Water at given densities. The diagram illustrates this approach. By manipulating the soil profile in this way, it is possible to provide a growing medium which will be conducive to good root development.

On the next page is a comparison of two soil profiles using similar materials but with very different properties. Profile (b) will be unfavourable for plant growth, whilst profile (a) is more carefully designed to optimise vegetation growth with good water availability in the soil profile.

(Continued overleaf)

Box 5.5 *(Continued)*

Depth (cm)	Soil type	Clay %	ρ_d Mg/m^3	L_d	AWC %	Profile Available Water
15	Sandy loam topsoil	15	1.36	1.5	16	0.16 × 15
40	Clay loam	30	1.3	1.57	15	0.15 × 40
45	Silty clay	40	1.5	1.86	12	0.12 × 45
	Compacted fill		2			PAW = 138 mm

(a) Carefully prepared profile with uncompacted layers and gradual transition between horizons. ρ_d = dry bulk density, L_d = packing density, AWC = available water capacity (*see* Section 2.4)

Depth (cm)	Soil type	Clay %	ρ_d Mg/m^3	L_d	AWC %	Profile Available Water
15	Sandy loam topsoil	15	1.5	1.63	15	0.15 × 15
20	Silty clay	40	1.7	2.06	6	0.6 × 20
20	Clay loam	30	1.7	1.97	9	0.9 × 20
	Compacted fill					PAW = 52 mm

(b) Typical earthworks profile with topsoil spread over compacted layers. Note that the silty-clay layer beneath the topsoil forms a low-permeability horizon, which roots would find very difficult to penetrate.

3. how performance will be measured/monitored;
4. any constraints on the construction operation due to the special requirements of soil and plant materials.

Box 5.6 gives guidelines on what provisions should be made in addition to those usually covered in engineering specifications.

Owing to the often specialist nature of bioengineering techniques, specifications will usually have to be prepared as method statements. An element of performance can be introduced for seed germination rates and survival of planted material, for example, but even then, when novel techniques are being applied, there may be scope for dispute about the cause of failures. The onus will be largely on the design team to prepare a proper method and to supervise construction adequately as it is being carried out.

The West German DIN Standards include several which deal specifically with landscaping, vegetation establishment and techniques for incorporating vegetation in engineering works. These standards provide a useful source of bioengineering techniques and specifications, in an area where there are few UK standards. The

Box 5.6 Specification guidelines

Section	Item	Coverage
Materials	Seeds	Types (species, quality, storage, sources, mixtures)
	Plants	Types (cuttings, container–grown, bare–rooted), size, handling and storage, source/provenance, pre-treatment and preparation
	Fertilisers	Content of N:P:K and other nutrients, lime, particle size, special requirements such as slow release
	Mulches	Material, source, size or grade
	Composts/manures	Organic bulk materials: material, source, content of nutrient and/or organic matter, moisture content
	Imported soils	Texture classes, source, pH, fertility, organic matter content
	Geotextiles	Trade name, product, grade or minimum/maximum properties, storage, testing
	Special materials	Such as soil stabilisers for erosion control, soil additives, geocomposites e.g. cribs, blocks, gabions
	Herbicides	Formulation, active ingredient, type e.g. liquid or granular
Earthworks	Soil stripping	Depth and location of horizons to be stripped, timing, moisture content
	Soil stockpiling	Size and shape of stockpile, temporary protection e.g. grassing
	Compaction	Density requirements for soil layers within 1 m of final surface, method of compaction, interim cultivations
	Soil handling	Methods, timing (especially in relation to wet periods), moisture content
	Deep cultivation	Ripping: implement and spacing of tines, depth, direction in relation to slope, timing (moisture content of subsoil)
	Trimming/finishing	Method, tolerances, scarification, finished surface condition, direction of passes in relation to slope

(Continued overleaf)

Box 5.6 *(Continued)*

Section	Item	Coverage
Seeding	Method	Drilling, broadcasting, hydroseeding, hand application; sequence of operations and materials applied; uniformity of application
	Timing	Acceptable seeding periods in relation to predicted or actual weather conditions
	Ground preparation	Site clearance (e.g. weeds), stonepicking, cultivation
	Aftercare	Follow-up fertilising, overseeding, weed control, cutting
	Performance and defects	Required germination success or density of groundcover, remedial work.
Planting	Method	Planting technique: excavation, preparation, backfilling, support (best illustrated by diagrams); size/type of plants, mulching, watering/irrigation
	Timing	Acceptable planting periods according to weather or ground considerations
	Ground preparation	Site clearance, cultivation
	Aftercare	Fertilising, pruning, weed control, watering; checking, adjustment and removal of tree supports
	Performance	Acceptable rate of failure, initial growth , replacement procedures
Management	Trees	Thinning, coppicing, replacement planting, checking for disease, pesticide application, trimming (hedges)
	Herbaceous/grass	Mowing: frequency, height, method, disposal of cuttings; fertiliser materials, rates, timing; overseeding; pest control; removal of pernicious weeds
	Fencing	Check and repair enclosures on a regular basis
Measurement	Performance	Acceptable level of failures, arrangements for replacements of defects
	Slopes	Areas measured on plan or plane of ground surface; allow for extra materials to maintain rates on slopes if measured on plan

coverage of these together with relevant British Standards is summarised in Appendix 3.

5.4.3 Construction programme

The overall programme for new or remedial works in which vegetation plays a significant role must be controlled to some extent by seasonal factors. For example, soil moisture deficit may determine soil stripping times and soil temperatures will determine the time of seeding. Seeding, planting and bioengineering construction should commence at an appropriate time of year, guidance on this aspect being given in Section 4.8. The completion time should be determined by the relationship between season and the elements which make up the last stages of construction. Section 4.8 describes the time of year when particular operations should be carried out, though it should be remembered that seasonal variations with geography and altitude in the UK can amount to three or four weeks.

Considerable variations can also occur from one year to the next and the construction programme should be sufficiently flexible to accommodate these changes. Nevertheless it is not always possible to arrange a programme that fits in neatly with seasonal requirements. In such cases several options are open:

1. delay completion until conditions are right;
2. delay completion but introduce some temporary cover such as grass which will establish quickly outside of the normal planting seasons;
3. complete the work, risk partial or complete failure and be prepared to undertake remedial work later.

Local circumstances must figure largely in deciding on which course of action to follow, and the supervising engineer should allow for whichever contingencies may be most appropriate.

5.5 Contractual arrangements

5.5.1 Options

Where vegetation work is to be carried out by a contractor, the question often arises of whether specialist or critical work should be arranged as a subcontract to a civil engineering contract or as a completely separate contract. Difficulty in resolving this general question means that the implementation of vegetation work in particular may be unnecessarily difficult and unreliable, unless undertaken by direct labour, or lies outside contractual restraints. Some of the advantages and disadvantages of various contractual options that can be considered for the construction and aftercare phases are listed below.

Option 1:

Vegetation work as a nominated subcontract to main civil engineering work

Advantages
- Conflicts between separate contractors are avoided.
- The engineering contractor has more incentive to accommodate the programme needs of the vegetation contractor.
- Some control over the vegetation work can be gained, by nominating the subcontractor or at least naming a list of acceptable firms.
- Vegetation work can be covered in civil engineering documents by a provisional or prime cost sum.

Disadvantages
- Conflicts will occur between the short maintenance period on an engineering contract and the possible need for a longer defects liability

period and certainly for a longer aftercare period under the vegetation subcontract.

- A separate vegetation management contract may be needed to cover aftercare.
- Few published subcontract documents deal specifically for vegetation work.
- There is a lack of special clauses in standard engineering contracts to cover the requirements of plants.
- There is less control over and communication with the vegetation contractor.
- The engineering contract period has to allow for planting seasons.
- The retention of payment under typical engineering conditions is inadequate for vegetation works.
- Quotations for nominated subcontracts may have to be obtained to prepare the main tender documents, and it may be difficult to finalise the bioengineering requirements before the civil engineering work has progressed some way towards completion.

Remarks
- This is perhaps the most widely used option where vegetation is a significant component of the works.
- Ease of contract administration and closer co-ordination of engineering and vegetation work are in its favour, but there are difficulties in accommodating sufficient aftercare.

Option 2:

Vegetation work included in main civil engineering contract (main contractor at liberty to do work himself, or sublet)

Advantages
- Simple and easy to arrange.
- Some aftercare operations can be included, but only for a short period, i.e. the engineering maintenance period.
- The contractor is already familiar with site conditions.
- The contractor knows he has to carry out vegetation work himself.

Disadvantages
- Workmanship may be poor due to inexperience.
- The arrangements for defects liability and aftercare may be poor.
- Additional clauses are needed to standard engineering contracts to cover requirements of plants; special contract conditions need to be included.

Remarks
- Suitable on normal contracts only if the work is very minor in scale and straightforward in type.
- Would be appropriate if the civil engineering contractor was suitably experienced and/or cooperative.

Option 3:

Entirely separate contracts

Advantages
- The most appropriate conditions of contract can be used.
- There is more control over the selection of contractor.
- There is direct communication with contractor.
- The final account for engineering work is not delayed until the end of vegetation defects liability and aftercare periods.
- An aftercare programme is straightforward to arrange as part of the vegetation contract if required.
- The final design of the scheme can be deferred until the engineering work is well advanced, providing this does not adversely affect the main contract (useful where there is uncertainty over materials, etc).

Disadvantages
- The civil engineering contractor may not undertake his work with vegetation establishment foremost in mind.
- There is lack of incentive for the civil engineering contractor to meet the vegetation contractor's programme.
- The engineering contractor could blame defects in his work on the activities of the vegetation contractor if periods overlap, and vice versa.
- Vegetation contractor may have to undo some of the civil engineering contractor's work e.g. excessive soil compaction.
- Delay in commencement of vegetation work until after engineering maintenance period is almost certainly undesirable, as the site will remain unprotected for some time.

Remarks
- Appropriate only when civil engineering and vegetation work are easily separated, such as where groundworks are minimal, or where bioengineering functions are not crucial to the success of the main civils works.

Option 4:

Vegetation work split between separate vegetation and main civil engineering contracts (i.e. a variation of Option 3)

Advantages
- Elements which may need shorter defects liability periods, such as grass seeding, can be done by engineering contractor or sublet to a specialist.
- This work may be straightforward and familiar to the main contractor.
- Less familiar elements, such as planting, can be done by specialists under more suitable contract conditions.
- These elements may only require access to limited parts of the site.
- The final design of special vegetation work can be deferred until engineering work is well advanced.

Disadvantages
- See notes under Option 3.
- Clauses may need to be added to the main contract and subcontract conditions to cover plants.
- Items of work done under the engineering contract will still have to be included in a longer term aftercare programme.

Remarks
- A useful option but does not solve all the difficulties.
- Since a large engineering project may well involve vegetation work which is not bioengineering, this option may be preferred.

Option 5:

Main contract is with vegetation contractor with civil engineering done by him, or subcontracted

Advantages
- The vegetation is the major objective, with a subsidiary civil engineering component which is a means to that end.
- Civil engineering works are programmed according to the vegetation requirements.
- The main contractor with overall responsibility has a greater appreciation of the vegetation requirements.
- Advantages of the single contract as for Options 1 and 2.

Disadvantages
- The vegetation contractor may be unfamiliar with the nature of civil engineering works, with similar subcontracting implications to Options 1 and 2.
- The value of the civil engineering works may be more than the vegetation works.
- The vegetation contractor may have difficulty in meeting specialist civil engineering requirements.

Remarks
- A common arrangement for larger landscaping and land reclamation contracts.
- Appropriate where the civil engineering element is secondary, or at least not overwhelming.
- Will encourage specialist bioengineering contractors to become established.

Whatever arrangements are chosen, two related aspects must be considered.

1. The division of the work between the engineering contractor and the specialist should be rationalised; in terms of earthworks, for example, the specialist contractor should take over and complete them prior to the establishment of vegetation, whenever the mechanical requirements of the soil are less significant than the vegetative requirements.

2. Provision must be made for aftercare work, in order to get the vegetation established and to facilitate more long-term management. Aftercare and management requirements for vegetation are discussed in sections 4.5 and 4.7. Aftercare must begin as soon as seeding or planting work has been carried out and is therefore likely to overlap with the contract maintenance period (i.e. the period during which defects are made good).

Good aftercare and management are likely to be the key to the long-term success of the vegetation. Owners and management authorities are often unwilling or unable to take on early management work themselves, so a sensible arrangement can be for 2–3 years of aftercare to be included in the vegetation part of the contract. Long-term management can be carried out under contract or by direct labour. This should be allowed for in the management programme.

5.5.2 Forms of contract

Standard civil engineering forms of contract do not generally include specific clauses to deal with vegetation work and will often need amendment to accommodate bioengineering applications. This arises largely because:

1. plants have different aftercare and maintenance requirements from normal civil works;
2. there are restricted times when they can be sown or planted;
3. extended periods of time are needed for plants to become properly established and for defects in performance to become apparent.

Modifications to standard conditions of contract should be considered for the following matters.

- A typical 6 or 12 months' maintenance period or defects liability period is not enough for planting or seeding of trees and shrubs. A minimum of 24 months after the first breaking of buds is desirable and 36 months is preferable.
- By contrast, as little as 6 months may be acceptable for grass and herb seeding, provided there is no intervening dormant season.
- As well as an extended defects liability period, vegetative work needs a period of aftercare. This phase of the work usually commences immediately after planting/sowing and therefore overlaps with the former period; responsibilities have to be defined clearly.
- The responsibility for aftercare following substantial completion of the works can fall to the contractor or to the employer; the defects liability period is waived in the latter case.
- At the end of the defects liability period, the contractor can be required to continue aftercare work either under the same contract or a separate management contract.
- If aftercare operations are carried out under the same initial contract, such work can be arranged in the contract documents as a separate and distinct part.

- It may also be useful to split a contract which includes both civil engineering and vegetation work into two parts, i.e. earlier completion could be certified on all but the vegetation work. The first part of the main contractor's retention is then released earlier and the start of the maintenance period on the engineering work is not unnecessarily delayed. Partial possession by the employer occurs at this time.
- A typical retention of 1.5% may be inadequate cover for the possible failures that can arise from poor materials or workmanship in the use of vegetation; 10% retention, reduced to 5% at substantial completion, is more appropriate. Alternatively, a bond can be arranged to cover the risk of failures beyond the contract maintenance period.
- Provided cover is adequate, arrangements can be made for the release of the final retention on the civil engineering work at the end of the one-year maintenance period. The remaining retention need only cover the vegetation work. However, sufficient retention should remain to cover any potential repair to the civil engineering works resulting from the failure or poor performance of the vegetation.

In the UK two Forms of Contract are available which are specifically for use in landscape work.

1. The Joint Council of Landscape Industries (JCLI) Form of Agreement for Landscape Works, April 1985 edition. This is only suitable for work of a relatively low value.
2. The Joint Contracts Tribunal (JCT) Intermediate Form of Contract (IFC 1984) with 1985 supplement for landscape work.

Maintenance contracts would normally be let on a one- or two-year term, perhaps renewed on a regular basis. The Joint Council for Landscape Industries publishes a model contract document for landscape maintenance which would be appropriate for bioengineering management.

5.6 Comparing costs

In justifying the use of vegetation in a civil engineering application, the engineer will usually need to carry out an economic comparison with alternative solutions. Initial interest in the use of vegetation is often partly due to its economic appeal compared with conventional engineering methods. The environmental benefits are also important, but are difficult to quantify. It is not possible to provide actual cost comparisons between vegetative and conventional approaches, though in Section 6 some indication of the relative costs involved is given for specific applications. Each application must be considered on its merits, comparing full life-cycle costs, i.e. the net present value of investigation, design and construction, plus future management and replacement.

In countries such as the UK, where bioengineering is frequently regarded as a novel approach, costs can be expected to be proportionally higher than in countries where practice is established, due to the additional time needed for working to unfamiliar design and construction procedures. As engineers become more familiar with the techniques, more confident in their use and as special materials become more readily available, however, unit costs can be expected to fall.

The additional cost of providing a good, reliable and functional vegetation system can be associated with the following activities:

1. investigation of additional parameters for design purposes;
2. greater design effort in some cases;
3. comparison between vegetative and conventional approaches in cost-benefit analysis;
4. greater care with soil preparation and handling during construction;
5. constraints on timing and progress during construction;
6. special materials;
7. special techniques, such as hydroseeding, direct tree seeding, planting with willows, etc, often with high manpower requirements;
8. intensive aftercare to ensure establishment;
9. management, monitoring and repair in the long-term.

Nevertheless the overall costs of an approach using vegetation may be lower, and will certainly follow a different expenditure profile, that of conventional structures, as illustrated in Figure 5.2. A conventional approach may well have a higher construction cost, a finite serviceable life with an element of maintenance, and then a substantial replacement or refurbishment cost. Vegetation, on the other hand, will usually have a lower construction cost, and for practical purposes an indefinite life. During this time, however, it will require regular maintenance and occasional repair or refurbishment. Where bioengineering works are constructed and/or

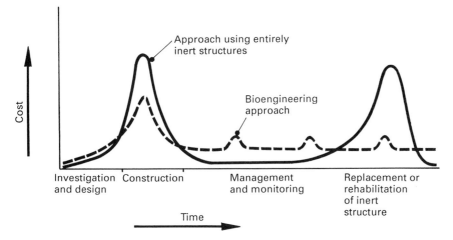

Figure 5.2 Illustrations of different expenditure profiles of inert structures and bioengineering works

maintained by the owner or authority, the economic cost of labour will be considerably lower than for externally contracted work.

The bioengineering approach may simply be adding a greater margin of safety, in which case the cost of providing the appropriate vegetation should be set against the cost of the conventional solution (including management implications) plus the repair cost associated with its lower margin of safety. This situation would apply, for example, to the incidence of small-scale shallow slips on highway slopes.

When considering a bioengineering approach, the risks associated with failure of the system must be taken into account:

1. the extent and nature of a potential failure in the vegetation;
2. implications of the loss of the function, perhaps temporarily, which it is performing;
3. costs of repair and making good any consequent damage;
4. risks to life, health or property which might be involved.

Environmental benefits are a major consideration. Some of these may be quantifiable, such as improvement in property values or reduction in downstream sedimentation and thus drainage maintenance costs. Others will be intangible, such as visual appearance and wildlife value. On many schemes the engineer is required to submit an environmental assessment; the benefits of the bioengineering approach which are difficult to quantify would be included in this and are likely to be greater than with a conventional engineering approach.

6 Applications – theory and practice

6.1 Rationale

The potential for using vegetation in an engineering role covers a broad range of applications, too broad for each to be considered in detail in this Guide. Only the principal applications, as selected by consensus among UK practitioners, are described. These are summarised, along with the relevant vegetation effects, in Box 6.1. For each case, attention is focussed on the ways of using vegetation, exemplified by the best of current engineering practice. The depth of coverage varies between different applications, reflecting the complexity of the application, the amount of published information, and the level of interest afforded it by practising engineers.

In attempting to make a fuller use of vegetation in practical applications, engineers may well find themselves facing uncertainties arising from:

1. a perceived variability and unreliability in the properties and performance of plants, and the susceptibility of the material to loss or damage beyond the control of the owner or designer;
2. a lack of experimental and field data on vegetation properties and behaviour in an engineering context.

For the former, the Guide has indicated throughout Section 2 that the performance and properties of plants are well understood and reasonably predictable, and that the susceptibility of vegetation to loss or damage can be reduced (*see* Section 2.7). With an informed approach to plant selection, site preparation and management, engineers will find that vegetation will behave fairly predictably according to a simple set of basic principles.

Experimental and field data is, however, lacking or sparse in respect of certain aspects of plant behaviour. The physical interaction between roots and soil is, for engineers, a particularly relevant example of these gaps in our knowledge, and there is uncertainty as to the actual mode of behaviour of roots and their long-term performance. There can be no doubt that in many circumstances vegetation does play an engineering role, but recourse to empirical design procedures means that it is impractical to work to specific limits for loadings or factors of safety.

Box 6.1 The applications of vegetation and the relevant effects

Application	Surface competence: Soil detachment	Surface competence: Mechanical strength	Surface competence: Insulation	Surface competence: Retarding/arresting	Surface competence: Erosion	Surface water regime: Rainfall interception	Surface water regime: Overland flow/runoff	Surface water regime: Infiltration	Surface water regime: Subsurface drainage	Surface water regime: Surface drag	Soil water: Evapotranspiration	Soil water: Soil moisture depletion	Properties of soil mass: Root reinforcement	Properties of soil mass: Anchorage/restraint	Properties of soil mass: Arching/buttressing	Properties of soil mass: Surface mat/net	Properties of soil mass: Surcharge	Properties of soil mass: Windloading	Properties of soil mass: Root wedging	Air flow: Surface drag	Air flow: Flow deflection	Air flow: Noise attenuation	Air flow: Filter particles
Slope stabilisation — Embankments and cuttings	●	●		●	●						●	●	●	●	●	●	●	●					
Slope stabilisation — Cliffs and rockfaces	●		●	●									●	●		●	●	●	●				
Water erosion control — Rainfall and overland flow	●	●	●	●	●	●	●	●															
Water erosion control — Gully erosion	●	●		●	●		●																
Watercourse and shoreline protection — Continuous flow channels	●				●			●	●	●			●	●		●	●	●					
Watercourse and shoreline protection — Discontinuous flow channels	●				●				●	●			●	●		●							
Watercourse and shoreline protection — Large water bodies (shorelines)	●	●			●					●			●	●		●		●					
Wind erosion control																				●	●		●
Vegetation barriers — Shelter																				●	●		●
Vegetation barriers — Noise reduction																						●	
Surface protection and trafficability	●	●	●		●		●				●	●	●			●							
Water management in small catchments						●	●	●	●	●	●												
Plants as indicators																							

Uncertainties in the practical application of vegetation must be viewed in the light of the considerable experience of bioengineering outside the UK and, for some applications, within the UK. There is a large body of relevant information and experience available, much of which is drawn together for the first time in this Guide. The applications which are described in this Section rely to varying extents on theoretical and empirical procedures combined with experience, and lead to two distinct approaches to the use of vegetation:

1. providing a positive increase in the ability of engineering works to resist a potential failure mode, such as erosion, channel flow or soil slippage;
2. reducing the risk of failure associated with natural variation in site or soil conditions, such as localised patches of weak soil, flow concentration or water seepage.

Vegetation may therefore amount to a way of adding an extra margin of confidence to safety or stability, and of reducing the incidence of problems requiring maintenance or repair. Its use will also guard against decreases in the margin of safety due to long-term geotechnical or hydrological changes, or local variations in soil condition.

The physical principles underlying the effects of vegetation can be combined in either analytical procedures, based on theory, or a series of general empirical relationships, based on observation and experience. The need for both emphasises the point made in Section 1 that, in many cases, bioengineering principles cannot be described by rigorous scientific theory and that good practice is as much an art as a science, involving considerable judgement and experience. In using vegetation, the engineer needs to combine an understanding of the underlying physical principles of its engineering role (*see* Section 3), with knowledge of the factors influencing vegetation growth (*see* Section 2), the procedures for selecting and establishing vegetation and for its short- and long-term maintenance (*see* Section 4) and an assessment of different methods of implementations and relative costs and benefits (*see* Section 5). This section brings these aspects together in the context of specific applications and the situations in which they are appropriate.

6.2 Slope stabilisation

Slope stabilisation is an element of construction in which vegetation can play a significant role (*see* Section 3.1). The effect of vegetation on slopes, cliffs and rockfaces has applications in mining, reclamation, highway, railway and dam construction, coastal protection and many other situations where the construction of embankments and cuttings forms slopes or steep faces. In the engineering of slopes, there is often a compromise between the admissable steepness from the viewpoint of stability and the cost of additional earthworks and land-take. Slopes also have a high visual impact and so their appearance is often particularly important.

6.2.1 Types of slope instability

The classification of the movement of material on slopes is difficult because of the extremely complex mix of processes which creates slope instability. For the sake of simplicity, the relationship between slope instability and vegetation is here discussed under three headings (*see* Walker and Fell, 1987):

1. surface movements
2. shallow-seated instability
3. deeper-seated instability.

Surface movements include those induced by soil creep (BS6031, 1981; *see* Appendix 3), solifluction (here defined as a process resulting from repeated freeze-thaw cycles), and soil erosion (*see* Section 6.3). These processes can have a significant influence on overall slope stability because heavy and prolonged erosion and continuous slow soil movement can alter slope geometry. Creep is usually associated with natural hillsides in upland areas rather than engineered slopes, although it is not necessarily exclusive to these environments. Plants selected to reduce the incidence of surface movements will usually have to be tolerant of hostile soil and climatic conditions.

Shallow-seated instability is taken to be slides, rotational failures or a combination of both which occur within 2 m of the ground surface.

Deeper-seated instability covers failures where the failure surface is several metres below the ground surface, beyond the limits to which the roots of the majority of trees and shrubs normally penetrate. Vegetation cannot therefore significantly affect deep-seated instability.

Possibly the most widespread form of slope failure, particularly in the UK, with its over-consolidated clays, is a shallow-seated slip, in which the depth of the failure plane is less than 2 m below the slope surface (Parsons and Perry, 1985). As seen in Section 2.1.5, appreciable concentrations of grass roots reach depths of 0.3–0.5, while shrub and tree roots reach depths of 2–3 m. Considerable scope then exists for using deeper-rooting vegetation to reduce the incidence of shallow-seated slope failures.

Most shallow slope failures tend to occur seasonally, during the early spring. It is not certain whether these failures occur as a consequence of steadily increasing soil moisture in clays due to very low evapotranspiration during winter; root decay and declining root strength before new spring root growth begins; or temperature effects. It is usually feasible to reduce the incidence of shallow slope failures by using plants where the seasonal variation in the critical factors is not so marked. Such plants should have:

1. substantial perennial root structures, i.e. plants other than grasses;
2. an evergreen habit;
3. a high water demand, so-called phraetophytes.

6.2.2 The effects of vegetation

The beneficial effects of vegetation on slope stability develop gradually over a period of time, and there is therefore a tendency for the effects to be underestimated. Paradoxically, as seen in Section 3 and illustrated in Box 6.2, it is the sudden removal of vegetation which can best demonstrate its effectiveness, as illustrated by the sometimes dramatic onset of slope instability after a wooded slope has been clearfelled. This can take the form of steady soil creep or sudden mud flows, shallow-seated slips and landslides or sometimes, though rarely, deep-seated rotational or translational movement (Gray, 1977; Wu, 1976).

Box 6.2 Long-term effects of clear felling on slope stability

The clear felling of trees can have a dramatic effect on the root reinforcement, anchoring and buttressing roles of vegetation. The rate of decay of Radiata pine roots in New Zealand, a temperate climate, has been found by O'Loughlin and Watson (1979) to decline exponentially after felling. The time to half strength was only 14 months. In western USA, Ziemer (1981) reported that about 30% of roots less than 17 mm in diameter (i.e. those contributing most to soil reinforcement) in a mixed conifer forest had totally decayed after 7 years. Burroughs and Thomas (1977) found that 75% of Douglas fir roots 10 mm or smaller were lost within 2 years of felling on the west coast of North America. They also discovered that root tensile strength of roots 10 mm diameter and less declined from about 26.5 kN/m^2 to about 2.3 kN/m^2 within 30 months of felling.

Similarly the ability of tree roots to anchor slope soil masses to fractures in underlying bedrock, in order to bind zones of weak soil to more stable ones, and the ability of the tree stem/root cylinder to buttress and support by soil arching an upslope area of soil, fall away as the roots weaken and disappear through decay. The decay rates are dependent upon climate and soil moisture levels, hotter and wetter slopes having greater decay rates.

The reduction in the stabilising role of vegetation due to clear felling and the onset of slope instability is clearly manifested by an increase in the frequency of landslides. Results from a study of felled areas in southeast Alaska are shown below.

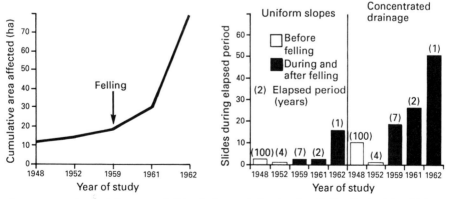

Frequency and cumulative area of slides before and after logging, Hollis, Alaska (after Bishop and Stevens, 1964).

The stability of the denuded natural slopes declines progressively due to a number of immediate, short-term and long-term effects.

Immediate effects due to loss of above-ground vegetation
  • increase in erosion and water runoff;
  • decrease in transpiration losses of soil water in relation to infiltration;
  • reduction in interception storage/losses.
These effects may be only temporary while a scrubby or ruderal vegetation regrows.

Short-term effects
  • decrease in soil strength as soil suction is relieved or, alternatively, as groundwater level increases;
  • loss of root reinforcement in the surface layers as smaller/softer root tissue deteriorates.

Long-term effects
  • loss of deeper root reinforcement, anchoring or buttressing effects as deeper and larger root tissues deteriorate;
  • increased weathering of the slope surface due to the loss of insulating cover and the erosion of surface soil.

The rates of decline in root strength and reduction of root biomass determine the speed at which a clear-felled slope will deteriorate. These rates are similar for many species. Roots with a high initial strength retain some strength for several years after felling, whilst those with low initial strength lose nearly all their reinforcing capacity in a short time.

Slopes can recover from clearfelling as vegetation regrows. The rate of recovery depends on the type of regeneration and management of the vegetation. Figure 6.1 illustrates this effect. Loss of root reinforcement of soil due to roots decaying with

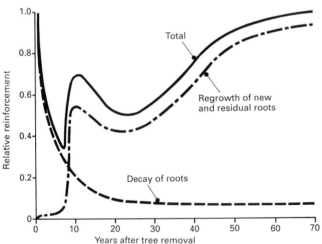

Figure 6.1 Relative reinforcement of soils by roots after tree removal (after O'Loughlin and Ziemer, 1982)

Box 6.3 Effects of vegetation on slope stability

Overall effect on	Influence[1]	Effect on slope stability		
		Surface movement	Shallow instability	Deeper-seated instability
Strength of the soil mass	Root reinforcement (3.5.1)	+	+	
	Soil arching and buttressing (3.5.2)		+	+
	Root anchorage (3.5.2)		+	+
	Surcharge (3.5.4)		–	
	Windthrow (3.5.5)		–	
	Surface mat (3.5.3)	+	+	
	Soil restraint (3.3.5)	+	+	
Moisture-related strength	Interception (3.2.1)	+		
	Infiltration (3.2.3)	+/–	+/–	+/–
	Evapotranspiration (3.4.2)	+	+	+
Microclimate	Shelter (3.7.1)	+		
	Insulation (3.3.4)	+	+	

[1] The principles behind these influences are described, as referenced, in Section 3.
+ Beneficial effect
– Adverse effect

time is compensated for by increasing reinforcement by regrowing roots, the total reinforcement reaching a maximum after about 10 years. This fits quite well with the observed accelerated incidence of landslides between three and seven years after tree removal. Nearly all the effects of vegetation on soil described in Section 3 are encountered on slopes and they contribute in one way or another to slope stability, as detailed in Box 6.3.

6.2.3 Stabilisation of soil slopes

Surface movements

The ability of vegetation to restrain surface material and prevent movement depends on how well it binds together the soil, provides some anchorage by its roots, and insulates and protects the soil surface by shoot growth. Extensive shallow rooting and dense surface growth are therefore necessary attributes of the plants used. Grasses, herbs and shrubs can all fulfil this role. The deeper that creep and other surface effects penetrate the slope, the more important deeper rooting becomes.

Shallow instability

Shallow-seated slope failures may take the form of one or a combination of the following:

• rotational failure

- translational block wedge or slab slide
- earthflow or mudflow
- slump and earthflow
- successive slips
- multiple retrogressive translational slides.

The depth to the underside of the down-slope movement, relative to the maximum rooting depth of vegetation growing on the slope, will determine the degree of stabilisation that vegetation can provide. Root reinforcement and other root-related mechanical forces will only influence the well-rooted zone. Indirect forces due to moisture related effects may well have a significantly deeper influence. Thus surface water infiltration and moisture extraction/transpiration by roots will have some effect well beyond the root zone.

Four classes of plant-root reinforced and anchored slope can be identified, as illustrated in Figure 6.2, depending on the relative depths of soil to bedrock (or stable stratum) and the rooting depths (Tsukamoto and Kusakabe, 1984). When

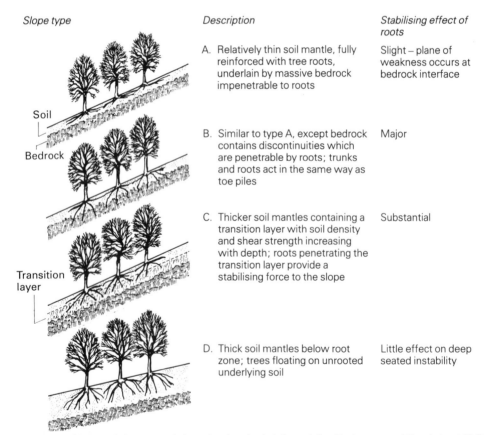

Slope type	Description	Stabilising effect of roots
Soil Bedrock	A. Relatively thin soil mantle, fully reinforced with tree roots, underlain by massive bedrock impenetrable to roots	Slight – plane of weakness occurs at bedrock interface
	B. Similar to type A, except bedrock contains discontinuities which are penetrable by roots; trunks and roots act in the same way as toe piles	Major
Transition layer	C. Thicker soil mantles containing a transition layer with soil density and shear strength increasing with depth; roots penetrating the transition layer provide a stabilising force to the slope	Substantial
	D. Thick soil mantles below root zone; trees floating on unrooted underlying soil	Little effect on deep seated instability

Figure 6.2 Classes of plant-root reinforced and anchored slopes (after Tsukamoto and Kusakabe, 1984)

vegetation is used to stabilise slopes, the principal requirement is to ensure optimum rooting in the weak soil zones, to the maximum practicable depth. This should form the basis of the design philosophy (*see*, for example, Box 5.5) and be a major objective during construction.

Shallow-rooting plants such as grasses are unlikely to be effective in overcoming shallow instability. Conventional slope seeding mixtures are therefore of little value, except for controlling surface movements. Deeper rooting vegetation, including herbs, shrubs and small trees, will be much more effective at reinforcing soil, anchoring soil layers and removing soil water.

Careful selection and management of vegetation can help deal with specific problems. For example, the adverse effects of surcharge can be reduced by tapering the height of plants on a slope to give greatest weight at the toe of the slope. This can be achieved by coppicing or by selecting species mixtures so that the heaviest trees are on the lower portion of the slope.

If trees are planted where the groundwater is close to the surface, the roots may not grow downwards but will extend laterally instead (*see* Section 2.1.5). A potential slip plane may then be formed along the plane of shallow rooting depth. To some extent this effect may be counteracted by the ability of vegetation to lower the groundwater table as a result of evapotranspiration. A layered vegetation structure (*see* Section 2.2.2) may be beneficial here. Shallow-rooted species, trees and shrubs, will increase soil suction in the upper soil layers while deeper rooting trees will reduce pore-water pressures at depth. These effects will, of course, occur only when transpiration is taking place and may therefore not be sufficient to increase the factor of safety during winter.

Deeper-seated instability

The ability of vegetation to enhance the factor of safety of slopes prone to deep-seated problems should be regarded as minimal. As discussed above, roots can influence soil moisture beyond their physical extent. Because soil suction is increased in the root zone, moisture from deep soil layers will move upwards by capillary action, thereby reducing pore-water pressure in the deeper layers. This may have some influence on deeper-seated instability. Nonetheless it is likely that the main role of vegetation will be aesthetic, unless it is combined with inert construction, such as retaining walls, toe loading with berms, geotextile reinforcement, ground anchoring and toe piling. It may be possible to obtain a degree of enhanced shear resistance at the emergent position of the failure plane by buttressing and soil arching. The emphasis on the use of vegetation, however, must be largely on enhancing the effectiveness of inert structures and on minimising any possible adverse effects, such as:

1. surcharging the upper portion of the slope;
2. decreasing soil strength along potential failure planes by infiltration;
3. introducing failure planes by planting in rows at close intervals across or down the slope.

6.2.4 Stabilisation of cliffs and rockfaces

This section applies to very steep slopes, between 45° and vertical, in rock or soils which form cliffs, quarry faces and steep cuttings. The influence of vegetation in a cliff or rockface environment can be limited. The main effects are:

1. rock wedging, whereby roots, especially of trees, force open joints in the rock and increase weathering action;
2. weight and leverage of larger trees or heavy creepers, which can topple or drag loose rock material from the face;
3. rock binding, whereby roots bind and restrain loosened rock fragments and prevent them falling;
4. insulation, protecting the surface directly with a mat of shoots and roots, thus reducing weathering action, or indirectly by retaining weathered material against the slope so that fresh material is not exposed.

In examining the stability of steep faces, it is convenient to divide them into three types:

1. formed hard rock masses of any angle
2. steep weak rock slopes
3. steep soil slopes.

Formed hard rock masses of any angle

The approach to slope stability here is controlled by the orientations of important discontinuities in the host rock mass; the method of slope stability analysis is entirely different from that for soil slopes. The basis of design is an amalgam of empiricism, using sets of standard designs based on rock hardness, relative jointing and slope orientations, and excavation techniques.

The long-term stability of hand-excavated rock slopes is generally superior to that of slopes formed by mass excavation using explosives. With the latter, less opportunity exists to adapt to local variations in ground conditions as work proceeds. Most stability problems are considered to be due to disturbance of the rock mass by dilation of pre-existing fractures during blasting (Matheson, 1985). Given this situation, the elimination of root wedging is highly desirable.

Steep weak rock slopes

The approach to slope design here is very dependent on the properties of the weak rocks forming the cliff, the location of the slope relative to property and transport corridors, and the risks to life and property. Design involves incorporating a combination of site stabilisation measures, such as scaling or removing loose slabs, lumps and rock fragments; netting; buttressing; and infilling with concrete structures or lean-mix, and associated safety measures such as rock trenches and fences. Design is based on judgement and experience. Vegetation has particular value for anchoring and restraining surface material and thermal insulation against freeze-thaw weathering. Generally these slopes are much more amenable to vegetation establishment, as they have softer areas with a larger potential rooting volume.

Steep soil slopes

These are oversteepened slopes resulting from either natural erosion processes, such as wave and current action on coastlines, river and stream banks, or human activities. In these situations vegetation can fulfil peripheral roles at the margins of massive inert construction, and also aid erosion control on regraded stabilised slopes.

Generally all the above types of steep face contain portions of soft soil or rock, sometimes of irregular and sometimes of well-defined extent. For example, irregularly occurring steep clay-filled pits which occur in chalk formations in the UK cause problems in cuttings. Similarly, bands of weathered soft overburden cause problems in cuttings in hard rock. Steep slopes in soils can be treated satisfactorily by either flattening them to a stable slope (*see* Section 4.2.3) or incorporating a composite form of construction such as vegetation in conjunction with a geogrid or mesh (*see* Section 6.2.10).

Vegetating cliffs and rock faces

Rockslopes and steep cliffs are generally quite hostile environments for plants. The absence of fine material to form a 'soil', either because of the nature of the rock itself or because of rapid erosion and removal, can inhibit the colonisation of plants. Nevertheless, plants often colonise a cliff-face, as long as the erosion or instability is not so great that the substrate is continually falling away faster than they can colonise it. Trees with deep tap-roots which penetrate the rock fissures for water are often the best colonisers but, unfortunately, these are the plants with the greatest destabilising characteristics.

Techniques for increasing the ability of cliffs and rockfaces to support vegetation are illustrated in Figure 6.3. Essentially these involve increasing the retention of fine material on the face by providing ledges, crannies and crevices. Some temporary, or even permanent, reinforcement or netting on the face can also be used to hold soil material in place until vegetation has become established. If conditions can be made less hostile, a wider choice of plant types is available, permitting selection of those which will minimise the destabilising influences and enhance the stabilising ones.

Vegetation, in particular naturally colonising trees, on steep rockfaces is usually considered to be undesirable from the engineering point of view. However, it is conceivable that if a vegetation cover which does not destabilise the rock can be selected and established, it may discourage the colonisation of undesirable species. The types of vegetation which might be more welcome on rockfaces include:

1. dense grass-dominated swards
2. shallow- or fibrous-rooted shrubby species such as willows.

Deep-rooting species, especially tap-rooted trees, are particularly undesirable.

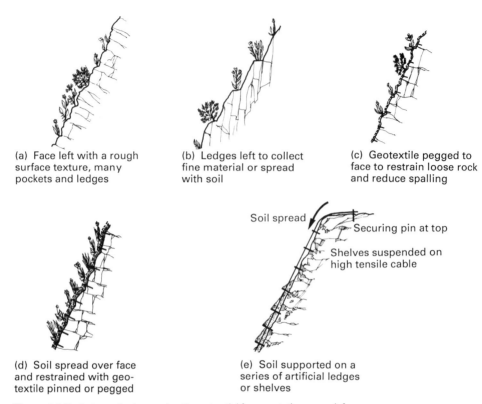

(a) Face left with a rough surface texture, many pockets and ledges

(b) Ledges left to collect fine material or spread with soil

(c) Geotextile pegged to face to restrain loose rock and reduce spalling

Soil spread
Securing pin at top
Shelves suspended on high tensile cable

(d) Soil spread over face and restrained with geo-textile pinned or pegged

(e) Soil supported on a series of artificial ledges or shelves

Figure 6.3 Techniques for increasing the potential for vegetation on rock faces

6.2.5 Quantification of the effects of vegetation on slope stability

It is not possible, with the present state of the art, to quantify precisely the individual effects of vegetation on slope stability but it is likely that feedback from laboratory and field research will allow this increasingly in the future. At present considerable judgement and experience are required when assessing the physical effects of vegetation on slope stability. The general scale of these effects may be evaluated using the approaches set out in Box 6.4.

Root reinforcement of the soil matrix can be quantified on an existing vegetated slope, using the procedure shown in Box 6.5 and applying the simplified perpendicular root model described in Box 3.1. This analytical approach is most suitable for interpreting field observations by applying numerical models of slope stability. The methodology is not yet sufficiently advanced, however, for use in predicting the effects of roots on soil strength for any given combination of plants and soil. Numerical models cannot, therefore, be used to give theoretical design parameters of root density and strength, but they do give an indication of the magnitude of the likely effects and the sensitivity of the stability of the slope to variation in significant parameters relating to soil/plant interactions.

Box 6.4 Assessing the physical effects on vegetation on slope stability

Effect	Physical characteristics	Method
Root reinforcement	Root area ratio, distribution and morphology	Weighing root mass in soil core, or counting root densities at vertical intervals in trial pits dug into slope
	Tensile strength of roots	In situ and laboratory tensile tests
Soil arching buttressing and anchorage	Spacing, diameter and embedment of trees, thickness and inclination of yielding strata	Site survey of trees
	Shear strength properties of the soil(s)	Laboratory and in situ testing of slope soils
Surcharge	Mean weight of vegetation	Site estimate or reference to published information for typical weights/biomass of trees (e.g. Cannell, 1982)
Wind loading	Design wind speed for required return period; mean mature tree height for groups of trees	By reference to BS CP3:V:2:1972 and windthrow hazard assessment (Miller, 1985)
Soil moisture	Moisture content of soil Level of ground-water Pore-pressure/soil suction	Field and laboratory tests, stand-pipes, piezometers and tensionmeters
Interception	Net rainfall on slope	Rainfall readings, slope runoff, ground detention estimates, density of foliage cover
Infiltration	Variation of moisture content of soil with depth	Field and laboratory tests to determine soil permeability, etc

A similar situation exists for the evaluation of arching and buttressing in soil, where the overall effect of root reinforcement can be due to both large and small diameter roots. The effects of soil arching and buttressing can only be assessed qualitatively based on an appraisal of slope geometry, soil depth, soil type, slope inclination and the vegetation. A theoretical analysis of buttressing on existing vegetated slopes is described in Section 3 (*see* Box 3.2 and Figure 3.16).

Surcharge, based on existing knowledge of weights of trees for different species and at different stages of growth, and windthrow, using calculated wind loadings (*see* Section 3.5.5) can be allowed for directly in present methods of slope stability analysis. Surcharge generally appears to be most beneficial as critical saturated conditions develop in a slope (Gray and Leiser, 1982). It should be noted, however, that even for wooded slopes surcharge is at most a secondary effect.

Although modelling of the soil/water/vegetation interaction is possible (*see* Section 3.4.2), the variability of *in-situ* soils, particularly in excavated cutting slopes, is so great that predicting the precise effect on the soil strength is extremely difficult. However the overall effects can be estimated in a very general way.

Box 6.5 Simplified procedure for studies of tree root reinforcement of soil (Greenway, 1985).

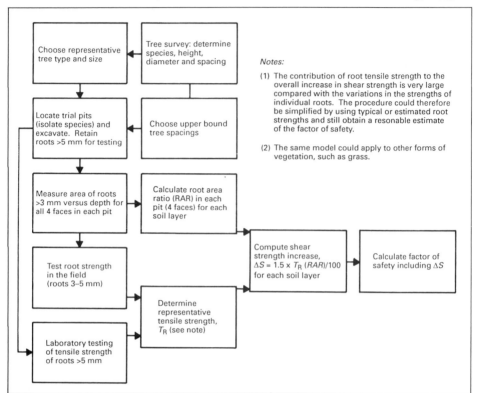

Notes:

(1) The contribution of root tensile strength to the overall increase in shear strength is very large compared with the variations in the strengths of individual roots. The procedure could therefore be simplified by using typical or estimated root strengths and still obtain a resonable estimate of the factor of safety.

(2) The same model could apply to other forms of vegetation, such as grass.

The existence of soil suction alone is rarely sufficient to affect the overall incidence of shallow slope failures associated with heavy rainfall (high intensity, long duration). In such events, storm water infiltration eventually saturates the soil and eliminates any soil suction in the potential failure zone as the wetting front advances. The process of pore-pressure equilibriation involving the dissipation of soil suction over time is also a very significant factor in slope instability.

Although vegetated slopes tend to be drier than bare ones (*see* Section 3.4.3) and are therefore able to absorb a storm of greater intensity or duration before the onset of saturation and consequent loss on strength, some dry surfaces, especially on peat soils, can shed water by a hysteresis effect when there is a lag between infiltration and water absorption in the soil. Modelling the soil water environment is also made more difficult by the need to allow for seasonal effects in transpiration rates (*see* Section 3.4.3).

6.2.6 Slope stability analysis

In view of the problems of adequately evaluating all the vegetation factors that influence slope stability, the most useful exercise that can be carried out using methods of slope stability analysis is to assess the sensitivity of the soil/plant system to changes in the parameters on which vegetation has some influence. In this way the designer can examine how vegetation increases the factor of safety, even though it is not possible to design to a particular factor of safety value.

The factor of safety, F, of a potential slip surface can be defined as:

$$F = \frac{\text{shear resistance along a slip surface}}{\text{shear force acting along the slip surface}}$$

Stability analysis to determine the factor of safety of a vegetated slope can incorporate five major affects of vegetation, as illustrated in Figure 6.4:

1. increased effective soil cohesion due to root matrix reinforcement, c'_R;
2. increased effective soil cohesion due to soil suction resulting from plant evapotranspiration, c'_S, or, a decrease in pore-water pressure u (*see* Section 3.6);
3. increased surcharge due to weight of vegetation, S_W;
4. increased disturbing force due to windthrow, D, acting parallel to and down the slope;
5. increased restoring force, T, due to large diameter inclined roots acting as discrete tensile elements.

As an example of the sensitivity of the factor of safety against slope failure to vegetation effects, proportionally large increases in the factor of safety, from less than 1.0 to over 1.5, have been shown to result from quite small increases in soil shear strength, in the order of 1 to $5\,kN/m^2$, due to the presence of plant roots (Greenway, 1987).

As indicated in Figure 6.4, in certain combinations of seepage, soil permeability and vegetation type, groundwater lowering may also result from suction induced by evapotranspiration. In considering both groundwater and soil suction effects, care must be taken that the values of these manifestations of the same influence are not double-counted.

Most common methods of slope stability analysis (Walker and Fell, 1987; Bromhead, 1986) can be modified to include the overall effect of vegetation. Those described here are selected because they cater for the type of shallow-seated failures where the influences of vegetation are most likely to be significant.

The most commonly used approach to soil slope stability analysis is the limit equilibrium technique, which assumes that the linear failure criterion (Mohr-Coulomb) is satisfied along the whole of the critical slip surface and that there is a constant factor of safety along this surface for the conditions under consideration.

The method of slices is a well-established limit equilibrium approach for assessing the stability of slopes. Its most basic form is the infinite slope method, in which a single vertical slice is representative of the whole slope, as detailed in Box 6.6. The failure surface is parallel to the slope, usually at shallow depth. The method may only be applied to slip surfaces where the length to depth ratio is large; in other words, the slope geometry for which vegetation is likely to be most effective as a stabilising agent. It is suitable for long slopes with shallow mantles of weathered soils over bedrock and with groundwater flow parallel to the surface.

Box 6.6 Infinite slope method for stability analysis of a shallow soil layer

In the case of a sloping shallow vegetated soil layer which is liable to fail as an elongated landslip, the toe and head portions are of negligible extent. This situation may be represented as a single slice. As shown in the diagram (after Bache and MacAskill, 1984) the failure plane is assumed to be just above the interface between the rooted soil and the bedrock.

For simplicity only the effects of increased cohesion (c_R), surcharge (S_W), and disturbing force (D) due to windloading are incorporated in this section. Under steady state conditions of seepage, with only partial saturation of the soil, as shown, the usual expression (Wu *et al*, 1979) for factor of safety, F, is:

$$F = \frac{c'l + (W\cos\beta - ul)\tan\phi'}{W\sin\beta} \tag{1}$$

is modified to allow for the effects of vegetation to:

$$F = \frac{(c' + c'_R)l + [(W + S_W)\cos\beta - ul]\tan\phi'}{(W + S_W)\sin\beta + D} \tag{2}$$

Under conditions of steady state seepage, pore water pressure (u) may be expressed as:

$$u = \gamma_W\, h_W \cos^2\beta$$

surcharge from vegetation as: $w = S_W/b$
windloading shear stress as: $d = D/b$

Hence $$F = \frac{(c' + c'_R) + (\gamma h_z - \gamma_w h_w + w)\cos^2\beta\,\tan\phi'}{[(\gamma h_z + w)\sin\beta + d]\cos\beta} \tag{3}$$

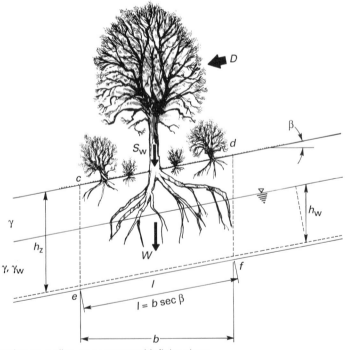

Forces acting on a slice on a vegetated infinite slope

Box 6.6 *(Continued)*

A parametric study described by Bache and MacAskill (1984), based on infinite slope stability analysis, used a similar expression to Equation 3 attributed to Wu *et al.*, (1979). The range of cases in the study involves the major influences of trees on slope stability i.e. soil root reinforcement, soil moisture content, surcharge and windthrow.

The fixed slope and soil parameters are:

$c' = 5.3\,kN/m^2$; $\phi' = 34.7°$; $\gamma = 18.0 + 2.0 h_w/h_z\,kN/m^3$; $\gamma_w = 9.8\,kN/m^3$; $\beta = 35°$; $h_z = 0.9\,m$; $l = 1.22\,m$

The variable vegetation and ground water parameters are:
h_z; h_w; c'_R; S_w; d

Table of Results:

Case	$h_z\text{-}h_w$ (m)	h_w (m)	c'_R (kN/m²)	S_w (kN/m²)	d (kN/m²)	F
1) Bare slope	0.4 (assumed)	0.5 (assumed)	0.0	0.0	0.0	1.36
2) Vegetated slope	0.7 (assumed)	0.2 (assumed)	6.0	3.8	0.1	1.93
3) Densely vegetated slope	0.9 (maximum)	0.0	6.0	3.8	0.1	2.18
4) Immediately after felling	0.9	0.0	6.0 (fresh roots)	0.0 (plants removed)	0.0	2.90
5) After felling mid-term	0.4 (case 1)	0.5 (case 1)	3.0 (50%)	0.0	0.0	1.75
6) After felling long-term	0.0	0.9 (maximum)	0.0	0.0	0.0	1.13

Interpretation:
Cases 1 to 3 show the factor of safety increasing as the soil moisture content is reduced, assumed to be the result of the ground cover intercepting rainfall and increasing evapotranspiration.

In case 4 clear-felling of the trees is assumed, and the slope factor of safety reaches a peak as a result of maximum root reinforcement, minimum soil moisture and zero wind loading.

Cases 5 and 6 reflect the gradual reduction of root strength and a corresponding increase in soil moisture content, producing in case 6 a minimum level of slope stability as the soil has reached saturation and root soil reinforcement has decayed to zero.

A theoretical sensitivity study (*see* Box 6.6), based on the infinite slope method, indicates the potential of vegetation to increase the factor of safety by considerable margins, compared with an unvegetated slope. It also shows how the factor of safety falls after vegetation clearance due to root decay.

The method of stability analysis for circular failure on long uniform slopes is the ordinary method of slices (Fellenius, 1936). A modification of this has been proposed by Greenwood (1983), in which a horizontal water surface across each slice is assumed. Ways of accounting for vegetation in this method are shown in Box 6.7.

There are many cases where the observed critical slip surfaces are non-circular, particularly the shallow-seated down-slope movements where vegetation is likely to

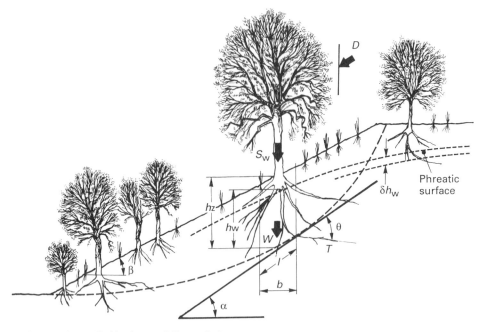

Parameters applied in slope stability analysis

W	Total weight of soil slice, kN/m²
c', ϕ'	Effective strength parameters at slip surface
l	Length of slip surface with slice, m (b sec α)
u	Pore-water pressure at slip surface, kN/m² ($\gamma_w\ h_w$)

<table>
<tr><td rowspan="5">Due to vegetation</td><td>u_v</td><td>Decrease in pore-water pressure to evapotranspiration by vegetation at slip surface, kN/m² (2)</td></tr>
<tr><td>c'_R</td><td>Enhanced effective soil cohesion due to root matrix reinforcement by vegetation along slip surface, kN/m²</td></tr>
<tr><td>c'_S</td><td>Enhanced effective soil cohesion due to soil suction due to evapotranspiration by vegetation at slip surface, kN/m² (2)</td></tr>
<tr><td>S_w</td><td>Surcharge due to weight of vegetation, kN/m</td></tr>
<tr><td>D</td><td>Wind loading force parallel to slope, kN/m</td></tr>
<tr><td>T</td><td>Tensile root force acting at base of slice, kN/m (assumed angle between roots and slip surface, θ)</td></tr>
</table>

h_z	Vertical height of surface of soil layer above slip plane, m
h_w	Vertical height of phreatic surface or water table above slip surface, m

Notes
1. The value of many of these parameters varies with depth and soil type.
2. In certain slope stability analyses (e.g. Lee, 1985) the decrease in pore-water pressure due to vegetation (i.e. increased soil suction from evapotranspiration) is expressed as an enhanced effective soil cohesion, as distinct from a pore-pressure reduction.

Figure 6.4 Typical slice in a slope, showing the five main influences of vegetation

have a significant effect. In such cases, the Janbu routine procedure may be a more appropriate method of analysis, especially if the geometry of the failure surface is known. Lee (1985) has applied this method to theoretical slopes, simulating typical conditions in Hong Kong, to compare the minimum factor of safety for a slope with and without vegetation under saturated and unsaturated conditions. The results are summarised in Box 6.8. It should be noted that the values assigned in Lee's example to the vegetated influences may, when taken together, give over-optimistic results and the use of Janbu's equation for slopes of such steepness, though the norm in Hong Kong's weathered soils, may not be applicable elsewhere.

The apparent coexistence of saturated soil conditions in the stability analysis given in Box 6.8 with a soil suction effect due to vegetation is not the anomaly it may at first appear. The situation is being assessed by way of superimposition in which the latter effect is represented either by an enhanced effective soil cohesion, as in Box 6.8, or by a reduction in pore-pressure, itself equivalent to a lowering of the phreatic surface, as in Box 6.7. The value of soil suction due to vegetation may be derived by monitoring tensiometers or piezometers installed in vegetated and bare portions of slopes.

Box 6.7 Stability analysis for a circular slip surface using Greenwood's simple method

The ordinary method of slices (Fellenius, 1936) tends in practice to be very conservative for most slip surfaces, because the assumption of seepage parallel to the slip surface is not appropriate where the slip surface enters at the top of the slope and emerges at the toe, as shown in the diagrams below. In the 'simple' method proposed by Greenwood (1983), the slip surface is assumed to be horizontal in each slice, and the factor of safety, F, is given by:

$$F = \frac{\Sigma[c'b\sec\alpha + (W - ub)\cos\alpha\tan\phi']}{\Sigma W \sin\alpha} \tag{1}$$

Greenwood's simple equation is easily modified to include the vegetation factors shown in Figure 6.4:

$$F = \frac{\Sigma\{(c' + c'_R)b\sec\alpha + [((w + S_w) - (u - u_v)b)\cos\alpha - D\sin(\alpha - \beta) + T\sin\theta]\tan\phi' + T\cos\theta\}}{\Sigma[(W + S_w)\sin\alpha + D\cos(\alpha - \beta)]} \tag{2}$$

This is an easy method to use and one that has been shown to give realistic consistent factors of safety for both shallow and deep, circular and non-circular, slip surfaces with either high or low pore water pressures.

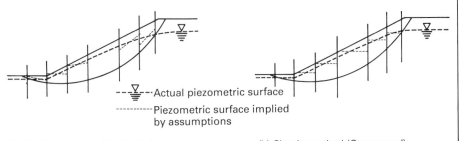

- - -▽- - -Actual piezometric surface

----------Piezometric surface implied
          by assumptions

(a) Ordinary method (Fellenius)   (b) Simple method (Greenwood)

(Continued overleaf)

Perhaps the most comprehensive example of the use of slope stability analysis to determine the contribution of large trees to slope stability is the investigation by Greenway (1987) of wooded slopes in Hong Kong. This study, demonstrated that tree roots can increase the factor of safety of a slope by about 30%, as detailed in Box 6.9. At present, however, such studies are unfortunately rare. The examples given above illustrate the potential for using slope stability analysis techniques to evaluate the effects of vegetation. Their present use remains limited as a design tool because of the lack of field data.

Box 6.7 *(Continued)*

For a typical mid-slope slice in Greenwood's analysis with the following parameters:

Soil	Slice	Vegetative effects acting on slice
$c' = 10.0\,\text{kN/m}^2$	$\alpha = 35°$	$u_v = 3.0\,\text{kN/m}^2$
$\phi' = 18°$	$\theta = 45°$	$c'_R = 2.5\,\text{kN/m}^2$
$\gamma = 18.5\,\text{kN/m}^3$	$h_z = 1.5\,\text{m}$	$S_W = 0.25\,\text{kN/m}$
$\gamma_w = 9.8\,\text{kN/m}^3$	$h_w = 0.66\,\text{m}$	$D = 2.5\,\text{kN/m}$
	$u = 6.5\,\text{kN/m}^2$	$T = 5.0\,\text{kN/m}$
slope $\beta = 30°$	$W = 40\,\text{kN/m}$	
	$b = 1.5\,\text{m}$	
	$l = 1.83\,\text{m}$	

Hence the factor of safety, F, for a single slice only:

1) Without vegetation

$$F_{\text{slice}_i} = [(10 \times 1.5\sec 35° + (40 - 6.5 \times 1.5)\cos 35° \cdot \tan 18°]/40\sin 35° \tag{3}$$

$$= \frac{18.31 + 8.05}{22.94}$$

therefore $F_{\text{slice}_i} = 1.15$

2) With vegetation

$$F_{\text{slice}_i} = [(10 + 25)1.5\sec 35° + [[(40 + 0.25) - (6.5 - 3.0)\,1.5]\cos 35° - 2.5\sin(35° - 30°)$$
$$+ 5\sin 45°)]\tan 18° + 5\cos 45°]/[(40 + 0.25\sin 35° + 2.5\cos(35° - 30°)] \tag{4}$$

$$= \frac{22.89 + 10.39 + 3.54}{23.09 + 2.49}$$

therefore $F_{\text{slice}_i} = 1.44$

It should be noted that this example is purely illustrative and does not indicate the total increase in factor of safety of an entire critical slip surface, merely that of a single slice.

In practice, the factor of safety calculation is carried out only once, by summation of the upper and lower terms in Equation 2 for all of the slices.

It is emphasised that the cumulative effect of vegetation on slope stability is unlikely to be of the same order as that shown in this hypothetical example for a single slice. It is unlikely that all the influences of vegetation will act simultaneously or, if they do, that they will act for any appreciable length of time.

In the event that major roots, windthrow and evapotranspiration are all absent, the factor of safety of the slice considered above is reduced to 1.35.

Box 6.8 Effect of vegetation on slope stability assessed by the Janbu routine method

A form of the non-circular routine developed by Janbu (1973) was used by Lee (1985) to calculate the factor of safety, F, of a vegetated slope in Hong Kong.

$$F = \frac{f_o \sum \left[\dfrac{[(c' + c'_R + c'_S)b + (W - ul + S_w)\tan\phi']}{[1 + (\tan\alpha\,\tan\phi')/F]/(1 + \tan^2\alpha)} + P_R \right]}{Q + D + \sum (W + S_w)\tan\alpha}$$

where f_o is the Janbu correction factor. Lee also considered for the first time soil arching P_R, and the hydrostatic force, Q, due to the water in a crest tension crack. Reinforcement by large diameter roots was not taken into account.

The theoretical slope was 10 m high and was assumed to be planted with grass and 6 m tall mature trees at 2 m spacing. Each tree was assumed to have a deeply penetrating root system extending 3 m both horizontally and vertically into the soil mantle. Five different slope angles were considered: 30°, 35°, 40°, 45° and 50°, together with two soil conditions, unsaturated and saturated. A peak wind gust of 73 m/s blowing down-slope was assumed.

The soil shear strength and vegetation-related parameters were as follows:

Assumed design parameters	Unsaturated condition		Saturated condition	
	With vegetation effects	Without vegetation effects	With vegetation effects	Without vegetation effects
ϕ' (degree)	35	35	35	35
c' (kN/m²)	5	5	5	5
γ (kN/m³)	20	20	21.5	21.5
Q (kN/m)	0	0	0	0
c'_R (kN/m²)	5	0	5	0
c'_S (kN/m²)	10	0	0	0
S_w (kN/m)	4	0	4	0
P_R (kN/m) per tree	38	0	38	0
D (kN/m) per tree	2 to 3.7 for 30°<β<50°	0	2 to 3.7 for 30°<β<50°	0

(*Continued overleaf*)

6.2.7 Time dependency in slope stability: role of vegetation

There will usually be some delay between the introduction of the vegetation components of a bioengineering scheme and the start of their active roles. It may be weeks or even months in the case of grasses and herbaceous vegetation, and several years in the case of shrubs and trees, before a scheme is fully effective. Temporary measures to control surface erosion during this stage are described in Section 4.2.7.

If the slope is in a critically unstable condition during this phase, some initial safeguard against failure may be implemented using, for example, biodegradable and synthetic geotextiles, live or dead wooden stakes, metal pins or spikes, soil nails, or concrete or timber piles. These will perform a temporary engineering function until the vegetation takes root and grows. There are also certain long-term time-dependent effects, whereby the soil forming a slope may increase or decrease

Box 6.8 *(Continued)*

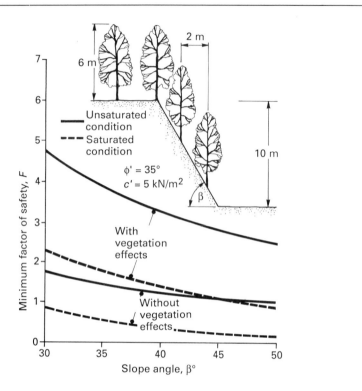

The results of the analysis illustrated in the diagram show that for both unsaturated and saturated soil conditions, the minimum factor of safety would be about two-and-a-half times higher than for the slope without vegetation. In theory, slope failure would have occurred in the 30° to 50° slopes without vegetation under saturated conditions. On the other hand, no failure would have occurred in saturated vegetated slopes inclined at 45° or less.

It should be noted that the values assigned to the vegetation influences in this example may, when taken together, give over-optimistic results for slopes of this steepness, which though normal in Hong Kong's weathered soils, may not be applicable elsewhere.

in strength due to weathering, changing moisture content and equilibration. In these cases the aim is to use appropriate plants in a complementary way, either rapid-growing ones to make up an early deficiency in soil strength, or slow-growing towards maturity at the time when soil strength loss would otherwise become critical. Figure 6.5 illustrates schematically how the use of vegetation can complement the progressive loss in stability of newly formed slopes, and extend the time to failure from, say, 15 years to 25–50 years or more.

Over consolidated clays in the surface layers of earth cuts or fills deteriorate in strength over time due to the process of equilibration (Vaughn and Walbanke, 1973). The mechanisms and occurrence of this phenomenon and the onset of

Box 6.9 Three-dimensional slope analysis of a wooded slope

In a study by Greenway *et al.* (1984) the stabilising influence of shallow roots on a slope was investigated using a simple three-dimensional stability analysis as described by Wu (1984). This work was based on very comprehensive field and laboratory work carried out in Hong Kong.

The distribution of the roots of candlenut (*Aleurites mollucana*) on a slope was found by examination of 3 m deep hand-dug trial holes located half-way between trees. Only a very small proportion of the roots were located below the top 1.2 m of the slope. A lower-bound estimate of the increase in soil shear strength due to root reinforcement in this layer was 15 kN/m². This was based on:

1. the measured root area ratios for trees 6.5 m apart;
2. field and laboratory measured root tensile strengths;
3. the relationship for the shear strength increase due to the roots given by:

$$c_R = 1.25 \, T_R \, (A_R/A)$$

This was a modification of the relationship given in Box 3.1: the coefficient of 1.25, as opposed to 1.15, was taken to reflect the high strength of the soil ($\phi' = 39°$). The reinforcing effect of all roots below 1.2 m was ignored.

The analysis of the 8 m segment of the slope, as shown in the diagram below, showed that the factor of safety of the slope was increased from 2.43, ignoring the tree roots, to 3.26 including them; an increase of 29%.

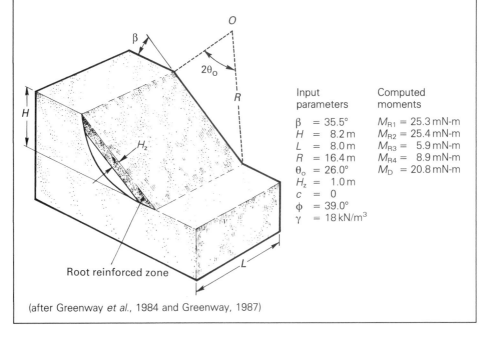

Input parameters	Computed moments
β = 35.5°	M_{R1} = 25.3 mN-m
H = 8.2 m	M_{R2} = 25.4 mN-m
L = 8.0 m	M_{R3} = 5.9 mN-m
R = 16.4 m	M_{R4} = 8.9 mN-m
θ_o = 26.0°	M_D = 20.8 mN-m
H_z = 1.0 m	
c = 0	
ϕ = 39.0°	
γ = 18 kN/m³	

Root reinforced zone

(after Greenway *et al.*, 1984 and Greenway, 1987)

consequential failure of slopes has been well documented (Parsons and Perry, 1985; Greenwood *et al*, 1985).

Vegetation may have considerable beneficial effects on the stability of overconsolidated clays, especially as these effects will develop and increase over time, particularly in the 1–2 m depth of soil within which most problems occur.

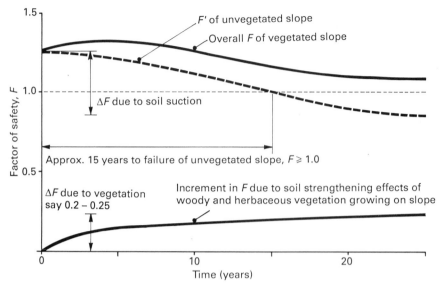

Figure 6.5 Long-term effect of vegetation on the factor of safety in clay soils

These effects include:

1. shading action, reducing the amount of surface dessication and cracking;
2. root bridging of cracks, thus restraining the cracks;
3. interception and evaporation of rainfall, thus reducing infiltration;
4. removal of infiltration water from soil by transpiration, maintaining soil suction and reducing pore-pressures deeper down.

6.2.8 Choice of vegetation

The selection of vegetation must reflect the need to maximise the benefits and minimise the adverse effects which vegetation can have on slope stability. Important characteristics of plants for maximising the benefits of particular effects, together with the implications for their establishment and management, are summarised in Box 6.10. Particular factors to take into account when selecting vegetation include the following.

1. Management implications in respect of working methods, manpower and machines.
2. The timescale involved; the problem may require a short-term solution, a long-term one, or both.
3. Time-dependent changes as the vegetation structure develops, succession proceeds and the soil/plant system matures.
4. Time-dependent changes in the soil characteristics affecting its strength.

5. Nature of the root system, its extent, depth and architecture.
6. Seasonal fluctuations in the scale of vegetation effects such as root growth, transpiration and interception.
7. Other cyclical fluctuations due to climate, disease, etc.
8. Man-influenced changes resulting from management, maintenance, or their absence.
9. Potential plant performance on the site, i.e. the response of the plant to climate and soil conditions (*see* Section 2).

Whether or not vegetation is chosen as a means of stabilising a slope depends on the factor of safety required and the degree of confidence that the proposed vegetation cover can perform its engineering role. Some circumstances demand a high factor of safety and degree of confidence. It is usual in these cases for inert materials to be the principal component of slope stabilisation and for vegetation to have only a secondary function. In less critical cases, where the consequences of failure are not costly or life-threatening, vegetation can have an equal or greater role to play compared with inert structures. It is therefore possible to consider a spectrum of solutions from totally live to totally inert, with vegetation contributing in different degrees to slope stability, as shown in Box 6.11.

6.2.9 Composite structures for slope stabilisation

The combination of vegetation and inert materials as composite structures can function in two ways. The inert or dead plant component can provide a short-term temporary function whilst vegetation develops. A long-term composite is produced where each component fulfils a different though complementary function. The design of composite bioengineering or biotechnical structures follows conventional soil mechanics theory for soil-retaining structures, as described in numerous ground engineering texts including Gray and Leiser (1982), Winterkorn and Fang (1975), and Clayton and Milititsky (1986). The design of reinforced earth and reinforced soil structures has been dealt with extensively, e.g. Vidal (1969), McGown *et al*, (1978), Department of Transport (1978), Ingold (1982), and Jones (1985).

Geotextile combinations

There is a wide range of geotextile materials available (*see* Appendix 2) ranging from biodegradable ones made of natural fibres to permanent ones of synthetic materials. They can be combined with vegetation in two ways (*see* Section 3.8.1):

1. as a surface-laid material
2. as a buried material.

Surface-laid geotextiles are used primarily for erosion control (*see* Section 6.3.3). Buried geotextiles combined with vegetation to form a hybrid structure can be used as an ideal 'soft' solution to a soil retention problem, on slopes where rigid concrete

188

Box 6.10 Selection, establishment and management of plants for slope stability

Mechanism	Plant selection characteristics	Establishment implications	Management implications
Root reinforcement	Extensive fibrous and branching root system at all levels; use mixture of plants to give stratified root mass. High tensile strength of individual roots	Close spacing for rapid development of root mass. Random mixtures to give uniform rooting pattern overall. Avoid heavy mulches around trees/shrubs, which encourage shallow rooting. Maximise soil rootability by careful soil profile and ground preparation. Encourage rooting into required soil horizons by fertiliser placement and good moisture availability	Allow maximum shoot growth; pruning or cutting shoot will reduce root mass. Encourage diversity and mixture of desired species. Maintain close spacing of individual plants
Soil arching and buttressing	Deep root system, tap-roots. Mainly larger trees	Using young plants where transplanting will do at least permanent damage to tap-roots. Correct spacing of buttress trees. Use direct tree seeding	Maintain correct spacing of buttress trees by thinning. Allow trees to grow to full mature size
Root anchorage	Deep root system, tap-roots. Vertical root orientation	Maximise soil deep rootability by careful soil profile and ground preparation. Deep placement of fertilisers to encourage deeper rooting	As above
Soil restraint	Ability to withstand partial burial. Root adventitiously from stems. Resistant to abrasion and damage. Deflect rather than break under impact. Suitable for bioengineering techniques. Usually woody plants with bushy habit	Plant in rows across slope (but avoid creating planes of weakness)	Coppice or cut to maintain high density of stems at ground level

(Continued overleaf)

Box 6.10 (Continued)

Mechanism	Plant selection characteristics	Establishment implications	Management implications
Surface mat	Shallow rooting Branching rather than deep tap–rooting habit	Close spacing Mulch to encourage surface rooting	Continue mulching
Surcharge and windthrow	Not large trees High root : shoot ratio Deciduous species have less weight in winter and less wind resistance	Avoid large trees in critical areas Deep soil drainage to encourage deeper rooting	Coppice to reduce tall growth
Soil moisture	Evergreen species maintain transpiration throughout year Phreatophytes: high rate of water usage Deep rooting	Phreatophytes are mainly damp soil species, so avoid planting them in drought-prone areas	Maintain high density of shoots and foliage and thus large transpiring and interception surfaces
Root wedging	Fine fibrous root system, not woody or tap roots		Leave stumps and roots *in situ* if control involves eliminating trees
Insulation	High density of shoots and foliage near ground level Mainly grasses and herbs		Mow or graze infrequently, allow regrowth before winter

Box 6.11 The choice between live and inert components in slope stabilisation

Method	Function	Not serious — Stability of unprotected slope High	Medium	Low	Serious — Stability of unprotected slope High	Medium	Low
1. Live construction							
Conventional planting and seeding — Grass seeding; Plant and geotextile reinforced turf; Trees and shrubs	Control of water and wind erosion; Insulation	●	●		●		
Woody plants used as reinforcement and as barriers to soil movement — Cordons; Live staking; Contour wattling/fascines; Brush layering; Hedge layering; Palisades	Control of superficial rainfall erosion (rilling and gullying); Control of shallow-seated (translational) mass movement	○	●	●	●		
2. Mixed construction							
Conventional plantings in geotextiles. Woody plants grown in interstices of low to moderate height porous structures or benches of tiered structures — Turfing, grass seeding and shrub transplants; Vegetated revetments (rip-rap, masonry, grids, gabions, mats, blocks, netting); Vegetated geotextile reinforced embankments and soil-nailed cuttings; Vegetated retained walls (open cribs, gabions, stepped-back walls, reinforced soil walls with geotextile, welded-wire, timber or precast concrete facings)	Protection against slope drainage erosion; Control of shallow mass movements and resistance to low-moderate earth forces; Boulder barriers; Environmental barriers; Blast bunds; Landscape and/or avalanche arresters; To reduce maintenance and/or increase service life of structure	○	●	●	●	●	

Consequences of slope failure*

Box 6.11 (*Continued*)

Method	Function	Not serious			Serious		
		High	Medium	Low	High	Medium	Low
Walls at foot and crest of slopes used together with planting on face Low to moderate height breast walls (stone, masonry, precast concrete blocks, timber and concrete crib walls) with vegetated slope above (grasses and shrubs)	Control of erosion on cut and fill slopes subject to under-mining at the toe or road/railway widening for sightlines and extra capacity etc Reduction of slope angle and/or length Improved slope drainage and maintenance access	○	○	●	○	●	
3. Inert construction Conventional structures with pockets of vegetation Gravity walls Cantilever walls Pile walls Reinforced soil walls	Control of deep-seated mass-movement and restraint of high lateral earth forces Retention of toxic or aggressive fills or soil Boulder barriers	○	○	○	○	○	●

Consequences of slope failure* (header above) — *Stability of unprotected slope* (sub-header)

● Suitable approach
○ Suitable but probably over-conservative and costly
* The consequences of slope failure depend on the risk to life and property relying on the integrity of the slope

or steel structures are both more expensive and aesthetically less acceptable. In this case, the geotextile performs a variety of roles of varying duration, from immediate to long-term, primarily reinforcing soil strength and contributing a surface mat effect in the upper soil layer (*see* Section 3.8.2). Techniques for using geotextiles are illustrated in Figures 6.6, 6.7 and Plates 6.A and 6.B.

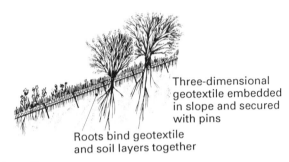

Three-dimensional geotextile embedded in slope and secured with pins

Roots bind geotextile and soil layers together

(a) Normal planting and seeding onto geotextile-reinforced slope

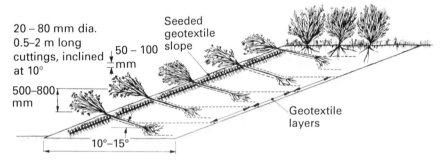

20 – 80 mm dia. 0.5–2 m long cuttings, inclined at 10°

Seeded geotextile slope

50 – 100 mm

500–800 mm

10°–15°

Geotextile layers

(b) Wrap-around geotextile-reinforced brush-layered fill slope

Crest shrub drought resistant

Envelopes of fill contained within geotextile layers

Slope varies, typically 2:1 or 4:1

(c) Geotextile-reinforced barrier or hedge with brush layering

Figure 6.6 Bioengineering techniques using planting and seeding with geotextile soil reinforcement

(*a*) Installation on the slope

(*b*) After completion and seeding

Plate 6A Stabilisation of steep cliffs using synthetic geotextile mats

(*a*) Construction showing formwork

Plate 6B Geotextile-reinforced soil walls, planted with turf

(*b*) With grass growing, which obscures the geotextile

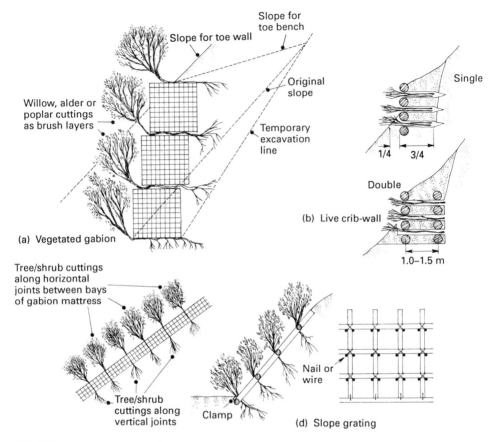

Slope for
toe bench

Slope for toe wall

Original
slope

Single

Willow, alder or
poplar cuttings
as brush layers

Temporary
excavation
line

1/4   3/4

Double

(b) Live crib-wall

(a) Vegetated gabion

1.0–1.5 m

Tree/shrub cuttings
along horizontal
joints between bays
of gabion mattress

Nail or
wire

Tree/shrub
cuttings along
vertical joints

Clamp

(d) Slope grating

(c) Gabion mattress revetment

Figure 6.7 Bioengineering techniques using woody plants combined with inert structures

Timber

Timber may be used together with live vegetation in a large number of bioengineering structures, as illustrated in Figure 6.8 (*see also* Figures 4.9, 4.10, 6.7 and 6.8 and Plate 6.C) including:

1. wattle fencing
2. brush layering
3. contour boarding
4. fascine drains, fascine plantings
5. slope grids/gratings
6. crib walls
7. post and rail retaining walls.

Timber can be used as a temporary structural element or a skeleton, pending full establishment of the vegetative component, or as a semi-permanent component to

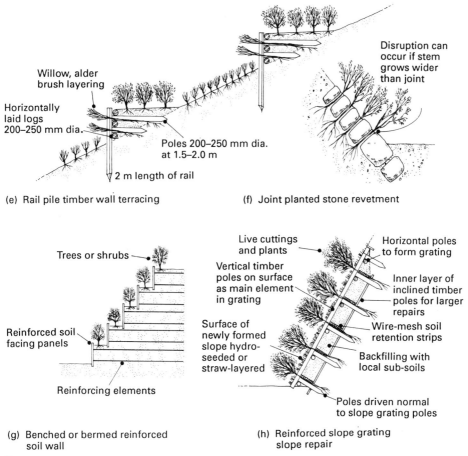

Willow, alder
brush layering

Horizontally
laid logs
200–250 mm dia.

Poles 200–250 mm dia.
at 1.5–2.0 m

2 m length of rail

(e) Rail pile timber wall terracing

Disruption can
occur if stem
grows wider
than joint

(f) Joint planted stone revetment

Trees or shrubs

Reinforced soil
facing panels

Reinforcing elements

(g) Benched or bermed reinforced
     soil wall

Live cuttings
and plants

Vertical timber
poles on surface
as main element
in grating

Surface of
newly formed
slope hydro-
seeded or
straw-layered

Horizontal poles
to form grating

Inner layer of
inclined timber
poles for larger
repairs

Wire-mesh soil
retention strips

Backfilling with
local sub-soils

Poles driven normal
to slope grating poles

(h) Reinforced slope grating
     slope repair

Figure 6.7 (continued)

augment the performance of the vegetation, as illustrated in Plates 6.D and 6.E. In the latter case, the timber is often treated or rot-proofed. Since for general timber use this treatment involves chemicals which are toxic to plants, special treatments should be used incorporating chemicals which are not phytotoxic for combinations of timber and vegetation.

Many of the techniques under this heading use live woody materials, especially willow, poplar and alder. These species have certain attributes which make them ideal for this application:

1. versatility, with many species and varieties providing tolerance to a wide range of environmental conditions;
2. high growth rates, many with shrubby habits;
3. fine fibrous extensive root systems;
4. high transpiration rates (when in leaf);

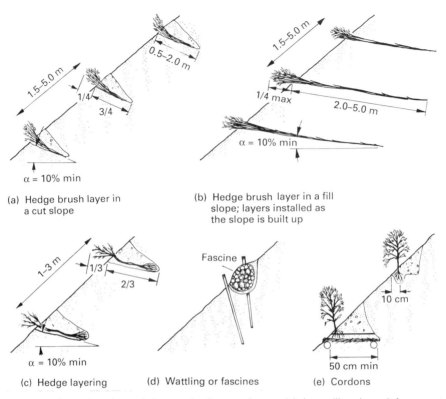

Figure 6.8 Bioengineering techniques using live woody materials (e.g. willows) as reinforcement and barriers to soil movement (after Scheichtl, 1980)

Plate 6C Willow fascines established on a highway cutting

Plate 6D Timber slope grafting or crib wall, planted with willow

Plate 6E Timber retaining wall with concrete piers, planted with willow

5. flexible stems resistant to abrasion and damage;
6. roots able to withstand exposure to air;
7. free rooting from cuttings and live wood;
8. easy management by coppicing or layering;
9. resistance to disease.

Concrete

Concrete can be combined with vegetation in a wide variety of structures including:

1. crib walls;
2. small or large planter boxes;
3. reinforced soil retaining walls with concrete facing panels, arranged in steps or a series of terraces and planted out with shrubs or ivy or other climbing plants.

Cellular concrete is used principally for erosion protection in waterways, but its surcharge load can also help to stabilise the subsoil against failure by a shallow slip. There can, however, be problems associated with the high alkalinity of concrete and its high thermal gain characteristic, which leads to high soil evaporation loss and high rates of evapotranspiration.

Steel

Combinations of vegetated soil with steel in hybrid structures may include one or other of the following:

1. wire mesh, as surface-laid erosion control netting or as wire-mesh mattresses and boxes (gabions) filled with stone to form slope retention structures;
2. steel rods, as part of a soil-nailing system for cuttings or embankments with surface mesh and layered shrubby or hydroseeded grassed vegetation;
3. steel rails, as supporting uprights/piles at intervals along rail-and-log terracing walls or the face of timber crib walls or timber;
4. steel sheets, as facings to temporary reinforced soil walls or abutments, as a variation of the pre-cast concrete panels of reinforced soil. These sheets can be provided with cut-outs for planting of trees or, as an alternative, with brush-layering between rows of panels.

Gabion-stepped retaining walls can be designed to incorporate brush-layering. These have a 100–150 mm thick organic layer laid between each course of gabion. Brush-layered willow twigs or other suitable live cuttings are then laid across the tops of the organic layer and back-filled with topsoil/subsoil so that the thickest end of the branches is in contact with the soil behind.

6.2.10 Costs

Typical costs for slope seeding work undertaken in the UK are given in Box 6.12. Accurate costs for individual construction methods cannot be given, since they vary greatly from site to site. Schiechtl (1980) gives some relative costs for slope stabilisation as a proportion of the total construction costs, compiled from several sources:

USA highway construction	1½–3%
USA freeway construction around cities	5–7%
West Germany, smaller roads – bioengineering	2–8%
– grass seeding	3½–6%
West Germany, highways	8–12%
Austrian Alps, highways, forest roads	1½–2%

The percentages are of the total construction costs and include the whole revegetation work incorporating bioengineering techniques as appropriate.

Cost indications given here only relate to construction and establishments costs. Maintenance costs are very site-specific and no general figures have been published.

Box 6.12 Typical costs for slope-seeding works in the UK

Establishment	pence/m^2
Conventional broadcast seeding, including tilth preparation, broadcasting, fertilising and incorporation on slopes 10° to 1 in 5	4–6
Conventional broadcast seeding as above but slopes 1 in 5 to 1 in 3	7–9
Surface preparation of slopes > 1 in 3	
by machine	5
by hand	7
Hydroseeding with normal mulch specification	9–14
Hydroseeding with high mulch specification	30–37
Hydroseeding with dry mulching of straw	35–40
Hydroseeding with fibreglass rovings	65–85
Installation of erosion control netting, including surface preparation but excluding broadcast or hydroseeding	100–200
Broadcast seeding by hand, no mulching or additional erosion control	10
Maintenance	
Mowing with tractor mounted flail, cuttings not removed, slopes 10° to 1 in 5	2
Mowing as above on slopes up to 1 in 3	5
Hand cutting on slopes > 1 in 3	15

Note: Costs vary considerably depending on the size of the area, the materials used and the remoteness
Typical costs given are at 1988 prices and are appropriate to medium-sized contracts
100 pence = £1 sterling

6.3 Water erosion control

6.3.1 The problem

A great deal of rain falls to the ground without producing runoff. Soil texture, soil structure and vegetation cover are important factors which determine when and where runoff, and the resulting soil erosion, occurs. In equable climates such as that enjoyed by the UK, there are minimal climatic restraints on vegetative growth; where soil erosion occurs, it is usually a symptom of impoverished soils, e.g. mine and quarry wastes, or bad management of an existing cover vegetation. Areas of mineral workings and construction sites are particularly vulnerable, as illustrated in Plate 6.F. Prevention is always more effective than cure when controlling erosion since, once started, erosion is a self-perpetuating process. The problems associated with erosion, such as the loss of surface layers and the formation of gullies, have their counterparts in areas of deposition, where channels and pipes can become choked.

Plate 6F Severe uncontrolled erosion on an erodible spoil tip which could easily be cured with vegetation. In this case the solution to downstream water pollution with sediment is to construct a series of settling lagoons

Soil erosion on slopes will usually take two forms:

1. erosion by rainfall and overland flow, often referred to as sheet and rill erosion;
2. erosion by gullies, usually occurring downhill of sheet and rill erosion as water flow is concentrated and channelled.

An eroding site needs stabilisation and one method of stabilisation is vegetating the slopes. However, healthy vegetation will not grow on an actively eroding slope: seeds will be washed out in the surface runoff and infertile subsoil may be exposed by erosion; runoff will also damage existing vegetation; and soil loss will reduce soil depth and hence limit profile available water, nutrient status and rooting depth for vegetation. Thus erosion will reduce the rate at which vegetation becomes established and affect its growth, so that the vegetation fails to reach its potential for erosion control.

A visual assessment of an eroded site will provide an indication of the rate of erosion and the scale of the soil loss. Eroded material is frequently transported into areas where it can cause severe problems. Sediments, for example, are deposited on flat land or in drains, reducing the transport capacity of the runoff. Failure to keep drainage systems clear of sediment will result in their hydraulic capacity being reduced. The effectiveness of reservoirs and canals is similarly limited by siltation, and costs are incurred in clearing or dredging the sediments. Water quality in rivers and man-made systems will also decline on account of the sediment load, affecting fisheries and the natural aquatic ecology. The consequences of high surface runoff and sedimentation are further considered in Section 6.8. Cross reference should be made between the two sections.

Erosion is a selective process; fine sands and silts tend to be preferentially eroded, because they lack the cohesion of clays and the inertia of larger-sized particles. These sediments, when deposited, are structureless, generally low in nutrients and organic matter, and have relatively low available water potential. As a result of these poor qualities the deposited sediment is usually infertile for vegetation establishment and growth. Nevertheless, sediments and silts from settlement lagoons, which may have a higher clay content and thus better water potential, are often considered suitable as substitute topsoil materials, with appropriate management (Section 2.4 and 4.2.2). It should always be remembered, however, that such materials when re-spread are potentially very erodible, particularly on slopes.

Erosion control is considered here in three stages:

1. the assessment of the problem;
2. control of erosion due to rainfall and overland flow;
3. control of gully erosion.

6.3.2 Erosion risk assessment

By modelling the erosion process and assessing the risk of erosion, it is possible to determine the scale and intensity of the potential problem. The model can also be used to assess which part of the erosion process is most active, and thus what particular functions of the vegetation are most likely to have a controlling effect. In this way an erosion control strategy can be developed.

Annual erosion risk

The extent of any erosion depends upon the interaction of the rainfall, soil, slope and land cover. These factors have been combined in a semi-empirical equation for predicting erosion which was developed by the United States Agricultural Research Service (Wischmeier and Smith, 1978). The equation, generally known as the Universal Soil Loss Equation (USLE), can be used to predict risk in terms of a mean annual erosion rate per unit area. The USLE was developed for agricultural land in the USA, but has been extended to apply to areas such as construction sites (Gray and Leiser, 1982). The parameters used in the equation would need re-calibration if the equation was to be used elsewhere.

An alternative procedure for evaluating erosion risk is described in Box 6.13, based on a model developed for predicting annual erosion and designed to combine the relative simplicity of the USLE with recent advances in the understanding of soil erosion processes. It is therefore more closely related to the processes of erosion described in Section 3. In the model, erosion is considered as resulting from:

1. the detachment of soil particles from the soil mass, usually by raindrop impact on the soil surface;
2. the transport of the detached particles down-slope by surface runoff.

The amount of sediment carried depends on either the sediment supply rate or the transport capacity of the runoff. Erosion will therefore occur at either the

Box 6.13 Erosion risk assessment (after Morgan et al, 1984)

RAINFALL			SOIL

Intensity, I (mm/h)	Volume, R (mm)	Rain days, R_n

Rainfall energy
$E = R (11.89 + 8.74 \log_{10} I)$

Mean rain per day, $R_o = R/R_n$

• Rooting depth, RD (m)
• Moisture at field capacity, FC (%)
• Bulk density ρ_d (Mg/m³)
• E_t/E_o ratio, use 0.05 for bare ground

Soil moisture storage capacity
$R_c = 1000 \times FC \times \rho_d \times RD \times (E_t/E_o)^{0.5}$

Rainfall interception H
Use zero for bare soil

Soil detachability, D

Volume of overland flow
$Q = R \exp(-R_c/R_o)$

Slope angle, $S°$

Crop/conserv. factor, C (value 1 for bare soil)

SPLASH DETACHMENT
$F = K E \exp(-0.5 \times H) \times 10^{-3}$

TRANSPORT CAPACITY
$G = C Q^2 \sin S P \times 10^{-3}$

F and/or G	<2.5	2.5–5	5–10	10–20	>20
Erosion risk class	1	2	3	4	5

Low   High

maximum transport capacity rate, when the runoff is carrying the maximum amount of sediment that it has the capacity to convey, or at the detachment rate, when supply of material is less than the transport capacity. The erosion rate is calculated as the lower of these two rates and then translated into an erosion risk class. This class assesses the risk in terms of an erosion rate per unit area over a period of one year. If the erosion rate is greater than 2.5, i.e. erosion risk class greater than 1, control measures will be required.

The procedure operates by taking the annual rainfall amount, R, expected at the site and calculating the energy of the rainfall available for soil detachment and the annual depth of runoff. The equations for these calculations are included in Box 6.13. Rainfall energy is dependent upon the intensity, I, and the amount of rain.

Box 6.13 *(Continued)*

---

1) Input parameters

R	Annual rainfall, mm
I	Typical value for intensity of erosive rain, mm/hr (typical values 25-75 mm/hr)
R_n	Number of raindays in the year
H	Rainfall interception, see table
D	Soil detachability, see table
RD	Soil rooting depth: depth of soil to an impermeable layer; or to the base of topsoil (if any); depth containing the majority of roots; or to 1 m, whichever is shallowest
FC	Soil moisture content at Field Capacity, % vol
ρ_d	Bulk density, Mg/m^3
E_t/E_o	Ratio of potential evapotranspiration (E_t) to open water evaporation (E_o), see table
C	Crop and soil conservation factor

2) Rainfall interception factor, H

Typical values:

Wheat	43		Mulch straw	95
Barley	30		fibreglass	95
Dense grass	50–70		woodfibre	20–50
Open grass	25–40		Netting	40
Woodland,				
conifer	25–30			
broadleaf	15–25			
Bare soil	0			

As a rule of thumb, *H* equates to the % ground cover of the vegetation, canopy or mulch layers combined.

H values can be estimated for each stage of establishment, development and succession of the vegetation.

3) Soil detachability, D

Defined as the weight of soil detached per unit of rainfall energy (g/J). Typical values:

Clay	0.02		Silt loam	[0.5]
Clay loam	0.4		Fine sand	0.2
Silty clay	[0.4]		Sand	0.7
Sandy loam	0.3		Loamy sand	[0.7]
Sandy clay loam	[0.4]			

[ ] guide value only

4) E_t/E_o ratio

Ratio of potential evapotranspiration to open water evaporation values:

Wheat	0.6		Woodland	0.95
Barley	0.6		Bare ground	0.05(*)
Pasture	0.85		Mulch – low	?
Tall grass	0.9		– high	?

* calibrated value

Annual runoff is estimated by assuming that runoff occurs when the daily rainfall total exceeds a critical value which represents the soil moisture storage capacity, R_c and that daily rainfall amounts approximate an exponential frequency distribution (Kirkby, 1976). The value of R_c is dependent upon the soil moisture content at field capacity, FC, the bulk density of the soil (ρ_d), the rooting depth, RD, and evapotranspiration from the plant cover. The latter is expressed by the ratio of annual potential evapotranspiration, E_t, to open water evaporation, E_o (*see* Section 3.4.1).

In the second stage of the procedure, the rainfall energy and annual runoff values are used to estimate respectively the amount of soil detachment and the transport capacity of the runoff. Soil detachment depends upon the energy of the rainfall, E, the detachability of the soil, K, and the interception factor, H, of the vegetation cover. The transport capacity of the runoff is a function of runoff depth, Q, slope steepness, S, the land cover (vegetation) factor, C, and an erosion control practice factor, P.

Compared with the Universal Soil Loss Equation, this procedure does not make an allowance for changes in slope length. This is not necessary, however, if it is assumed as a working approximation that soil loss increases proportionally with increasing slope length. A unit increase in length brings a unit increase in area, so that soil loss per unit area remains the same.

Applying the procedure

Experience with the method in agricultural situations (Morgan *et al*, 1984) and at recreational sites in mountain areas (Morgan, 1985) has shown that best results are achieved if measured values are obtained for the soil parameters of particle-size distribution, from which to determine texture and assign a soil detachability value, moisture content at field capacity and bulk density. These properties should therefore be included in the analysis carried out as part of site investigations.

For the other input data, it is sufficient to use the guide values given in Box 6.13, but noting the following points. Reasonable annual average values for RD are 0.05 m for grasses and 0.10 m for trees. These are based on calibration. A value of $E_t/E_o = 0.05$ is recommended for bare soil. Values of the C and P terms are represented by the appropriate C- and P- factor values used in the Universal Soil Loss Equation. Thus $C = 1$ for bare soil. Values for other conditions are given in Table 6.1.

Evaluating the role of vegetation

It is recommended that the procedure be applied to obtain estimates of risk with and without a vegetation cover respectively. The difference between the two is then an indicator of the role of vegetation in protecting the site from erosion.

Where the procedure is used in advance of land clearance, the difference reveals the likely consequences of the removal of the vegetation. Where it is applied to an existing area which may be largely bare soil, the difference between the risk prediction for the actual conditions and the value of 2.5 is an indicator of the amount of effort that needs to be made to reduce erosion to acceptable levels. By modifying the values of the input parameters used in the procedure to express the effects of vegetation, it is possible to evaluate different strategies for controlling the erosion.

The effects of vegetation on erosion described in Section 3 are represented in the risk assessment procedure by four parameters:

1. The interception factor, H. This accounts for the changes in the volume and energy of the rainfall reaching the ground surface as a result of the interception of rainfall by the plant cover. Its effect is to decrease the amount of soil detachment.
2. The evapotranspiration factor, E_t/E_o. This accounts for the transfer of moisture from the soil to the atmosphere through the plant cover. Its effect is to reduce runoff by maintaining a drier soil and therefore greater soil moisture storage capability at the start of each storm. To evaluate the sensitivity of this factor to the time of year, different ratios for monthly variation in E_t/E_o can be used.
3. The rooting depth, RD. This accounts for increases in pore spaces along the lines occupied by plant roots, which help to reduce runoff by increasing infiltration rates. In the procedure described here, its effect is to increase the depth of the effective soil moisture store that controls runoff generation.
4. The ground cover factor, C. This accounts for the effect of a vegetation cover in decreasing the transport capacity of the runoff through reductions in flow velocity and the physical restraint of soil particle movement. The effects of different soil surface preparation can also be accounted for in this factor (see Table 6.1).

The ability of this procedure to evaluate these separate effects of vegetation is an advance over the Universal Soil Loss Equation. The procedure demonstrates that effective erosion control is accomplished as much through the hydrological effect of vegetation, in reducing runoff, as through a direct effect on sediment transport.

Sediment discharge

The risk assessment procedure can be used to estimate the amount of sediment reaching the bottom of a slope and therefore leaving an area. This can be done by taking the erosion rate per unit area as predicted by the lower of the two values of F and G, and, assuming a unit width of 1 m and that soil loss increases proportionally with slope length, multiplying this value by the slope length, m. This will give a sediment yield in kg per metre-width.

Storm appraisal

It is often useful to supplement the evaluation of erosion risk over a year with more detailed information on the likely effect of individual storms. Most of the erosion in any one year usually takes place in two to five major storms. Analysis of storm rainfall data will indicate the season or months of the year when these are likely to occur. Site operations can then be planned so that the ground is not bare of cover or recently seeded during periods when erosive storms are likely to occur. Such

Table 6.1 C factor values for soil erosion risk assessment (after Wischmeier and Smith, 1978, via Gray and Leiser, 1982)

1) Grass swards and scrub[1]

| Type and height of canopy[2] | Canopy cover[3] (%) | Type[4] | C factor Ground cover at surface (%) | | | | | |
			0	20	40	60	80	95–100
No appreciable canopy		G	.45	.20	.10	.042	.013	.003
		W	.45	.24	.15	.090	.043	.011
Canopy of tall herbs or short scrub (0.5 m fall ht.)	25	G	.36	.17	.09	.038	.012	.003
		W	.36	.20	.13	.082	.041	.011
	50	G	.26	.13	.07	.035	.012	.003
		W	.26	.16	.11	.075	.039	.011
	75	G	.17	.10	.06	.031	.011	.003
		W	.17	.12	.09	.067	.038	.011
Appreciable scrub or bushes (2 m fall ht.)	25	G	.40	.18	.09	.040	.013	.003
		W	.40	.22	.14	.085	.042	.011
	50	G	.34	.16	.085	.038	.012	.003
		W	.34	.19	.13	.081	.041	.011
	75	G	.28	.14	.08	.036	.012	.003
		W	.28	.17	.12	.077	.040	.011
Trees but no appreciable low scrub (4 m fall ht.)	25	G	.42	.19	.10	.041	.013	.003
		W	.42	.23	.14	.087	.042	.011
	50	G	.39	.18	.09	.040	.013	.003
		W	.39	.21	.14	.085	.042	.011
	75	G	.36	.17	.09	.039	.012	.003
		W	.36	.20	.13	.083	.041	.011

1. All values shown assume: random distribution of mulch or vegetation, and mulch of appreciable depth where it exists.
2. Average fall height of waterdrops from canopy to soil surface.
3. Portion of surface area that would be hidden from view by canopy in a vertical projection.
4. G cover at surface is grass, grasslike plants or litter at least 50 mm deep. W cover at surface is mostly broadleaf herbaceous plants (as weeds) with little lateral-root network near the surface, and/or undecayed residue.

2) Tree cover

Tree canopy[1] (% of area)	Ground litter[2] (% of area)	Undergrowth[3]	C factor
100–75	100–90	Managed[4]	.001
		Unmanaged[4]	.003–.011
70–40	85–75	Managed	.002–.004
		Unmanaged	.01–.04
35–20	70–40	Managed	.003–.009
		Unmanaged	.02 –.095

1. When tree canopy is less than 20%, the area will be considered as grassland or cropland for estimating soil loss.
2. Forest litter is assumed to be at least 50 mm deep over the ground surface area covered.
3. Undergrowth is defined as shrubs, weeds, grasses, vines, etc., on the surface area not protected by forest litter. Usually found under canopy openings.
4. Managed - grazing and fires are controlled. Unmanaged - stands are overgrazed or subjected to repeated burning.

Table 6.1 *(Continued)*

3) Ground surface conditions

Surface condition with no cover	C factor[1]
Compact and smooth, scraped with bulldozer or scraper up and down slope	1.3
Same condition except raked with bulldozer scarifier up and down slope	1.2
Compact and smooth, scraped with bulldozer or scraper across the slope	1.2
Same condition except raked with bulldozer scarifier across the slope	0.9
Loose as a disced or cultivated layer	1.0
Rough irregular surface; equipment tracks in all directions	0.9
Loose with rough surface greater than 300 mm depth	0.8
Loose with smooth surface greater than 300 mm depth	0.9

1. Values based on estimates.

4) Newly seeded areas

Type of cover		C factor	%[1]
None (fallow ground)		1.0	0.0
Temporary seeding (90% cover)			
Ryegrass (perennial type)		0.05	95
Ryegrass (annual)		0.1	90
Small grain		0.05	95
Millet or sudan grass		0.05	95
Field bromegrass		0.03	97
Permanent seeding (90% cover)		0.01	99
Mulch[2]			
Hay, rate of application,	1.25 tonne/ha	0.25	75
	2.5	0.13	87
	3.75	0.07	93
	5.0	0.02	98
Small grain straw	5.0	0.02	98
Wood chips	15.0	0.06	94
Wood cellulose	4.4	0.1	90
Fibreglass	3.75	0.05	95
Bitumen emulsion	1.4 l/m²	0.02	98

1. Percent soil loss reduction as compared with fallow ground.
2. Fibrematting, excelsior, gravel, and stone may also be used as a protective cover.

analysis is most useful in seasonal climates, where the probability of erosive storms occurring at particular times of year can be made with confidence. In the UK, erosive storms can occur at any time of year and their probability of occurrence cannot be so accurately predicted. This means that greater care over erosion control is required, since planning the timing of site operations with respect to erosive rains will be less certain.

Some measure of erosion risk from a single major storm is also of value in indicating the amount of sediment that might have to be safely disposed of from one event. This can be estimated by predicting the volume of peak flow using standard hydrological methods such as the Rational formula (*see* Section 6.8), converting that volume to a depth by dividing by the catchment area, and then applying the same sediment transport capacity equation as used in the procedure for assessing annual erosion risk.

In addition to these methods of evaluating risk, perhaps the best indicator of all is the previous history of similar slopes in the area. If mine spoils or cut road banks have given problems in the past, it is reasonable to expect that new spoils and new cuts will give similar problems if treated in the same way as before.

6.3.3 Control of erosion by rainfall and overland flow

The erosion control system must be designed to deal with runoff and sediment production on the slope itself as well as its safe disposal downstream. Ground surface preparations and erosion control during plant establishment are discussed in Section 4.2 (Section 4.2.7 and Box 4.7).

Runoff diversion

Water originating on higher ground should be collected and diverted away from the land to be protected. This then minimises the problem of runoff generated on site. Diversions and on-site drainage systems can consist of channels, possibly lined with vegetation, which will convey the water at safe velocities (*see* Section 6.4.3 on watercourses with discontinuous flow, Section 4.2.3 on slope preparation). All channels should incorporate some simple means of collecting sediments. Where sediment loads are large, it will be necessary to construct sedimentation basins at the down-slope end of the site; these are likely to need maintenance to ensure continued effectiveness. Sediment traps are often required as a temporary measure until a sufficient vegetation cover has been established to control the erosion. Vegetation can be used in these traps as a filter.

Selection of vegetation

The more quickly that the right kind of vegetation cover can be established, the more rapidly will erosion control be achieved, as shown in Plate 6.G. Quick establishment requires proper selection of species for the soil and climatic environment of the site, and the preparation of a suitable soil environment for plant growth. These factors become especially important where toxicity or infertility in the soil may restrict the choice of species, and where compaction of the soil may inhibit seed germination and plant emergence. The guidelines on plant selection and site preparation for vegetation growth (*see* Section 4) must be followed carefully.

Plate 6G Demonstration panel of seeded vegetation on an otherwise bare slope, illustrating the effect of vegetation in controlling runoff erosion

As explained in Section 3.3, the wrong kind of plant structure can actually exacerbate erosion. The most effective vegetation cover for controlling erosion is a dense, uniform, ground cover of herbs and grass, which will:

1. intercept a high proportion of the rainfall;
2. prevent or minimise the effect of leaf-drip;
3. promote a uniform pattern of arrival of rain at the soil surface and a uniform pattern of infiltration into the soil;
4. impart a high level of roughness to runoff.

These effects provide the key to the control of erosion, since they bring about directly a reduction in the detaching power of the rainfall and in the transporting and detaching powers of the runoff, and they promote re-deposition of sediment.

Vegetation types to be avoided are tall trees or clumpy bushes without an adequate surface cover or plant litter. Grasses, herbs and legumes with a bunched growth habit are less effective in providing surface cover. Tussocky grasses are undesirable because they promote channelling of the runoff. Where, for other reasons such as slope stabilisation, these types of vegetation are being considered, they may need to be introduced in combination with groundcover plants.

The C factors for vegetation cover used in modelling and assessing erosion risk include a wide variety of vegetation types (*see* Table 6.1). From this it is possible to select the most appropriate or achievable vegetation cover to give the degree of protection required. It is not, however, possible to select individual species or mixtures to provide a given design value of the C factor. All that can be (or needs to be) done is to maximise the degree of protection which the selected vegetation type can provide, bearing in mind the guidelines given above.

Groundcover seeding and planting

As a general rule, at least 70% of the soil surface should be covered with grasses or herbaceous plants, uniformly distributed to give a roughness level equivalent to a Manning's *n* value greater than 0.05. Similarly the lateral root system should occupy more than 60% of the surface area. This is considered to be sufficient to control the velocity of overland flow in most situations. Good groundcover can be achieved using a variety of seeding methods, which are described in Section 4.3. Site preparation both to reduce the erodibility of the soil surface and to facilitate rapid plant establishment and growth needs particular attention (*see* Boxes 4.7 and 4.8).

Contour barriers

There are limits to the role that vegetation alone can play in controlling erosion. Although vegetated slopes in the natural environment appear to be stable and experience extremely low erosion rates, it should be noted that these conditions of stability have evolved over many years. Also, many cut-and-fill slopes are steeper than those which occur naturally and the soil on these slopes and those of mining spoil is often more erodible than natural soils.

On very steep man-made slopes with highly erodible soils, or in anticaption of very intense rainfall events, vegetation may need to be supplemented by other measures to intercept and divert any overland flow. Experience from agricultural situations suggests that terracing should be considered for all slopes steeper than 7° which are longer than about 20 m. Generally, vigorous vegetation alone will be effective in controlling erosion on slopes with gradients up to the stable angle of the soil, i.e. about 8–11° on clays, 19–21° on sands and 33–38° on loose scree. Once these slopes are exceeded, surface erosion is no longer the major problem and slope stabilisation becomes critical.

Vegetation can be used to simulate the effect of terraces when it is planted in strips on or at a slight grade to the contour to form a barrier across the slope. The spacing of the strips should be varied according to the slope steepness, from about 25 m apart on a 5% (3°) slope to 2 m apart on a 25% (14°) slope, as shown in Figure 6.9. Tall dense grasses and thick bushes can be used to form barriers, which should be about 1 m wide. Alternative methods are to plant live stakes in horizontal rows across the slope or to use contour wattling or contour brush layering (*see* Section 6.2.9; Figures 4.9, 4.10, 6.8). The barriers will reduce the velocity of flow, filter out the sediment, and encourage deposition within and up-slope of the barrier, thereby creating a set of benches over time .

Mulching

When using a vegetation option to control erosion on slopes, the speed with which a vegetation cover can be established on bare soil is critical. Rapid erosion can remove the soil in which the plants are to grow and also wash away the seeds or young plants before they can become established. Where erosion is likely to inhibit

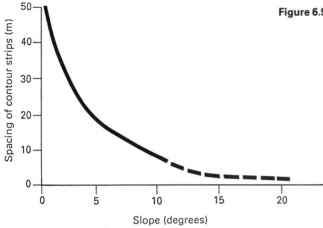

Figure 6.9 Spacing of contour grass strips

the establishment of vegetation cover, or to be a problem until such cover is established, temporary protection is required. This can be achieved by applying a surface mulch. Mulches should cover 70–75% of the soil surface to give adequate protection against erosion. The use of mulches in vegetation establishment is described more fully in Sections 4.3.3 and 4.3.4.

Composite solutions

Many of the disadvantages of mulches can be overcome by using a biodegradable geotextile (*see* Section 3.8.1). Different geotextiles (listed in Appendix 2) provide different degrees of cover. As well as affecting the proportion of soil protected against raindrop impact, the cover affects the amount of light penetrating through to the soil surface. Soil temperatures may also be modified by the colour and composition of the geotextile material. Depending upon the moisture holding properties of the material, geotextiles, like mulches, will affect the soil moisture regime. All these factors will affect seed germination and growth, so that geotextiles will act as both a mulch and an erosion control material.

The protection against erosion from a combination of geotextile and vegetation is greater than that offered by the geotextile or the vegetation alone. If the final vegetation cover is going to be effective in controlling erosion, temporary protection with a biodegradable geotextile in the early stages of plant growth and establishment will be sufficient. If there is a danger that the vegetation alone will give inadequate protection in the long-term, back-up support should be provided using a permanent erosion control geotextile. Installation of geotextile materials for erosion control is illustrated in Figure 4.5.

Aftercare and maintenance

The ability of the vegetation cover to control erosion depends upon its maintaining the properties required. Since both surface cover and root density decline during dormancy and therefore vary seasonally, it is important to establish when the period of erosion risk occurs and to ensure that the vegetation cover performs well at that time. For the UK, this means ensuring that adequate cover exists throughout the winter. Regular inspection of the vegetation cover is needed as part of the long-term maintenance. Areas of vegetation failure should be carefully noted and remedial action taken immediately. Aftercare and management requirements are discussed fully in Section 4.7. As a general rule, high levels of management are not usually necessary to maintain an erosion control function, though other considerations such as the use of the area concerned may be relevant.

6.3.4 Gully erosion control

Vegetation can be used both to prevent and to cure in gully erosion. Gullies form in two ways. Small eroded channels such as rills will concentrate runoff, which in turn erodes the channel further until large gullies are created. Alternatively, gullies may form when subsurface flow is concentrated beneath the soil surface, particularly along boundaries between impermeable and permeable layers or where hard pans have formed. The concentrated flows form subsurface pipes and tunnels which enlarge and eventually collapse when their roofs are no longer supported from below.

Prevention of gully erosion

Gully erosion can be prevented using vegetation in two ways:

1. to control overland flow, preventing the formation of rills or their development into gullies, using techniques described in Section 6.3.3;
2. to control subsurface erosion, minimising dangerous flow concentration and piping at depth. Subsurface piping often results from concentrated infiltration of surface water. A dense, uniform vegetation cover on the soil surface will encourage infiltration to be spread over a larger area. Roots can break up any hardpans along which flow may concentrate. Species with different rooting depths will also distribute infiltrating water throughout the soil profile.

Cure of gully erosion

If no preventive measures have been taken previously, the engineer may be faced with an area with deeply incised gullies. The long-term objective here will be to establish vegetation that will be self-regenerating, and thus will provide permanent erosion control. The plants selected must be good soil binders, crowd out weeds and form good groundcover. They must be easy to establish and their seeds must germinate rapidly. However, it may be impossible to reach this long-term objective of vegetation until the gully and adjacent hillside are stabilised. Initially it is important to solve any hydrological problems and to stabilise the gully head-cut, perhaps by grading, prior to stabilisation with vegetation. Some of the techniques used in gully stabilisation are outlined below.

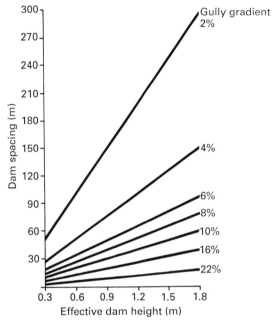

Figure 6.10 Spacing of check dams installed in gullies with different gradients (after Heede, 1976)

Wattling

Wattling consists of lengths of live, freshly-cut brush wood, packed together to form thick cables of plant material, which will root and sprout once placed on the slope (Figure 6.8). The wattling is placed in hand-dug trenches on the gully wall (following the contour, so that the lines of wattling lie across-slope) and staked for stability until the wattling roots into the gully wall. As the plant material begins to sprout, the restraint of soil particles by the roots and the increase in the shear strength of the gully wall reduce slumping. Also, any overland flow will be interrupted by the wattling and any eroded soil in the flow may be deposited behind or within the wattles, which act as a filter.

Check dams

The use of dams in gully erosion control reduces the high rates of erosion associated with gullies in a number of ways. Any structure within the gully will impede flow and will reduce flow velocity where it creates an upstream pond, so that eroded material transported by the flow may be deposited behind the dam. Dam structures thus encourage sedimentation, producing a longer, more gentle profile of deposited sediment on which vegetation can grow (and thus reduce flow velocities further). Deposited sediments behind the dam may also act as an aquifer and increase the channel storage capacity, again reducing the erosive effect of peak flow volumes. Channel deposits may also raise the groundwater level in the adjacent hillside.

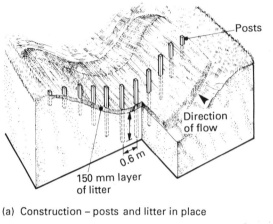

Posts

Direction
of flow

0.6 m

150 mm layer
of litter

(a) Construction – posts and litter in place

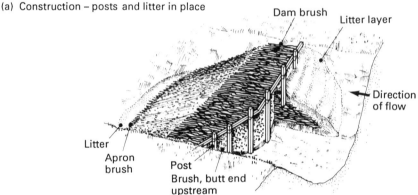

Dam brush

Litter layer

Direction
of flow

Litter

Apron
brush

Post

Brush, butt end
upstream

(b) Completion-note that the longer brush is on the bottom to form an apron

Figure 6.11 Single post-brush dams for gully erosion control

All dams made of vegetative material will be temporary, but they must provide short-term stabilisation of the gullied slope so that natural vegetation can re-colonise the area and provide long-term erosion control. Dams made from vegetative material allow some of the flow to pass through their porous structure, which decreases the head of flow over the dam and the hydrostatic forces against the dam.

The number of check dams needed to control erosive flows and stabilise the gully will depend on the slope gradient of the gully and the effective height of the dam. The latter will depend on the materials used in dam construction. The recommended spacing of dams can be determined from Figure 6.10. The simplest form of vegetative erosion control within a gully is the post-brush dam, illustrated in Figure 6.11. Gully erosion control using vegetative dams is very similar in principle to the use of brush-reinforced waterways using transverse barriers, described in Section 6.4.2.

6.4 Watercourse and shoreline protection

6.4.1 Approaches

In both the engineered and the natural environment, there is a range of situations in which the flow of water creates erosion. If this is to be controlled, there must be a clear understanding of the causes (*see* Sections 3.2.2 and 3.3.2) before remedial or preventive measures are begun. Merely to repair an eroding river bank or to stabilise a shoreline at a particular location without such an understanding can result in similar problems appearing elsewhere. The river bank and shoreline are also areas of considerable human and animal activity which can cause damage. That the solutions to these problems must be acceptable in engineering terms is taken for granted. Less obvious, however, is the need for solutions to be sensitive to the public perception of environmental quality. This is particularly relevant to the aquatic environment, because of its inherent beauty, its ecological status and its amenity value. Bioengineering methods fit well into this scenario and offer the attraction of cost savings.

In the aquatic environment, plant distributions are largely controlled by flow, water level and movement, together with the key factors such as soil, light and nutrient availability discussed in Section 2. The domain of interest can therefore be roughly divided into three categories:

1. watercourses with continuous flow, such as rivers and canals;
2. waterways with discontinuous flows, such as spillways, flood banks and drainage channels;
3. large water bodies in which wave attack is the principal erosive agent, such as reservoirs, lakes and the coastal environment.

The value of vegetation for protecting the soil depends on the combined effects of roots, stems and foliage. As indicated in Section 3, roots and rhizomes reinforce the soil. Immersed foliage elements absorb and dissipate flow energy and may promote sufficient attenuation by interference with the flow to prevent scour. In other circumstances, they can promote deposition from a sediment-laden flow. Although this buffering capability is advantageous, excessive foliage can also create problems of reduction in channel capacity, such as during spate flows in rivers, when large bushy plants with poor anchorage are liable to be torn from the banks.

The vegetative or composite vegetative/structural protection of waterways and watercourses is also considered in two other CIRIA reports, on the design of reinforced grassed waterways (Hewlett *et al*, 1987) and the protection of river and canal banks (Hemphill and Bramley, 1989). The German DIN 19657, *Sicherungen von Gewässern, Deichen und Küstendunen; Richtlinien* (Protection of watercourses, dykes and coastal dunes; guidelines) is also available in English translation; *see* Appendix 3.

6.4.2 Watercourses: continuous flow

When planning bioengineering works on watercourses, it is important to recognise that ditches, streams and rivers are important components of land drainage, whose primary function is the removal of surplus water. Flow must not be constrained by the vegetation and, in general, drainage authorities possess considerable power to ensure this. Authorities responsible for drainage may object to plants which impinge unduly on watercourses because they restrict the channel capacity and reduce velocities, thus encouraging sediment deposition and accretion. The effect of vegetation on channel capacity can be roughly determined by selecting the appropriate roughness coefficient for inclusion in the Manning formula (*see* Figures 3.3 and 3.4; Bache and MacAskill, 1984).

An important feature of river morphology is that channel patterns are not entirely random but either conform to or are seeking to achieve a 'regime', reflecting an equilibrium between the river and its environment. Thus alterations in channel shape may promote changes in the channel gradient and the conveyance capacity. A useful case-book example is described in Miller and Boorland (1963), in which local attempts to stabilise a channel by bank shaping and planting vegetation were thwarted by erosion taking place more rapidly. When revised control measures were implemented, taking account of regime principles, they were successful.

The bank can be considered as two separate areas:

1. that above normal water level, which is subject to attack under higher flow and flood conditions;
2. that in the vicinity of or below mean water level, which is under continuous attack from the stream flow and waves.

Among the many factors which should be considered, the maximum velocity and the flow duration at the area requiring protection are particularly important. The extent of the vulnerable area can also be influenced by changes in wave height resulting from boat wash.

Many types of plant can be used for bank protection and four natural bankside zones can be identified, as shown in Figure 6.12.

Aquatic plant zone

Plants in this zone will survive only with a slow current and sufficient light. They have little engineering function, although they may provide limited protection against erosion and help to absorb wave energy. It is important that they do not become too luxuriant and obstruct the flow; considerable effort is therefore expended on their clearance.

Marginal (reed bank) zone

Reeds and other marginal plants can form an effective buffer-zone by absorbing wave energy and restricting flow velocity adjacent to the bank. They therefore have a protective value. Specific functions which they can perform include the following.

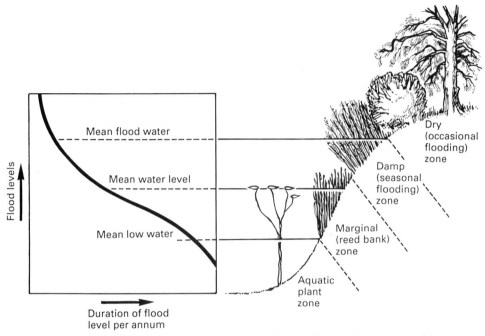

Figure 6.12 Vegetation zones on a river bank, correlated with water level and flood duration (after Seibert, 1968)

1. Absorbing and dissipating wave-wash energy; a reedbank 2 m wide can absorb about two-thirds of the wave energy generated by wash from pleasure craft, as shown in Plate 6.H (Bonham 1983);
2. Interference and protection of the bank from flow; reeds can be used successfully on their own where the main stream velocity does not exceed 1 m/s;
3. Reinforcement of the surface soil through the root mat and prevention of scour of the bank material;
4. Sediment accumulation brought about by the dense plant stems.

(a) Erosion of an unprotected bank

(b) Bank protected by reeds

Plate 6H Boatwash action

Plate 6J Marginal vegetation (Greater Pond Sedge)

Marginal plants require very wet ground and generally will not survive in water which is more than 0.5 m deep for long periods of time, as illustrated in Plate 6.J. They flourish in conditions of low velocity (about 0.2 m/s). Reeds are weakened by severe wave-wash or high flow velocity, which loosens the ground around the rhizomes and removes soil particles by backwash.

Species differ in the extent to which they will dissipate wave-wash, as detailed in Table 6.2. With substantial wave action (say waves >0.3 m high) and in faster-flowing waters or in navigable rivers, plants by themselves may be ineffective and it is often necessary to protect critical areas using inert materials. Rip-rap is commonly used and there are now many techniques utilising geotextile meshes and pocket fabrics, as shown in Figure 6.13 and Plates 6.K and 6.L).

Table 6.2 Dissipation of wave-wash by different reed species (after Bonham, 1980)

Reed species	Width of reedbed (m)	Boatwash energy dissipated (%)
Common Reed (*Phragmites australis*)	2.0	60
Reedmace (*Typha latifolia*)	2.3	66
Sweet-flag (*Acorus calamus*)	2.4	75
Bulrush (*Schoenoplectus lacustris*) (bed-slope 1 in 4)	2.5	70

The energy dissipated is dependent on the relative size of the reeds to the wave height, which is not given in this example. However, boatwash waves are typically in the height range 100–300 mm. (See also Bonham, 1983)

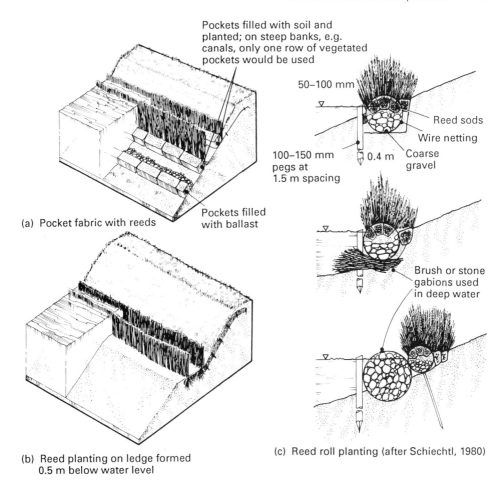

Pockets filled with soil and planted; on steep banks, e.g. canals, only one row of vegetated pockets would be used

50–100 mm

Reed sods

Wire netting

100–150 mm pegs at 1.5 m spacing

0.4 m

Coarse gravel

(a) Pocket fabric with reeds

Pockets filled with ballast

Brush or stone gabions used in deep water

(b) Reed planting on ledge formed 0.5 m below water level

(c) Reed roll planting (after Schiechtl, 1980)

Figure 6.13 Bank stabilisation using reeds and geotextiles

(a) Installation and planting of pocket fabric   (b) Marginal vegetation established

Plate 6K Bank stabilisation using reeds and geotextiles

(a) Installation of mat on river diversion

(b) Vegetation growth after two years

(c) Composite photograph and diagram showing installation detail

Plate 6L River bank reinforcement with synthetic geotextile mat and vegetation.
The mat provides protection above and below the waterline

Damp (seasonal flooding) zone

In the absence of mowing or other management, this zone is colonised by fast-growing shrubby or tree species (e.g. willow and alder). These species can tolerate regular inundations in the root zone (Gill, 1977) and can form 'adventitious' roots on stems. This valuable property enables them to develop secondary roots on cut stems, making them particularly useful for implantation techniques using live poles, fascines or mattresses.

Stands of full-grown trees are of little use for protecting banks (Seibert, 1968), except by soil reinforcement through their root structure. Large trunks can project into the flood flow and are pushed over or torn out. Above-ground growth in this zone is most effective when it is treated as scrub wood and coppiced. The thin whippy stems easily deflect under high water flows and cause least obstruction.

Trees should be planted within 0.5–1.0 m of the mean summer water level if protection of this zone is to be achieved. Greater distance has little value unless grass or a perennial herb cover is used in the intervening space. Live wood, particularly willow and alder, used on its own as a brush mattress or combined with a geotextile as a composite material, is frequently used to give both immediate and long-term protection of this zone, as illustrated in Figure 6.14 and Plate 6.M. It can also be planted in the joints of stone rip-rap and masonry to bind the structure together, thereby turning discrete blocks into an anchored monolithic mass. This can be an effective erosion-control measure as well as a means of improving visual appearance. There are, however, no definitive guidelines on the flow conditions and the timescales of the stresses that these structures can withstand.

Grass can only be used above the normal summer water level because its roots do not survive prolonged submergence. Some species and varieties have a degree of flood tolerance (*see* Appendix 1) and these should be selected as appropriate. Where very high flows are expected, geotextile-reinforced grass may be used, as in channels and spillways. The reinforcing and hydraulic properties of grass and reinforced grass are considered in more detail in Section 6.4.3.

Dry (occasional flooding) zone

Trees are less significant in bank protection in this zone because it is less often flooded and less easily eroded by water. They are a useful means of controlling by shading the growth of aquatic plants which obstruct a waterway, as detailed in Box 6.14. The right amount of shade has to be attained from the height and spread of larger trees in the drier zone, sufficient to control aquatic vegetation but not enough to shade out the shrub, grass or reed growth nearer or at the waterline which is protecting the bank. Grass is also often used to protect the dry zone part of the bank (*see* Section 6.4.3) and this must receive sufficient light to grow and function properly.

As already noted, natural methods represent the ideal basis for environmentally acceptable solutions to bank protection. Aspects of this work were highlighted by the Water Space Amenity Commission (1980) and NCC (1983). For example, when undertaking schemes to increase channel capacity, one possibility is to preserve one

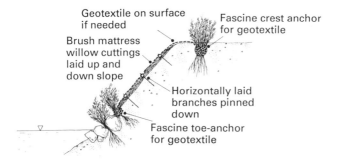

Geotextile on surface if needed

Fascine crest anchor for geotextile

Brush mattress willow cuttings laid up and down slope

Horizontally laid branches pinned down

Fascine toe-anchor for geotextile

(a) Stone rip-rap with joint planting

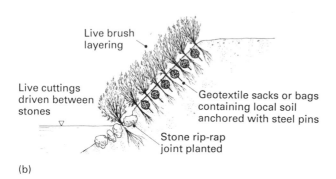

Live brush layering

Live cuttings driven between stones

Geotextile sacks or bags containing local soil anchored with steel pins

Stone rip-rap joint planted

(b)

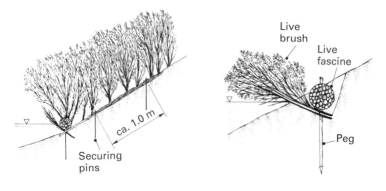

ca. 1.0 m

Securing pins

(c) Shoreline protected with a brush mattress

Live brush

Live fascine

Peg

(d) Live shore fascine

Figure 6.14 Bank protection using live wood

(*a*) Fascine hurdles along the waterline

(*b*) Brush mattress on a flood bank

(*c*) Well-developed willow growth; regular
pruning keeps it thin and flexible

Plate 6M River bank planting using live willows

Box 6.14 Tree planting for shade to control aquatic weed growth

Altering the amount of light reaching a channel is a simple way of controlling emergent and submergent weed growth, which can choke a waterway. The degree of control depends on the degree of shade tolerance of the weed species concerned (see Haslam, 1978), though no plants can live under permanently heavy shade. A 70% reduction in light will inhibit nearly all growth, a 50% reduction, which is achievable with tree-shading, will exclude all shade-intolerant plants and reduce the growth of others.

Orientation	Bank for shade belt	Effectiveness for weed control
E——W NW SE	South bank South-east bank	Maximum Moderate to good
NE SW	South-west bank	Moderate to good
N S	East bank East and west bank	Poor Moderate

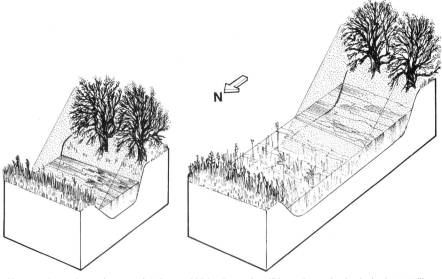

Narrow channels can be completely shaded from one side	Wide channels will be only partly shaded, plants still flourish on the south-facing bank

(after Lewis and Williams, 1984; Dawson and Haslam, 1983)

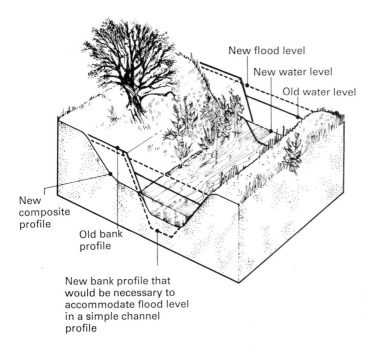

New flood level

New water level

Old water level

New
composite
profile

Old bank
profile

New bank profile that
would be necessary to
accommodate flood level
in a simple channel
profile

Figure 6.15 Simple and composite channel sections

bank in its natural state and carry out widening on the opposite bank. There is also considerable merit in making use of a complex rather than a simple cross-section, at little extra cost and effort, as shown in Figure 6.15.

In rivers with braided flow or very high seasonal fluctuations in flow levels, trees or shrubby vegetation can be used for channel training. Planting is mainly in the form of retards, groynes or close-planted belts 8–20 m wide (van Kraayenoord & Hathaway, 1986). These are usually located well away from the main stream of summer flow, on the edge of peak flood flow.

The plant material used in much of the bank protection work in the UK is rarely available commercially in the conventional way, with the exception of normal grass and herbaceous seed mixtures. Reeds, sedges and live-wood (willow) materials are usually collected from nearby waterway areas, often resulting from maintenance works that are being carried out anyway.

Techniques for bank stabilisation and channel protection using vegetation are summarised in Box 6.15, together with the locations for which they are suitable. Many bank protection schemes involve a combination of vegetation and geotextiles. For example a number of reinforcement methods were investigated by the British Waterways Board (1986) for use on canal banks. These are summarised in Box 6.16, together with an indication of costs estimated at that time.

Box 6.15 Selection of bioengineering techniques for bank protection in watercourses with continuous flow (rivers, canals, drains).

Seasonal variation in water level	Zone	Annual inundation (days)	Reed Planting			Grass & herbs		Shrubs		Trees
			Alone	Reinforced or in pockets	Combined with gabions or rip-rap	Alone	Reinforced	Alone	Combined with gabions or rip-rap	Alone
More than 1 m (approx)	Below flood level	<100				L		L		
	At or above flood level	<50					L	H	H+	H+
Less than 1 m	Marginal	100–365	L	L/H				L/H	H+	
	Damp	70–100	L	L				L/H	H+	L
		50–70			H	L	L	H	H+	H
	Dry	<50				L	H+	H	H+	L/H

Note: L = conditions of low wash, wave or current energy
H = conditions of high wash, wave or current energy
H+ = conditions of very high wash, wave or current energy

Box 6.16 Costs of reinforced vegetative bank protection on canals in the UK (after British Waterways Board, 1986)

Canal	Location	Boat traffic	Soil	Date	Costs per lineal metre (£)				Material	Length of site (m)	Comment
					Labour	Plant	Materials	Total			
Rushall	Aldridge	Very light	Shale spoil and clay	1982	1.79	1.26	6.72	9.77	Pocket fabric and reeds	150	
Ashby	Shenton	Moderate	Loam	1982	3.59	1.79	7.88	13.26	Pocket fabric and reeds	100	
Leicester	Kilworth	Moderate/heavy	Loam	1982	4.79	2.19	6.98	13.96	Pocket fabric and reeds	100	
Staffs & Worcs	Compton	Heavy	Sandy	1982	2.00	0.66	6.98	9.64	Pocket fabric and reeds	150	
Staffs & Worcs	Average costs 4 sites			—	3.04	1.48	7.14	11.66	Pocket fabric and reeds	—	
Staffs & Worcs	Compton	Heavy	Sandy	1982	1.66	0.55	1.33	3.54	Reeds only	180	
Leicester	Kilworth	Moderate/heavy	Loam	1984	11.33	9.46	19.23	40.02	Bitumen impregnated polypropylene 3D mat	47	Experimental not effective
Leicester	Kilworth	Moderate/heavy	Loam	1984	11.33	9.46	9.15	29.94	Polypropylene 3D mat	35	Experimental not effective
Leicester	Kilby	Moderate/heavy	—	1984	21.30	13.57	44.68	79.55	Trench sheets/bitumen impregnated polypropylene 3D mat	—	
Various								50.00	Standard 2 m trench Sheet piling	—	Usual non-vegetative method

6.4.3 Waterways: discontinuous flow

The most common application of grass, and indeed other types of herbaceous vegetation, is for protecting the banks of rivers, drains and canals in the intermittently washed zone above the normal water level. There are, however, situations, such as drainage ditches, auxiliary spillways and crests of flood banks, in which grass alone is unable to withstand the erosion hazard posed by low frequency but high intensity-short duration flows. Here, reinforced grass provides an economically attractive and easily constructed alternative to hard lining or heavy armouring. Reinforcement can be achieved using either geotextiles or cellular concrete products through which grass can grow forming a composite protective layer (Hewlett *et al*, 1987).

When considering whether herbaceous vegetation can provide reliable long-term protection, it must be borne in mind that it requires time to recover between periods of immersion. The length of this recovery time determines its suitability for use in intermittent flow situations. Besides estimating the likely frequency of flow, the designer will need to consider the effect of the grass on the hydraulic conveyance capacity and on the erosion resistance of the waterway.

Hydraulic capacity is usually assessed using the Manning formula, the retardance coefficient being selected according to the grass height and discharge intensity (i.e velocity times depth over discharge per unit width; *see* Section 3.2.2 and Figure 3.4). Note that for any given discharge intensity the erosive effort will vary according to the length of the grass. The minimum velocity and the maximum depth occur when the grass is longest. The maximum velocity occurs when the grass is shortest, perhaps after mowing or during winter. The effect of increasing hydraulic loading or discharge intensity on flattening the grassed surface is shown diagrammatically in Figure 6.16. Such flattening clearly helps to protect the subsoil from erosion.

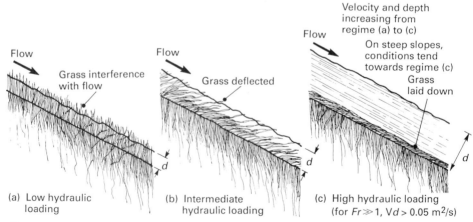

Figure 6.16 Effect of hydraulic loading (discharge intensity) on grassed surfaces (after Hewlett *et al.*, 1987)

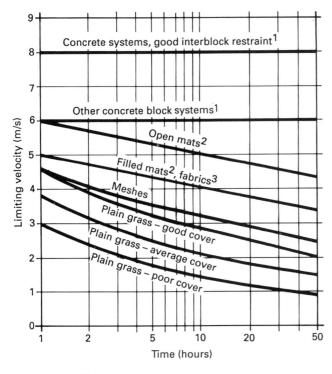

Figure 6.17 Recommended limiting velocites for erosion resistance of plain and reinforced grass against unidirectional flow (after Hewlett *et al.*, 1987)

For plain grass in UK conditions with relatively cohesive subsoils, the erosion resistance is usually considered simply in terms of the hydraulic parameters of velocity, length and cover of sward, and duration of flow. The velocity-duration diagram shown in Figure 6.17 is recommended for assessing the erosion resistance, based on a limiting velocity selected according to the estimated flow duration. This appears in the Manning formula as the maximum permitted velocity commensurate with the flow, channel dimensions and roughness (*see* also Table 3.2). If the permissible velocity and duration are exceeded, loss of vegetation cover and uncontrolled erosion of the subsoil are likely to occur.

Hewlett *et al,* (1987) provides basic guidance for the use of grass in hydraulic engineering practice and recommends that a well chosen grass cover can withstand the following velocities:

2 m/s for prolonged periods (more than 10 hours)
3–4 m/s for periods of several hours
5 m/s for brief periods (say less than 2 hours).

In general, long-term stability will be maintained provided the velocity is less than 1 m/s. The limiting velocity is reduced as the quality of the cover decreases, as indicated on the velocity-duration diagram (*see* Figure 6.17). Similar criteria apply to reinforced grass. In the case of steep grassed waterways in which supercritical flows occur, Hewlett *et al* (1987) indicates that grass reinforced with a geotextile can resist significantly higher short-duration velocities than a good cover of plain grass, or can increase the time for which a specific velocity can be resisted.

The length of grass is a major component in determining its erosion resistance. However, other factors also play a significant part.

1. The density of stems, foliage and surface mat; this is related to the age and management of the sward.
2. The growth habit and structure of the sward; this is related to the species that are present as well as their management.
3. The uniformity of the sward; clumped or tussocky growth will cause localised eddies and may exacerbate erosion in their immediate vicinity (*see* Section 3.3.2).
4. Flexibility and robustness of the foliage and shoots; these affect the behaviour of the grass as the flow characteristics change.

In addition to the data given in Figure 6.17, Temple *et al,* (1987) have developed more detailed models for predicting permissible velocity and soil erosion taking account of both vegetation and soil type and thus extending the approach shown in Table 3.2. The so-called 'stability design method' can be useful for indicating the likely sensitivity to flow erosion with different vegetation and soil types.

In central Europe widespread use is made of brushwood and live-wood techniques for protecting storm or meltwater channels from erosion during flood flows. These techniques are relevant for flood relief channels where grassed protection is not sufficiently robust. Several variations of the techniques are given in Schiechtl (1980).

6.4.4 Large water bodies

The shorelines of open waters and closed water bodies, such as lakes and reservoirs, are affected by the problems of changing water levels, wave attack and currents. Of these, wind-generated waves and water-borne craft produce the most critical forces affecting structures and the shore environment. In considering wave attack on banks, bank slope and wave period are determining factors but the dominant parameter affecting the design of protective measures is the wave height, since this defines the incipient wave energy.

Generally, plants stand little chance of survival in the wave breaking zone. However, in the wave run-up zone (above the breaking zone) reinforced grasses or more substantial shrubs can survive. It is often appropriate to adopt a gradual transition in protection and vegetation types through the marginal zone. Above this level, unreinforced vegetation is sufficient. A bank protection scheme should be designed to accommodate waves likely to arise in the severest conditions (say a continuous wind-speed of about 25 m/s).

Changes in water level are important in that they control the level of wave attack. In a lake or reservoir, the mean winter water level would be the main factor when planning the location of the toe of a protection structure. Similar criteria apply at coastlines, but taking account of the tidal pattern.

Protection systems for shorelines are similar to those used for banks of watercourses. Widespread use is made of composite techniques utilising permanent geotextiles and herbaceous vegetation, with different combinations of materials used depending on the degree of protection required in the various zones up the shore. Revetments constructed from inert materials are necessary where wave attack is likely to be severe. Vegetation and geotextile combinations are mainly designed to protect the soil surface from scour and erosion in the zone which is washed intermittently by wave run-up. Longer, denser herbaceous vegetation and reeds can be used to absorb wave energy, reducing its effects, in much the same way as on the marginal zone of a river bank. The use of trees and shrubs for stabilising the margins of water bodies has attracted some interest; documented examples can be found in Gill (1977). The role of woody plants is mainly to absorb wave energy, but they also give some degree of surface protection, as illustrated in Plate 6.N. Denser, coppiced, shrubby growth is preferred to taller mature trees in the lower wave run-up zone.

The main environmental factor that shoreline vegetation has to contend with is the seasonal variation in the water level. Reservoirs particularly can have a substantial draw-down zone with operational or hydrological regimes characteristic for each type of reservoir. The implications of this for tree and shrub growth have been extensively reviewed by Gill (1977). Most trees can survive short periods of flooding, but their tolerance varies from species to species. In general adapted species, such as alders and willows, appear to thrive well in areas which are flooded fewer than 100 days in an average year. This type of factor is useful for deciding the offshore limit of planting. Judged by natural plantations they are unlikely to thrive below summer median water level.

Trees planted and established some time before the initial flooding generally survive more successfully than those planted retrospectively. Such trees will have had an opportunity to grow taller and thus a smaller proportion of the shoot will be inundated, with correspondingly less damage as a result. The trees are also better able to respond to inundation by producing new surface roots, and the larger root system, although vulnerable to initial flooding, can provide firm anchorage against wave action. Mulching at the time of planting may be desirable to promote the development of a relatively shallow root system, which will be at an advantage when flooding eventually occurs. The Countryside Commission for Scotland has implemented trials at Loch Lomond to study the long-term growth of trees planted on a beach. A valuable set of information sheets covering an array of techniques using plants and geotextiles in lochshore management has been produced (C.C.S., 1985); these are summarised in Box 6.17.

Box 6.17 Selection of bank stabilisation techniques to control lochshore erosion (after CCS, 1985)

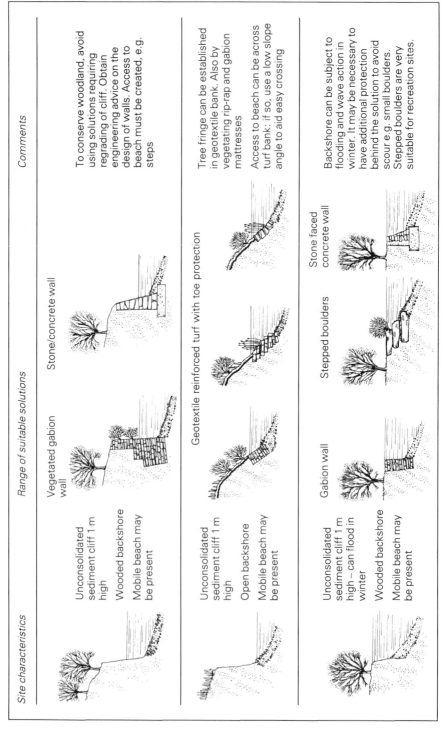

Site characteristics	Range of suitable solutions	Comments
Unconsolidated sediment cliff 1 m high Wooded backshore Mobile beach may be present	Vegetated gabion wall Stone/concrete wall	To conserve woodland, avoid using solutions requiring regrading of cliff. Obtain engineering advice on the design of walls. Access to beach must be created, e.g. steps
Unconsolidated sediment cliff 1 m high Open backshore Mobile beach may be present	Geotextile reinforced turf with toe protection	Tree fringe can be established in geotextile bank. Also by vegetating rip-rap and gabion mattresses Access to beach can be across turf bank; if so, use a low slope angle to aid easy crossing
Unconsolidated sediment cliff 1 m high – can flood in winter Wooded backshore Mobile beach may be present	Gabion wall Stepped boulders Stone faced concrete wall	Backshore can be subject to flooding and wave action in winter. It may be necessary to have additional protection behind the solution to avoid scour e.g. small boulders. Stepped boulders are very suitable for recreation sites.

Box 6.17 (Continued)

Site characteristics	Range of suitable solutions			Comments
Unconsolidated sediment cliff 1 m high can flood in winter Open backshore Mobile beach may be present	Geotextile reinforced turf with toe protection			The same solutions can be used as if backshore is wooded. Without the shading of trees, additional protection against scour can be gained by geotextile reinforced turf.
Open shore flooded in winter Aquatic vegetation fringe can be present Absence of mobile beach	Reinforced reed fringe	Rip-rap	Gabion mattress	Reed fringes can be planted in sheltered sites with waves less than 0.3 m high. Otherwise, use solutions which encourage the aquatic fringe to colonise Reed fringes do not survive recreational pressures – access points must be provided
Unconsolidated sediment cliff on bedrock Mobile beach may be present	Gabion wall	Stepped boulders	Stone pitching	It is essential to key into the bedrock to obtain good foundations for a wall, or use a heavy, flexible structure such as gabions or stepped boulders that will deform to take up the change of shape as the bedrock erodes

Note: Water level shown is winter water level.

(a) Original problem

(b) Construction with willow withies woven between stakes; note the jute netting at the waterline to protect reed planting

(c) Growth after six months

Plate 6N Live willow 'spiling' to protect an eroding bank from wave erosion

Herbaceous plants can survive in more sheltered areas with a water level variation of less than 1 m or so. Little and Jones (1979) have examined the uses of such vegetation in the draw-down zone. They give specific guidance on the selection of species and their tolerance to varying hydraulic conditions, including their erosion control potential.

There is relatively little data on the design of vegetation-based shoreline zones, although some guidance for herbaceous communities can be gleaned from experience with salt marshes, described below. The approach therefore has to be largely based on judgement, using design criteria and procedures for inert structures applied to a vegetative or combined system.

6.4.5 Salt marshes

Salt marshes in temperate climates are dominated by the herbaceous plant communities that grow in areas where there is regular tidal flooding by brackish water or seawater. There is a marked vertical zonation of vegetation, the plants growing in the lowest areas being best able to withstand tidal flooding. The salt marsh vegetation zones extend from mid-tide or mean sea level up to mean high water level. A strong marine influence also extends up to mean high water spring tide level, due to regular salt spray and occasional inundation.

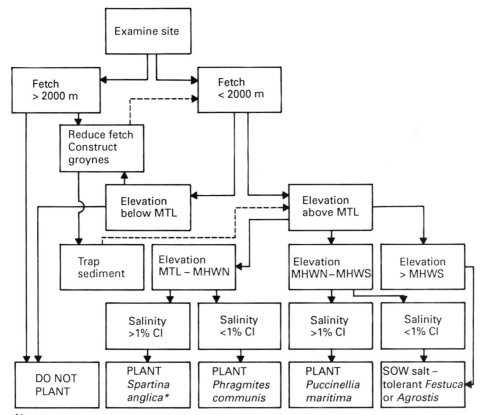

Notes
MTL = mean tide level; MHWN = mean high water neap tides; MHWS = mean high water spring tides; Fetch = maximum extent of open water beyond marsh in metres; salinity in % concentration of chloride ion, sea water being approx. 3.5%

* *Spartina anglica* is an invasive species on mud flats and should not be planted in the UK without reference to the Nature Conservancy Council.

Figure 6.18 A key to the selection of salt marsh stabilisation techniques for the UK (after Boorman, 1977)

Salt marshes are dynamic, with the level of the surface increasing by the accretion of sediment from the muddy water that flows over the marsh. The rate of sedimentation depends on the sediment supply and the duration of flooding, but rates of accretion from 3–25 mm/yr are typical. As the marsh level builds up, so the species composition of the vegetation changes with the decrease in the frequency and duration of submersion. The width of the salt marsh fringe will thus depend on the angle of slope of the shore. Marshes can form a narrow fringe along steep shorelines or can extend over wide areas in shallow, gently sloping bays and estuaries.

Where there is a sea wall protecting low-lying areas inland, the salt marshes outside the wall perform a vital function in protecting the wall from wave attack, especially at the toe. Loss of the salt marsh may necessitate artificial protection of the sea wall (Whitehead, *et al*, 1976). Losses are occurring extensively in southern England and, to avoid the necessity of expensive wall reinforcement, various measures are being attempted to encourage salt marsh growth. An alternative that is also being tried is the reconstruction of the sea wall 30 m inland, thus allowing fresh high level marsh vegetation to develop on land exposed outside the new wall.

The use of marsh vegetation for the stabilisation of mudflats and in coast protection has been practised in many parts of the world. Much excellent work, specifically for the USA but relevant elsewhere, has been carried out under the auspices of the US Army Coastal Engineering Research Centre. Knutson (1977) reviewed the procedures for establishing marsh vegetation as buffer regions on the North American coast and summarised the salient criteria in the form of a decision key. Figure 6.18 gives similar information for the UK. This highlights the inter-relationships between site requirements, species selection and planting techniques.

The question of the vegetation appropriate to the sea walls themselves is a different matter. The walls are not usually liable to tidal flooding and the vegetation only has to withstand a certain amount of salt spray. The normal principles for bank protection apply (*see* Section 6.4.2) but with the use of species and varieties that have a degree of salt tolerance (*see* Appendix 1).

6.5 Wind erosion control

6.5.1 The problem

Wind erosion can be a problem in areas where:

1. the soil surface has a high proportion of silt and fine sand, the most erodible fractions;
2. the terrain is very open and exposed to moderate and high winds;
3. there is little or no vegetation cover.

Such situations can occur on construction sites, spoil tips, tailings dams and on coastal sand dunes. In addition to the loss of soil on site, which may seriously hamper long-term restoration or reclamation, severe problems of air pollution and dust nuisance can be created. The risk of wind erosion is greatest when the soil is dry; moisture increases the adhesion between particles. Thus wind erosion is often a seasonal occurrence, though the soil surface can dry out sufficiently to cause a risk of erosion during any short dry period.

The process of movement of particles by wind takes three main forms:

1. saltation, rolling and bouncing of heavier particles along the surface, which accounts for most soil movement during erosion;
2. surface creep;
3. suspension of the finest particles in the air.

The mechanisms of wind erosion are described fully in several standard texts (Chepil and Woodruff 1963, Hudson 1981, Morgan 1986, Bache and MacAskill 1984).

6.5.2 Wind erosion risk assessment

The assessment of wind erosion risk can be based on two factors: the erosivity of the wind and the erodibility of the soil. A simple procedure is outlined in Box 6.18.

6.5.3 Use of vegetative cover

The effect of vegetation on wind erosion is twofold:

1. to bind the soil;
2. to reduce surface windspeed due to foliage drag (*see* Section 3.7.1).

Thus the best protection against wind erosion is provided by establishing a dense, uniform stand of ground vegetation, comprising plant elements which are basically cylindrical in structure. These are less prone to streamlining and therefore offer greater resistance to air flow. Grasses with at least 70% surface cover are the best way of achieving this requirement as long as bunch or tussocky types are avoided, since these may promote localised funnelling of air.

Where erosion is severe, it is generally not possible to establish the intended longer-term vegetation cover from the outset. A succession of vegetation can be used, with the first-established plant species being tolerant of blowing soil or sand and capable of stabilising the material. This approach is commonly used on sand dunes (*see* Section 6.5.6) but can be applied elsewhere, as detailed in Box 6.19.

In a mobile, wind-eroding situation, rapid establishment of the initial vegetation cover is of prime importance. However some temporary artificial stabilisation may still be necessary, the usual options being:

1. a chemical soil binder or soil stabiliser, as commonly used in hydroseeding (*see* Section 4.3.3);
2. a mulch similar to those used for water erosion control and hydroseeding (*see* Sections 6.3.3 and 4.3.3), which may need tacking down with a binder as well;

Box 6.18 Wind erosion risk assessment

The risk factor is an estimate of the potential soil loss in t/ha per year, and is given by the simple product of the wind erosivity value, E and the soil erodibility index, I.

1. Wind erosivity value

$$E = \sum_{j=1}^{16} \sum_{i=1}^{n} (v_{ij}^3 \, f_{ij})$$

where $j = 1$ to 16 represents the wind sectors (each sector is 16/360° wide around the compass
i = windspeed group (above a threshold velocity of 19 km/hr)
v = mean velocity of wind in the ith speed group
f = duration of wind (% frequency) for direction j in the ith speed group

The erosivity value can be calculated for each wind sector or group of sectors separately, if required.

2. Soil erodibility by wind

	% of dry stable aggregates <0.84 mm				
	<20	20–50	50–70	70–80	>80
I (t/ha per year)	>220	166–220	84–166	4–84	4

3. The value of the product $E \times I$ can be modified to allow for reduction of wind erosion by:
   - soil roughness
   - length of open wind blow
   - vegetation cover (see opposite)

3. long-fibred straw disced or punched into the soil surface so that it sticks up, simulating the effect of vegetation;
4. a biodegradable geotextile such as jute, which has to be well pinned down to prevent it blowing away.

These materials all have the added benefit of improving the soil microclimate and reducing soil/water loss, thus improving the germination and establishment of vegetation.

Box 6.19 Use of vegetation succession in stabilising blowing soil or sand

Common upland grazing areas on volcanic sands in the hostile climate of central Iceland are very prone to overgrazing of the fragile natural vegetation of mosses and dwarf shrub. Vast areas become denuded by wind erosion and are impossible to revegetate using normal methods.

These areas can be reclaimed, first by planting with sand dune grass species to stabilise the mobile surface, then seeding with normal rough pasture grasses. These are maintained by aerial application of fertilisers for two to four years, before being allowed to die back. In the soil environment thus created, the natural but slow-growing moss and shrub heath take hold, leading eventually to low-growing woodland in the absence of further grazing.

A similar approach would be appropriate for mountainous areas in the UK, where the severity of the climate (mainly low temperatures and a short growing season) means that the natural hardy vegetation is very slow to establish and grow.

This example illustrates the importance of using the right vegetation in the right way, and that establishment of the most appropriate vegetation can be achieved in successive stages.

Box 6.18 *(Continued)*

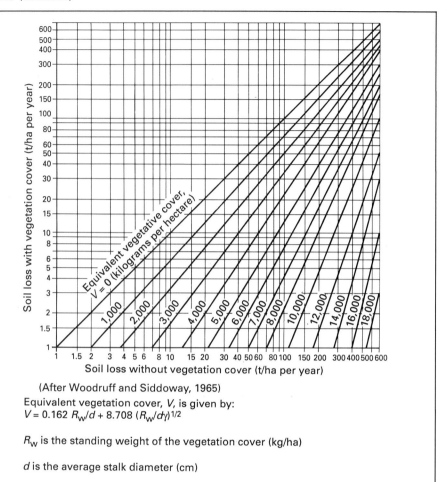

(After Woodruff and Siddoway, 1965)

Equivalent vegetation cover, V, is given by:

$$V = 0.162\ R_W/d + 8.708\ (R_W/d\gamma)^{1/2}$$

R_W is the standing weight of the vegetation cover (kg/ha)

d is the average stalk diameter (cm)

γ is the average specific weight of the stalks (Mg/m³)

For further details, see Morgan (1986)   (After Lyles and Allison, 1981)

6.5.4 Within-site shelter

Shelter can be obtained within a site by planting vegetative strips at right-angles to the direction of the erosive winds, as illustrated in Figure 6.19. Based on the research on in-field shelter systems used in agricultural situations, the most suitable plants are those with bladed leaves aligned full-face to the wind. Thus cereals or even lines of planted straw are very effective. In hostile environments more

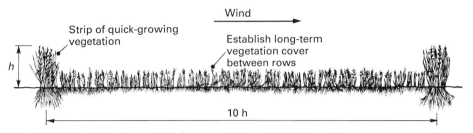

Figure 6.19 Strip planting to provide temporary shelter against wind erosion

tolerant grasses, particularly those naturally occurring on sand dunes, may be used. Plants to avoid are those with ovate leaves, as they streamline downwind too easily, and those with bladed leaves in random alignments or with tussocky forms, as these can enhance the risk of erosion in steady winds.

Where it is difficult to establish vegetated strips quickly, temporary shelter can be provided by erecting sand fences of wooden slats, synthetic meshes or brushwood.

6.5.5 Boundary shelter

Where long-term shelter is required, belts of more substantial vegetation such as trees and shrubs can be used. This is a form of vegetation barrier, and is discussed in Section 6.6. To protect large areas, belts are arranged in regular rows or arrays with appropriate spacing to give the desired degree of protection.

6.5.6 Sand dune stabilisation

The effect of wind on soil and vegetation in the coastal situation is complex. There are the direct effects of both soil loss (erosion) and soil addition (accretion). The growth of plants in the coastal zone can be adversely affected by salt spray even at some considerable distance from and above the high tide line. Onshore winds can cause the sea level to rise well above the normal high tide line and plants in this zone must be able to tolerate occasional flooding by salt water. The greatest wind effects are on sand dune coasts, where the loose soil is readily worked by the wind.

Sand dunes are composed of sand of marine origin, transported and built up by the wind and stabilised by the growth of specialised sand dune plants. They owe their rich and varied flora to a degree of continuing natural mobility. Much of their biological interest is lost if they are completely stabilised. However dune stabilisation may be required to preserve or strengthen sea defences, to reinstate areas damaged by construction operations, by trampling or the passage of wheeled vehicles, and to prevent excessive sand movement affecting nearby roads or buildings. Dune stabilisation can be achieved by the establishment of suitable plants but such plants are particularly sensitive to trampling (*see* Sections 3.3.3 and 6.7.1) at early stages of growth and thus access must be prevented or severely restricted while establishment is in progress.

A careful survey of the situation is necessary before such works are attempted, to select the most appropriate methods and materials for each situation. Questions to be asked include present and likely future sand movements, the occurrence and fluctuations of fresh and salt water as well as the chemistry of the substrate itself. The main steps in the assessment process are summarised in Figure 6.20. An understanding of the basic principles of sand dune growth and development is necessary for effective sand dune management. Further information can be obtained from ecological reference works (such as Boorman, 1977, Ranwell and Boar, 1986).

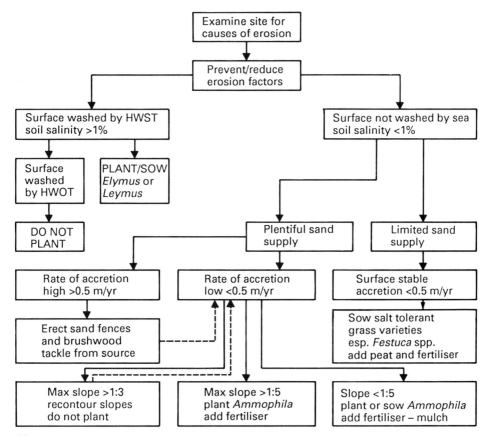

Notes
HWOT = high water ordinary tides; HWST = high water spring tides;
Elymus = *Elymus farctus* – sand couch; *Leymus* = *Leymus arenarius*
– lyme grass; salinity in % concentration of chloride ion, sea water
being approx. 3.5%; accretion refers to the potential for the site after
control of erosion.

Figure 6.20 A key to the selection of dune stabilisation techniques (after Boorman, 1977)

In the pioneer stages of dune growth, the low dunes may still be affected directly by sea water. Only specially adapted species are able to tolerate these conditions (*see* Appendix 1). These can spread horizontally but their ability to grow vertically and thus withstand rapid sand accretion is limited. The major dune building species in the UK is Marram Grass (*Ammophila arenaria*), which can withstand burial by sand at rates of up to a metre per year but cannot tolerate direct immersion in sea water. Once sand accretion falls to a low rate, other plant species are able to invade. Thus in dune situations where there is little or no accretion, salt-tolerant varieties of ordinary grasses can be used for sand stabilisation.

Dune grasses can be established by sowing seed, but it is usually necessary to stabilise the sand surface with chemical binders or an organic mulch. More often dune grasses are established by planting offsets. This can have the advantage of achieving an effective plant cover more quickly, and the young plants themselves help to stabilise the surface (*see* Section 4.5). The plants are usually set at 500 mm intervals, with the rows staggered to cover the gaps. Cuttings are obtained by the division of mature plants and should be planted 150–200 mm deep, as soon as possible; in any case the cuttings must be kept moist until planting. Planting is best done in the period mid-March to the end of April.

Dune sands usually have very low levels of the necessary plant nutrients especially nitrogen, and dune grasses respond well to the addition of fertilizer with up to 80 kg/ha of nitrogen.

If it is necessary to accumulate sand rapidly in a particular place, either to build dunes there or to prevent the sand moving elsewhere, then open-work fences of wattle, split chestnut or geotextile mesh can be used. These are set at right angles to the main direction of the wind and any necessary gaps are staggered. As the first fences become covered by sand, new ones will be needed. Any works to stop sand movement must be directed at the primary source of the sand to limit further activity.

If the mechanical reshaping of sand dunes is necessary, the new surface should be graded to a natural aerodynamic shape, with gentle slopes to reduce air turbulence and thus the possibility of further erosion.

Where public access cannot be restricted by the use of fencing, spiny shrubs (such as Sea Buckthorn, *see* Appendix 1) can be planted, to control erosion or to limit the extent of public access. Shrubs producing extensive rhizome systems can spread rapidly and should therefore be used with discretion.

In situations where sand movements have largely ceased, stabilisation can be achieved by the use of ordinary species of grass, although salt-tolerant strains may be needed. There are, however, special problems arising from the nature of sand as a substrate for plant growth. Although the plants will not have to withstand burial by sand, their growth will be limited by the low nutrient status and low water-holding capacity of the soil. Areas of bare sand have usually lost most of the soil organic material by windblow as the sand dries out. Special care therefore needs to be taken to improve the soil with organic matter and fertilisers, in order to encourage and maintain plant growth. Guidance is given in Sections 2.4.5 and 4.2.6, but specialist advice should be sought.

6.6 Vegetation barriers

In the context of the applications of vegetation, barriers are considered here for
two separate purposes:

1. shelter from wind, reducing the erosivity of wind and improving the
   microclimate;
2. reduction (or attenuation) of noise.

These are dealt with separately below. Barriers are used for other situations, of
course, such as visual screens on highways and as property boundaries. Hedgerows
in the UK are known to have existed for several hundred years and bear testimony
to the long-term effectiveness of vegetation management. They are an extremely
valuable ecological resource but, shelter and noise reduction apart, these uses are
not considered further here. The use of vegetation to reduce wind erosion of soil is
a special case of the general usefulness of vegetation to create barriers and is
discussed in Section 6.5.

6.6.1 Shelter from wind

Where long-term shelter or erosion control is desirable, for example around
buildings, alongside highways or to protect open, exposed ground, belts of trees
can be considered. The principal effect is a reduction in the velocity of the airflow
(Section 3.7.1 and Figure 3.22). However, the shelter in the lee of a windbreak also
produces a change in the microclimate, summarised in Figure 6.21; air and soil
temperature and humidity are increased, evapotranspiration is reduced. Away
from the immediate vicinity of the belt the combination of factors generally leads to
an increase in plant growth potential.

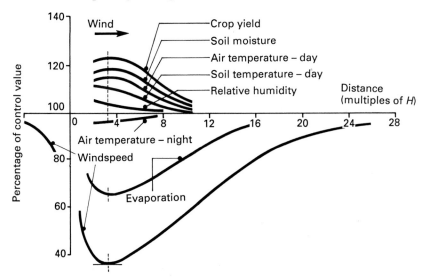

Figure 6.21 Effect of barriers on microclimate (after Marshall, 1967)

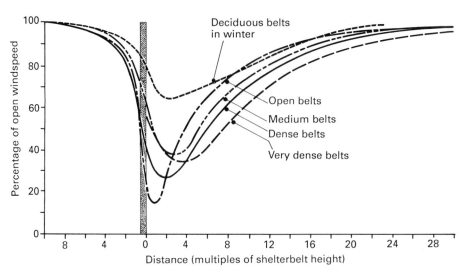

Figure 6.22 Wind abatement in the vicinity of shelterbelts of different density (after Caborn, 1965)

The effectiveness of a shelter belt is measured by the distance downwind at which wind velocity remains less than 80% of the open wind speed at the same height. This is affected by the height, width, length and shape of the barrier, and the resilience and porosity (or openness) of the vegetation. The wind abatement effect of barriers of different density is illustrated in Figure 6.22. Open belts give the greatest degree of shelter immediately downwind, but this effect lasts for only about nine times the shelterbelt height. Dense belts give protection over a greater distance, but produce eddying and downdraughts immediately downwind.

Tree belts at right angles to the wind afford protection for a distance theoretically seventeen times their height (17H) for open wind velocities up to 44 km/h (Woodruff and Zingg, 1952). This may be reduced to 12.5H in unstable air (Jacobs, 1984). In practice, variability in the growth, structure and maintenance of tree belts means that the effective shelter rarely exceeds 12H, provided that the length also exceeds 12H for barriers at right angles to the wind, or 24H for barriers at 45° to the wind (Bates, 1924; Bache and MacAskill, 1984).

Tree belts should rise sharply from the ground on the windward side, and have a degree of openness equivalent to about 50% porosity, to allow air to approach the barrier uniformly and be diffused through it. It should extend to the whole height of the barrier, which means including bushes and short trees to fill gaps between trees close to the ground surface. This is particularly important if the shelter belt is being used to control wind erosion because between 50 and 70% of wind-blown soil is moving within 1 m of the ground surface.

The Danish Land Development Service (Hedeselskabet) has developed a shelterbelt system to meet these design requirements, which is illustrated in Figure 6.23. It is based on mixing a variety of tree and bush species, adapted to the local

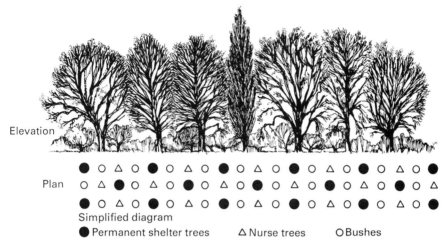

Elevation

Plan

Simplified diagram
● Permanent shelter trees   △ Nurse trees   ○ Bushes

Figure 6.23 Danish shelterbelt system (after Olesen, 1979)

soil and climatic conditions, planted in three rows at intervals of 1.25 to 1.5 m. It is also based on using a plant succession, to give an effective barrier within three years but with a life of 50 to 80 years. The belts comprise the following three groups of plants.

1. Nurse trees: these are fast growing, intended to give acceptable shelter after four or five years and, as a result, encourage the growth of the more durable trees.
2. Durable trees: these are tall and long-lived species designed to grow up with the nurse trees and to replace them when the latter are either felled or die.
3. Bushes: these are shade-tolerant, designed to provide undergrowth in the lower portion.

The moderate degree of permeability required suggests that narrow belts are the most effective. Often the width of multi-row belts is limited by the availability of land. Tanner and Naegeli (1947) suggest that low belts (about 5 m high) should be 2.5 m wide, whereas high belts (about 25 m high) should be 10-15 m wide. If windbreaks are too wide there is a tendency for the sheltered area to be reduced.

Tree shelterbelts can be applied to a variety of situations:

- buildings – as a windbreak to improve the microclimate and reduce heat loss
  – to reduce wind loading;
- farmland – for wind erosion control
  – to give shelter from exposure;
- highways – to control glare, especially in the central reservation
  – for snow control
  – as windbreaks, to check cross-wind gusts.

Vegetation barriers will also act as filters for gaseous and particulate pollutants, by encouraging deposition in the canopy (Bache, 1979). The design of barriers or belts for these situations can be quite complex; the possibilities are fully reviewed in Bache and MacAskill (1984).

Guidance on tree species for shelterbelts is given in Appendix 1, and generally species should be selected for the following characteristics:

1. pliable branches, able to bend with the wind and not break off;
2. deep widespread roots to provide firm anchorage;
3. conical or cylindrical shape, with branches spread up the whole trunk, avoiding large top-heavy crowns;
4. a degree of porosity (or openness) in the crown, especially during winter when windspeeds are higher;
5. tolerance of exposure, particularly wind; near the coast salt tolerance is also necessary.

Windthrow hazard should also be taken into account (*see* Section 2.5 on exposure). Evergreens are generally more vulnerable to toppling. To encourage deeper rooting, the ground must be well-drained and without any shallow impermeable soil horizons to restrict deep root growth. Many conifers are too dense to make good shelterbelts and may actually increase wind damage downwind due to funnelling effects.

6.6.2 Planting for noise reduction

Excessive noise is one of the most widespread social irritants and is particularly prevalent in the urban environment. Many studies have identified traffic noise as a major source of annoyance. Amongst the control measures, the placement of barriers between the source and the receiver represents a useful technique for modifying noise levels during transmission. Though artificial barriers are most often employed, there has been considerable interest in the use of vegetated barriers to act as acoustic buffer zones.

As discussed in Section 3.7.2, sound diminishes naturally with distance. In the context of traffic noise and under wind conditions favourable to the propagation of noise, the attenuation rate can be represented by:

$$dB(A) = -13.6 \log x + 20.1$$

where x (in m) is the distance from the nearside lane of the road. When the distance from the road is fully planted, the additional attenuation can be roughly represented by adding together the noise loss over the unobstructed distance and that due to the trees, i.e.

$$dB(A) = \frac{-nx}{100} - 13.6 \log x + 20.1$$

where n is the number of decibels of sound reduction per 100 m of planting. For example, when a reduction of 15 dB(A) is sought between a road carrying heavy traffic and a planned housing development, by means of a buffer zone, when trees are absent ($n = 0$), the necessary zone width is 400 m, whereas planting over the full

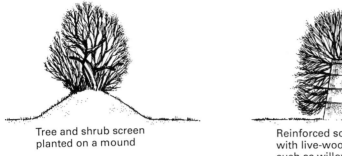

Tree and shrub screen
planted on a mound

Reinforced soil wall planted
with live-wood cuttings
such as willows

Figure 6.24 Types of barrier for shelter and noise attenuation

distance with trees characterised by $n = 3$ reduces the necessary buffer zone to
170 m.

The structure of the vegetation barrier will have a fundamental effect on the rate
of noise attenuation, though this is not allowed for in the theoretical equations.
Dense foliage right down to ground level will be most effective in absorbing,
reflecting and dispersing noise, but such conditions only occur at the edge of a
plantation. Simply increasing the width of the plantation, when this consists of an
open sub-canopy with stems or tree trunks only, will have relatively little additional
effect on noise attenuation. Most of the noise attenuation will occur at the vertical
barrier edge.

Dense hedges of quick-growing trees or shrubs are frequently used instead of
fences as noise barriers, as illustrated in Figure 6.24. Buffer plantings between 7
and 15 m in depth are also most effective and multiple barriers formed by planting
several rows or hedges together are a very good way of achieving dense growth
down to ground level throughout the depth of the buffer. A buffer should be
planted as close to the noise source as possible and, ideally, should be lower
towards the source and higher further away. This directs noise upwards and away
from the receiver. Similarly, planting on embankments or cuttings above a road is a
very effective means of reducing traffic noise.

6.7 Surface protection and trafficability

Vegetation can be used to protect surfaces against damage by pedestrian and
vehicular traffic. Its role is mainly that of cushioning and protecting the surface and
of reinforcing the surface layer of soil with roots, either alone or in combination
with inert reinforcing materials. As such, the functions are superficial to
engineering structures.

One interesting potential role of vegetation is to deflect traffic from protected
areas by making access difficult or unpleasant owing to texture or roughness. This
can be achieved by selecting plants with appropriate characteristics, such as spikes

and prickles, stiff woody stems, tussocky growth, tall, dense or many-branched growth form; and management such as infrequent mowing, or coppicing. This role, whilst of some application in visitor management, is not an engineering one and so is not considered further here.

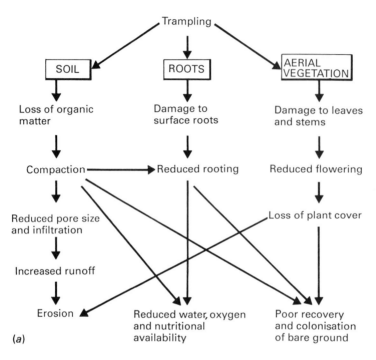

(a)

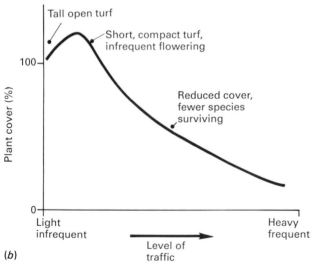

(b)

Figure 6.25 Effects of trampling on soil and vegetation

6.7.1 Damage to soils and vegetation by traffic

When a vegetated surface is heavily trampled there are a number of adverse effects on the soil, plant roots and shoots, which are illustrated in Figure 6.25. At very low levels of disturbance, trampling, like mowing, can stimulate plant growth by encouraging branching but the benefits of this are slight and, in practice damage, can usually be regarded as increasing progressively with the level of disturbance.

There are substantial differences in the way different plant communities respond to traffic and trampling. One effect is to eliminate sensitive species and favour more resistant ones, often with invasion by wear-tolerant species which might otherwise not occur. This process of replacement by resistant plants can actually result in a gradual improvement in vegetation cover after the initial damage.

The trafficability of any soil material is determined by its bearing capacity, which is a function of:

1. soil strength or cohesion
2. moisture content
3. organic matter content
4. density.

Deformation of the soil surface will result from both foot and wheeled traffic, by a combination of vertical compression and transverse slippage as a foot or wheel passes across (*see* Section 3.3.3). Figure 6.26 illustrates the tensile and compressive forces that a soil surface reinforced with a grass sward will be exposed to. If the bearing capacity is exceeded by the traction force, then severe deformation will occur.

The crushing and shearing forces exerted by traffic vary both with the type of traffic and the activity involved. Types of impact range from simple crushing and compaction of soils and vegetation to impaction of tread patterns, rutting and various combinations of damage, summarised in Table 6.3). Heavy vehicles are not always the most damaging, since a large wheel surface area can greatly reduce point loadings. However some tracked vehicles with low ground pressure, such as ski piste machines, can still cause extensive cutting damage to soils and vegetation by grips that penetrate the surface. The compaction effect of even low-pressure vehicles such as agricultural tractors can still be considerable. Reaves and Cooper

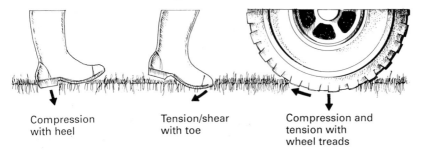

Compression
with heel

Tension/shear
with toe

Compression and
tension with
wheel treads

Figure 6.26 Forces exerted on a soil surface by traffic

Table 6.3 Types of damage under different forms of traffic

	Soil compaction/ vegetation	Root or shoot	Tread impaction	Rutting
Walkers – flat shoes	+			
Walkers – vibram soles	+		+	
Skiers		+		
Horses, cattle, sheep	+	+	+	
Motor cycles	+		+	+
Balloon-tyre cross-country vehicles	+			
Piste machines	+	+ +		
Cars, vans, 4-wheel drive vehicles	+ +		+ +	+ +
Heavy tracked vehicles	+ +	+ +	+ +	+ +

(+, light; + +, heavy effect) The severity of impact will depend a great deal on vegetation type and soil and moisture conditions (*see* Box 6.20)

(1960) detected stresses imposed by tractor wheels to a depth of 1.1 m, and Soane (1970) concluded that compaction problems arise with practically every type of agricultural vehicle.

The impact of pedestrians and animals tends to be more superficial than those of vehicles, but can be locally very damaging when use is concentrated. Feet and hooves can exert remarkably high static and torque forces on the ground, which can sometimes equal or even exceed those of vehicles. Static forces range up to about $40 \, kN/m^2$ for pedestrians, $100 \, kN/m^2$ for cattle and $150 \, kN/m^2$ for a small car, with much higher point loadings possible during movement.

The nature of traffic or trampling damage can take two forms.

1. A short-duration, high level of traffic with an intensive force, such as a large wheeled vehicle; there may be long periods between use when recovery can take place or remedial work undertaken. In this case a fairly high tensile strength in the surface root mat and foliage is required to protect the soil.
2. A long-duration or regular but relatively light level of traffic, such as on a footpath; periods of recovery may be quite short. In this case durability and rate of recovery become important factors, and tensile strength less so.

Damage to the soil surface will result in overall loss of traction, itself an undesirable consequence in footpaths, roadways and sports pitches. Compaction and smearing of the soil lead to further problems with impeded drainage and loss of soil productivity. In addition, exposed or loosened soil may be eroded by wind or water, leading to extensive further damage in heavily trafficked areas.

The relative trafficability of soil can be estimated from its depth and properties, described in Box 6.20. Van Wijk (1984) suggests that to prevent top layer deformation of sports pitches receiving moderately heavy wear, penetration resistance of $1 \, MN/m^2$ is required (measured using a cone of $60°$ angle and $100 \, m^2$ base), or $1.4 \, MN/m^2$ for intensive wear. He also reports that the contribution of roots of a grass sward to penetration resistance can be in the order of

Box 6.20 Estimation of trafficability of a grass sward surface (after Jarvis and Mackney, 1979)

Wetness class[1]	Depth to impermeable layer (mm)	Climate					
		Dry			Moist		
		Moisture content at FC[2]			Moisture content at FC[2]		
		Low	Medium	High	Low	Medium	High
C	>800	1	1	1	1	2	2
	800–400	1	1	2	2	2	3
B	>800	1	2	2	3	3	3
	800–400	2	2	3	3	3	4
	<400	3	3	4	4	4	5
A	>800	4	4	5	5	5	5
	800–400	5	5	5	5	5	5
	<400	5	5	5	5	5	5

Trafficability and damage risk categories are as follows:

Category	Trafficability	Damage risk
1	Very high	Very low
2	High	Low
3	Moderate	Moderate
4	Low	High
5	Very low	Very high

Notes
1. Wetness classes: refer to Figure 2.14
2. Moisture content at field capacity, FC (*see* Box 2.6):

Low	<35%
Medium	35–45%
High	>45%

0.8–1.6 MN/m^2. Canaway (1975) found that the torque to cause shear in turf ranged from about 50 to 80 Nm, with significant differences between species and turfgrass mixtures. Turf strength can often be related to the biomass of the roots and rhizomes, but is also dependent on root tensile strength, which varies between species, with season and with stage of plant development.

6.7.2 Species that tolerate wear

Plant characteristics that tend to make them resistant to wear include:

1. short or prostrate growth form;
2. stems and leaves that are flexible rather than brittle or rigid;
3. basal or underground growth points;
4. ability to spread vegetatively as well as by seeds;
5. a deciduous growth habit;

6. a rapid rate of growth;
7. a long growth period;
8. ability to withstand burial by soil or rock or exposure of the root system.

Grasses have many of these characteristics, but there are also many herbs with rosette or creeping growth forms that are tolerant of trampling. Many annual plants (ruderals, *see* Section 2.2.4) colonise disturbed patches of ground very quickly and are also very useful for areas subject to wear. Wear-tolerant species of different habitats in the UK are given in Appendix 1.

It is often desirable to plant or seed with species mixtures that are visually attractive ('amenity' mixtures including wild flowers – *see* Nature Conservancy Council, 1981, 1986) or mixtures that resemble the vegetation of the surrounding ground (for example in moorland situations). Many of these species will not establish where much trampling occurs, but may manage to grow under conditions of light disturbance. They tend to be most successful under conditions of low to moderate fertility, whereas trampling resistance tends to be assisted by fertiliser application. There are thus potential conflicts of interest in managing for both amenity and wear-tolerance.

6.7.3 Techniques to increase wear resistance

Improving drainage, thereby reducing soil moisture content and increasing soil strength, has an immediate benefit on surface trafficability. The timing of traffic or vehicle movements to coincide with periods when the soil is drier and to avoid periods when it is wet, has the same effect. Specific techniques to increase the trafficability of the vegetation are described below.

The resistance of vegetation to wear can often be increased by applying fertilisers. Low nitrogen, slow-release fertilisers are widely used (Section 4.2.6). This increases the rate of growth of the plants and reduces the time taken to recover from damage. Other management techniques to improve plant vigour, that have been mainly used for camp sites in the USA, include drainage of wet ground, watering during dry spells, and restricting use to permit partial recovery (Hammitt and Cole, 1987).

Modifying soil structure by adding organic matter (peat or alginates) or sand, can improve bearing properties, aeration and plant rooting. Reinforcement geotextile and perforated plastic and concrete cribs or blocks will give added tensile strength to the root mat and can reduce much of the direct mechanical disturbance of plants and soil, as illustrated in Figure 6.27. Examples of these techniques are given in the following pages.

6.7.4 Footpaths

The criteria for species selection are wear resistance, appearance and use deflection. Ground preparation should include landscaping, to concentrate use on a well-drained stable path surface; path margins vegetated with trample-resistant species. Cost is 0.2–0.6 £/m^2 (vegetation).

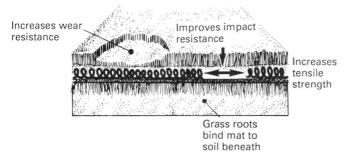

Increases wear resistance

Improves impact resistance

Increases tensile strength

Grass roots bind mat to soil beneath

Figure 6.27 Roles of reinforcement geotextiles in surface protection

Vegetation cover can rarely be maintained in the centre of paths unless the traffic is light, or ground conditions are ideal (i.e. well-established short-turf grassland on freely-drained, fertile soil over a stable, broken rock or gravel subgrade). It is usually feasible, however, to construct or reconstruct paths with a discrete wearing surface of wood, stone or gravel, and with wear-resistant vegetation on either side, as shown in Figure 6.28. In the case of new paths, any excavated turves should be retained and transplanted along the path margins. Any surviving turves on reconstructed paths should be similarly recycled, and remaining bare ground seeded.

Lightly-used paths or the margins of heavily-used ones can be reinforced with a three-dimensional geotextile (*see* Appendix 2) embedded in the soil surface. This gives extra resistance to wear and damage when the soil itself is in a poor condition, for example, very wet. This technique is prone to problems with exposure of the geotextile, however, which subsequently snags and pulls out if wear is locally heavy enough to remove the turf and soil covering.

6.7.5 Car parks and vehicular access areas

The criterion for species selection is wear resistance. Ground preparation should include soil reinforcement with cellular concrete load-bearing blocks. Light reinforcement with geotextile mesh may be sufficient in occasionally used areas. Costs are approximately:

5–20 £/m^2 (total)
0.4–0.6 £/m^2 (vegetation).

In areas used by wheeled traffic, vegetation on its own is rarely sufficient to protect the surface, unless the ground beneath is very stable. Well-drained firm soils of high bearing strength will sometimes be suitable for use by light vehicular traffic, with a cover of durable perennial grasses. Maintenance will consist of dressings of fertiliser to maintain vigour and resting areas where wear becomes excessive.

Where the soil is of insufficient bearing strength or traffic is too heavy or frequent, soil reinforcement may be necessary. Reinforcement can take the form of

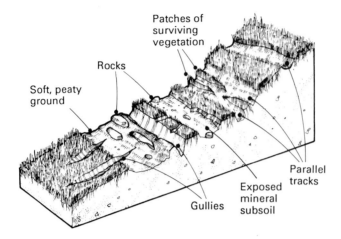

Patches of
surviving
vegetation

Rocks

Soft, peaty
ground

Parallel
tracks

Exposed
mineral
subsoil

Gullies

(a) Badly worn footpath

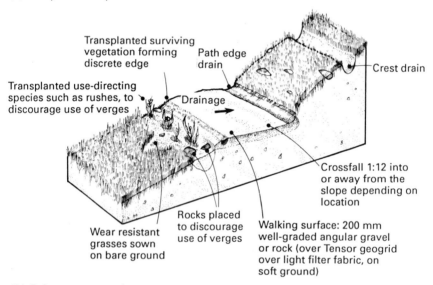

Transplanted surviving
vegetation forming
discrete edge

Path edge
drain

Crest drain

Transplanted use-directing
species such as rushes, to
discourage use of verges

Drainage

Crossfall 1:12 into
or away from the
slope depending on
location

Wear resistant
grasses sown
on bare ground

Rocks placed
to discourage
use of verges

Walking surface: 200 mm
well-graded angular gravel
or rock (over Tensor geogrid
over light filter fabric, on
soft ground)

(b) Reinstatement works

Figure 6.28 Footpath restoration in heavily used recreation areas

steel or plastic meshes, laid on the surface or just below the surface to spread the
load, or cellular concrete or plastic blocks that act as the bearing surface, with
vegetation filling the interstices. It is advisable for such blocks to be laid over
well-graded angular gravel or broken rock to provide a firm base. The interstices,
however, should be filled with free-draining soil to provide a good rooting medium,
and seeded with durable grasses or a grass-herb mixture, as illustrated in Figure
6.29.

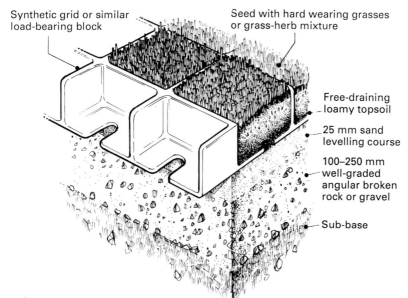

Synthetic grid or similar
load-bearing block

Seed with hard wearing grasses
or grass-herb mixture

Free-draining
loamy topsoil

25 mm sand
levelling course

100–250 mm
well-graded
angular broken
rock or gravel

Sub-base

Note Similar ground preparation applies to perforated
concrete slabs

Figure 6.29 Reinforcement of soils for heavy pedestrian or light vehicular traffic using plastic grids

6.7.6 Country parks, campsites, around buildings

The criteria for species selection are wear resistance, appearance, use deflection. Ground preparation ranges from simple seedbed preparation to soil amendment or reinforcement. Costs are very variable.

Heavily trampled ground around buildings, play areas, camp sites, gateways and stiles can be reinforced with cellular concrete blocks or with boardwalks, slab or stone-vegetation mosaics, as shown in Figure 6.30. Landscaping to channel use to reinforced or wear tolerant areas can be valuable. This can range from planting areas of coarse, tussocky grasses to spiny or bushy shrubs and trees (these may need fencing until established). Management can include watering in dry weather, the addition of fertiliser and seed to bare patches, and periodic resting from use (Hammitt and Cole, 1987).

6.8 Control of runoff in small catchments

This section deals with hydrological aspects of vegetation and erosion control in small catchments, such as construction sites and mineral workings. Uncontrolled water runoff can have serious consequences in the form of:

1. scour and erosion of soil material;
2. downstream pollution by suspended solids;

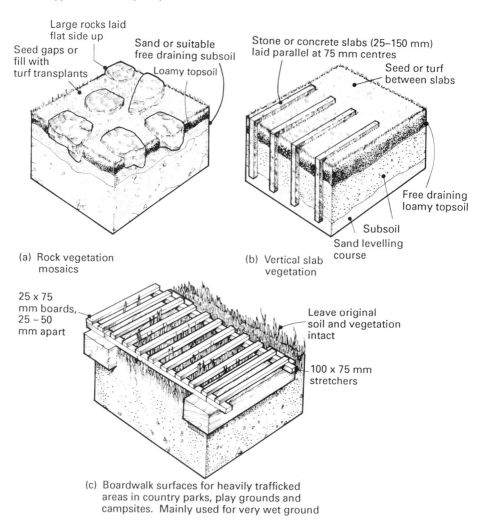

Large rocks laid
flat side up
Seed gaps or
fill with
turf transplants
Sand or suitable
free draining subsoil
Loamy topsoil

Stone or concrete slabs (25–150 mm)
laid parallel at 75 mm centres
Seed or turf
between slabs

Free draining
loamy topsoil

Subsoil
Sand levelling
course

(a) Rock vegetation
     mosaics

(b) Vertical slab
     vegetation

25 x 75
mm boards,
25 – 50
mm apart

Leave original
soil and vegetation
intact

100 x 75 mm
stretchers

(c) Boardwalk surfaces for heavily trafficked
     areas in country parks, play grounds and
     campsites. Mainly used for very wet ground

Figure 6.30 Reinforcement of swards for heavily trampled areas

3. rapid concentration of runoff from heavy rainfall leading to downstream
   flooding.

A widely-used solution to these problems is to construct flood attenuation and
sediment settlement lagoons at the outfalls of a site, before drainage water is
discharged to a normal watercourse. These may need to be very large to cater for
rapid runoff and erosion.

The establishment of vegetation on completed construction areas is usually
considered vital for controlling runoff, erosion and sediment. However, vegetation
can also play a useful role during the construction itself, in reducing the size of
attenuation lagoons. This can be achieved in two ways:

1. temporary seeding of bare areas, using quick-growing species (such as ryegrass or a cereal crop);
2. leaving the existing vegetation in place until the last moment, and not stripping turf too far in advance.

The effect of vegetation on soil erosion and thus on sediment yield has been discussed extensively elsewhere (*see* Section 3.3 and Section 6.3). The procedures for modelling erosion (*see* Box 6.13) can also be used to assess the sediment loading of runoff water.

The effect of vegetation on the balance of moisture in the soil, as a function of gross rainfall input, interception by the canopy and evapotranspiration via the roots and leaves, is to create a soil moisture deficit (*see* Section 3.4.2). The deeper the roots, the greater the potential deficit. From the hydrological point of view, this is extremely important because the soil moisture deficit (SMD) serves as a buffer against runoff, reducing overland flow by facilitating greater infiltration and soil storage.

Table 6.4 shows an example of a schematic calculation of the relationship between monthly rainfall, potential evapotranspiration and the type of cover, insofar as they influence the soil moisture deficit and the drainage (*see* Section 3.4.2; Figure 2.18). No distinction is made between drainage by deep percolation and that by overland flow, but it can be seen that most drainage occurs from bare soil and least from terrain with deep-rooted vegetation.

Land cover effects are included in procedures used for estimating peak runoff discharge. For small catchments the Rational method is often sufficient for design

Table 6.4 Effect of vegetation cover on soil/water relationships (after Bache and MacAskill, 1984)

Month	R (mm)	E_t (mm)	$R-E_t$	C = 200 mm deficit	drainage	C = 75 mm deficit	drainage	Bare soil deficit	drainage
March*									
April	23	50	−27	27		27		25	
May	51	81	−30	57		57		25	
June	12	95	−83	140		111		25	
July	72	100	−28	168		145		25	
Aug	48	76	−28	196		116		25	
Sept	52	53	−1	197		116		25	
Oct	109	29	+80	117		36			55
Nov	65	8	+57	60			21		57
Dec	66	7	+59	1			59		59
Jan	106	11	+95		94		95		95
Feb	22	18	+4		4		4		4
March	16	26	−10	10		10		10	
Year	642	554			98		179		270

* Assumed that there is no deficit at the end of the month.

C is the root constant (*see* Section 3.4; Table 3.3), taken as C = 200 mm for long-rooted vegetation (such as trees) and C = 75 mm for short-rooted vegetation (such as grass).

Box 6.21 The Rational method for estimating runoff

Suitable for catchments up to 25 km² in rural areas. The peak runoff rate, Q, is

$Q = 0.278\ CIA$ m³/s

where C is the runoff coefficient, I the rainfall intensity (mm/hr) and A is the area (km²).

The runoff coefficient depends on catchment characteristics and expresses some of the storage effects of a catchment in attentuating flood peaks. Dunne and Leopold (1973) list accepted ranges of C for urban and suburban areas; for rural areas, Schwab *et al.* (1966) give a procedure for estimating C for various soil-vegetation combinations. A rough guide is as follows:

Values of the Rational runoff coefficient, C

	Watershed cover		
Soil type	Cultivated	Grass	Trees
Sandy and gravelly soils	0.20	0.15	0.10
Loams and similar soils without impeding horizons	0.40	0.35	0.30
Heavy clay soils or those with a shallow impeding horizon; shallow soils covering bedrock	0.50	0.45	0.40

Where a catchment consists of several soils and vegetation combinations, C can be weighted according to the proportion of the area under each type.

The appropriate rainfall intensity, I, is chosen with reference to the recurrence interval of the storm to be designed for, a duration equal to the time of concentration for the catchment, i.e. the time required for overland and channel flow to reach the outlet from the hydraulically most distant part, which can be estimated in a variety of ways (Bache and MacAskill, 1984).

purposes, as shown in Box 6.21. More complex procedures have been developed which model the actual situation much more closely, such as that of the US Soil Conservation Service (1972) (see also Bache and MacAskill, 1984). However the Rational method is still in widespread use and is simple to apply. The duration of the design storm, required for estimating the rainfall intensity, I, in the Rational method, refers to the time of concentration of the catchment. Generally, when the time of concentration is increased through infiltration and reduction in the velocity of overland flow due to drag, the peak flow is reduced (*see* Figure 3.2).

The above discussion only aims to remind the reader of basic principles of hydrological design. These are fully explained in standard hydrology texts, notably Dunne and Leopold (1973), Gray (1970), US Soil Conservation Service (1972) and Bache and MacAskill (1984).

6.9 Plants as indicators

In Section 2 the importance of the environment, notably the soil conditions, in determining the occurrence and distribution of different plant species was stressed. It therefore also follows that the composition of the vegetation can be used to interpret or delineate the nature and characteristics of an area. It should be stressed that using plants as indicators in this way requires a reasonable understanding of the ecology of the plants concerned, and sometimes very complex plant/environment interactions can be involved.

Vegetation can 'indicate' site conditions in a number of ways:

1. the presence of particular indicator species for certain conditions, such as wetness or soil chemistry;
2. the absence of particular sensitive species to similar conditions;
3. the overall density or vigour of the plants, particularly plants under stress from drought, contamination, etc.;
4. variation in the overall structure and composition of the plant community, reflecting variation in the soil or climatic environment.

At its very simplest, plants are used as indicators during a site investigation by observing the naturally occurring species to see which might be the appropriate ones to introduce during revegetation. In doing so however, care should be taken to include investigation of the soils concerned, and whether the engineered soil formation will differ in terms of fertility, acidity and water relationships. The existing management of, or interference with, the vegetation should also be noted, particularly whether the area has been grazed.

Local variation in the nature of vegetation usually reflects changes in the underlying soils and therefore rocks. This can be a considerable help when mapping the geology or soils, provided that variations due to management, microclimate or biological cycles are taken into account. Differences in the ground conditions that can be mapped in this way include:

1. changes in the underlying rock type, particularly between alkaline and acidic rocks;
2. changes in the depth or nature of soil/drift material;
3. variations in soil moisture and subsurface hydrology.

A specific example of mapping geological conditions is bio-geochemical reconnaisance, i.e. using plants as an aid to mineral prospecting. Plants are very sensitive to the presence of metals in the soil and there are a number of characteristic 'metallophyte' species. These are used widely by geologists as an aid during preliminary prospecting activities. As well as the presence or absence of particular species, the plants themselves can be chemically analysed for metals, and a metal 'shadow' can often be detectable when the ore is buried several metres below the surface.

Soil moisture is perhaps the most useful and easily interpreted vegetation characteristic. The soil moisture regime, including seasonal variations, is a major determinant in the colonisation and development of different species. The kind of conditions which can be interpreted using vegetation include:

1. very drought-prone soils, suggesting thin, rocky or highly permeable strata;
2. continually wet or boggy areas, suggesting a high groundwater level;
3. wet flushes, springs, or seepage patches in an otherwise well-drained area;

4. seasonally or periodically flooded areas, for example delineating bankside zonation and thus frequency of inundation (*see* Section 6.4).

The presence of rushes, for instance, indicates a high soil moisture content. This can be due to either a high groundwater level, seepage, or impeded drainage resulting from soil compaction.

Vegetation that is showing signs of distress, (e.g. die-back, loss of foliage colouring and decreased vigour) often indicates a recent change in ground conditions. Examples of this include:

1. changes in the groundwater regime or level;
2. chemical pollution due to contaminated ground or surface waters or to aerial deposition;
3. gaseous pollution such as methane from decomposing buried wastes (which may be migrating some distance through the subsurface strata).

On slopes which have gradually or in the past undergone movement, the inclination of the surface may have changed. Trees and shrubs growing on such slopes will therefore show signs of having changed their vertical orientation, with curved or kinked stems. The nature and location of kinks in the main stem, relative to the overall age of the plant, will often give clues to the past history of any slope movements.

There are two principal approaches to plotting the distribution of vegetation which can help to interpret contemporary or past site conditions.

1. Ground reconnaisance. Individual species, distributions and growth characteristics can be noted. Quantitative techniques, using quadrats and transects to sample, describe and analyse the vegetation cover systematically, can be used to distinguish finer variations or gradients in plant communities.
2. Aerial survey. The spatial pattern and distribution in vegetation type and cover can be easily mapped using aerial photography. This will only distinguish visual differences in the density, appearance and texture of the vegetation, and should therefore be calibrated by ground reconnaisance. The use of colour, false colour, infra-red and multi-spectral scanning (e.g. remote sensing) techniques will help to define or enhance the recognition of differences in vegetation, although these should be used with care.

Using vegetation as an indicator is rarely a definitive method of determining site conditions. Its main use is as an aid to investigation or mapping, alerting the investigator to certain possible conditions, which then need more intensive survey or investigation using normal techniques. It is thus a means of gathering useful preliminary information or extending a more conventional survey using relatively cheap and simple sampling techniques.

Bibliography and References

Agricultural Development Advisory Service (ADAS) (1981) *The analysis of agricultural materials.* RB427, HMSO, London

Allen, S. E. (1974) Editor *Chemical analysis of ecological materials.* Blackwell, Oxford

Anderson, M. G., Hubberd, M. G. and Kneale, P. E. (1982) The influence of shrinkage cracks on pore-water pressures within a clay embankment. *Q. J. Engng. Geol.* London, **15** (1), 9–14

Anon. (1973) *Erosion control on highway construction.* National Cooperative Highway Research Program, Synthesis of highway practice No. 18, Highway Research Board, National Academy of Sciences, Washington DC

Armstrong, C. L. and Mitchell, J. K. (1987) Transformations of rainfall by plant canopy. *Trans. Am. Soc. Agric. Engnrs.* **30** (3), 688–696

Bache, D. H. (1979) Particulate transport in plant canopies. 11. Prediction of deposition velocities. *Atmospheric Environment,* **13**, 1681–1687

Bache, D. H. (1986) Momentum transfer to plant canopies: influence of structure and variable drag. *Atmospheric Environment,* **20** (7), 1369–1378

Bache, D. H. and MacAskill, I. A. (1984) *Vegetation in civil and landscape engineering.* Granada Publishing, London

Bache, D. H. and MacAskill, I. A. (1987) Vegetation in coastal and stream-bank protection. *Landscape Planning,* **8**, 363–385

Bagnold, R. A. (1941) *The physics of blown sand and desert dunes.* Chapman and Hall, London

Barker, D. H. (1986a) The enhancement of slope stability by vegetation. *Ground Engineering,* April, 11–15

Barker, D. H. (1986b) Biodegradable geotextiles for erosion control and slope stabilisation. *Civil Engineering,* June, 13–15

Barker, D. H. (1988) Geotextiles in slope protection and erosion control. *Civil Engineering,* March, 52–55

Bates, C. G. (1924) *The windbreak as a farm asset.* Farmers' Bulletin 1405, US Department of Agriculture

Beckett, K. and Beckett, G. (1979) *Planting native trees and shrubs.* Jarrold, Norwich

Bendelow V. C. and Hartnup, R. (1980) *Climatic classification of England and Wales.* Technical monograph 15, Soil Survey of England and Wales, Harpenden

Biddle, P. G. (1983) Patterns of soil drying and moisture deficit in the vicinity of trees on clay soils. *Geotechnique,* **33** (2), 107–126

Birse, E. L. (1971) *Assessment of climatic conditions in Scotland.* Macaulay Institute for Soil Research, Aberdeen

Birse, E. L. and Dry, F. T. (1970) *Assessment of climatic conditions in Scotland.* Macaulay Institute for Soil Research, Aberdeen

Bishop, A. W. (1955) The use of slip circle in the stability of earth slopes. *Geotechnique,* **5**, 7–17

Bishop, D. M. and Stevens, M. E. (1964) *Landslips on logged areas in Southeast Alaska.* US Department of Agriculture Forest Service Research Paper NOR-1,18

Bohm, W. (1979) *Methods of studying root systems.* Springer-Verlag

Bonham, A. J. (1980) *Bank protection using emergent plants against boatwash in rivers and canals.* Report IT206, Hydraulic Research, Wallingford

Bonham, A. J. (1983) The management of wave-spreading vegetation as bank protection against boat wash. *Landscape Planning,* **10** (1), 15–30

Boorman, L. A. (1977) Sand dunes. In *The coastline* (ed. R. S. K. Barnes), Wiley, London, 161–197

Bradshaw, A. D. and Chadwick, M. J. (1980) *The restoration of land.* Blackwell, Oxford

Branson, F. A., Gifford, G. F. and Owen, J. R. (1972) *Rangeland hydrology.* Society for Range Management, Range Science Series, No. 1

Brechtel, A. M. and Hammes, W. (1985) Influence of vegetation cover on the soil water relations, with special consideration of soil consistency on slopes. In *Ingenieurbiologie; Wurzelwerk und Standsicherheit von Böschungen und Hängen.* Jahrbuch 2 (1985) der Gesellschaft für Ingenieurbiologie, Sepia Verlag, Aachen

Brenner, R. P. and James, S. M. (1977) *Effect of roots on the shear strength of a colluvial soil.* Proc. 5th Danube European Conf. Soil Mech. and Foundation Engng, Bratislava, 77–98

British Railways Board (1985) *The management of lineside vegetation; a guide to good practice.* Civil Engineering Department Handbook No. 43. British Railways Board, London

British Waterways Board (1986) *Reinforced vegetative bank protection.* Internal report, Birmingham Area Engineer

Bromhead, E. N. (1986) *The stability of slopes.* Surrey University Press, Guildford

Brown, C. B. and Sheu, M. S. (1975) Effects of deforestation on slopes. *J. Geotech. Engng. Div. ASCE,* **101** (GT2), Feb. 147–165

Building Research Establishment (1987) *The influence of trees on house foundations in clay soils.* Digest 298, BRE, Watford

Burroughs, E. R. and Thomas, B. R. (1977) *Declining root strength in Douglas fir after felling as a factor in slope stability.* Research Paper INT-190, Intermountain Forest and Range Experiment Station, US Department of Agriculture Forest Service, Ogden, Utah

C.C.S. (1985) *Plants and planting methods.* Lochshore Management Information Sheets, Section 6, Countryside Commission for Scotland, Perth

C.P.S.E. (1985) *Code of Practice for Plant handling.* Committee for Plant Supply and Establishment, c/o H.T.A., 19 High Street, Theale, Reading RG7 5AH

Caborn, J. M. (1965) *Shelterbelts and windbreaks.* Faber and Faber, London

Canaway, P. M. (1975) Fundamental techniques in the study of turfgrass wear; an advance report on research. *J. Sports Turf Res. Inst.* **51**, 104–115

Cannell, M. G. R. (1982) *World forest biomass and primary production data,* Academic Press, London

Carter, M. (1983) *Geotechnical engineering handbook.* Pentech, Plymouth

Chandler, T. J. and Gregory, S. (1976) *The climate of the British Isles.* Longman, London

Chang, T. T. (1972) A study on the tensile stress of root systems for conservation grasses in Taiwan. *J. Chinese Soil & Wat. Conserv. Taiwan,* 3(1), 58–81

Charutamra, D. (1981) *Vegetation and the stability of earth slopes.* MSc thesis, University of Strathclyde, Glasgow

Chepil, W. S. and Woodruff, N. P. (1963) The physics of wind erosion and its control. *Advances in Agronomy,* **15**, 211–302

Clarke, R. T. and Newson, M. D. (1978) Some related water balance studies on research catchments. *Proc. Royal Soc. Lond.* (A), **363**, 21–42

Clayton, C. R. T. and Milititsky, J. (1986) *Earth pressure and earth retaining systems.* Surrey University Press, Guildford

Colwill, D. M., Thomson, J. R. and Rutter, A. J. (1982) *An assessment for the conditions of shrubs alongside motorways.* TRRL Laboratory Report 1061, Department of the Environment, London

Cook, D. I. and van Haverbeke, D. F. (1970) Trees and shrubs for noise abatement. *Proc. Symp. on Trees and Forests in an Urbanizing Environment, University of Massachusetts, Boston*

Coppin, N. J. and Bradshaw, A. D. (1982) *Quarry reclamation – the establishment of vegetation in quarries and open pit non-metal mines.* Mining Journal Books Ltd., London

Countryside Commission (1980) *Grassland establishment for countryside recreation.* Advisory Series No. 13, Countryside Commission, Cheltenham

Dawson, F. H. and Haslam, S. M. (1983) The management of river vegetation with particular reference to standing effects of marginal vegetation. *Landscape Planning,* **10**, 147–169

De Beer, E. and Carpenter, T. (1977) Methods to estimate lateral force acting on stabilizing piles, soils and foundations. *Jap. Soc. Soil Mech. & Foundation Engng.* 17(1), 68–82.

De Ploey, J., Savat, J. and Moeyersons, J. (1976) The differential impact of some soil factors on flow, runoff creep and rainwash. *Earth Surface Processes,* **1**, 151–161

Department of Transport (1978) *Reinforced earth retaining walls and bridge abutments for embankments.* Technical Memorandum (Bridges) BE 3/78, Department of Transport, London

Doorenbos, J. and Pruitt, W. O. (1977) *Guidelines for predicting crop water requirements.* Irrigation and Drainage Paper No. 24 (revised edition), Food and Agriculture Organisation, Rome

Dunne, T. and Leopold, L. B. (1973) *Water in environmental planning.* W. H. Freeman and Company, San Francisco

Elias, C. O. and Chadwick, M. J. (1979) Growth characteristics of grass and legume cultivars and their potential for land reclamation. *J. Appl. Ecol,* **16**, 537–544

Endo, T. (1980) Effect of tree roots upon the shear strength of soil. *Jap. Agri. Res. Q.* **14**, 112–115

Endo, T. and Tsuruta, T. (1969) *On the effect of tree roots upon the shearing strength of soil.* Annual Report of the Hokkaido Branch, Forest Place Experimental Station, Sapporo, Japan, 167–183

Etherington, J. R. (1982) *Environment and plant ecology* 2nd ed. Wiley, Chichester

Fellenius, W. (1936) Calculation of the stability of earth dams. *Trans. 2nd Congress on Large Dams.* Washington DC, **4**, 445–459

Felt, E. J. (1953) Influence of vegetation on soil moisture contents and resulting volume change. *Proc. 3rd Int. Conf. Soil Mech. Found. Eng.,* Zurich, **1**, 24–27

Finney, H. J. (1984) The effect of crop covers on rainfall characteristics and splash detachment. *J. Agri. Engng. Res.* **29**, 337–343

Garwood, E. A. (1967a) Seasonal variation in appearance and growth of grass roots. *J. British Grassland Soc.* **22**(2)

Garwood, E. A. (1967b) Studies on the roots of grasses. *Ann. Rep. Grassland Res. Inst.* **166**, 72–79

Garwood, E. A. and Williams, T. E. (1967) Soil water use and growth of a grass sward. *J. Agri. Soc. Camb.* **68**, 281–292

Gerald, C. J., Sexton, P. and Shaw, G. (1932) Physical factors influencing soil strength and root growth. *Agronomy J.* **74**, 875–879

Gill, C. J. (1977) Some aspects of the design and management of reservoir margins for multiple use. *Applied Biology,* **2**, 129–132

Gray, D. H. (1970) Effects of forest clear-cutting on the stability of natural slopes. *Bull. Assoc. Engng. Ecol.* 7(1), 45–61

Gray, D. H. (1978) Role of woody vegetation in reinforcing soils and stabilizing slopes. *Proc. Symp. Soil Reinforcing and Stabilizing Techniques in Engineering Practice,* NSW Inst. Tech., Sydney, Australia, 253–306

Gray, D. H. and Leiser, A. J. (1982) *Biotechnical slope protection and erosion control.* Van Nostrand Reinhold, New York

Gray, D. H. (1977) *Creep movement and soil moisture stress in forested versus cutover slopes: results of field studies.* Final Report ENG 74-02427, University of Michigan, Ann Arbor, Michigan

Gray, D. H. and Megahan, W. F. (1981) *Forest vegetation removal and slope stability in the Idaho Batholith.* Research Paper INT-271, Intermountain Forest and Range Experiment Station, Ogden, Utah

Greenway, D. R. (1985) *Tree root study at So Uk Estate.* Advisory Report ADR 4/85, Geotechnical Control Office, Hong Kong

Greenway, D. R., Anderson, M. G. and Brian-Boys, K. C. (1984) Influence of vegetation on slope stability in Hong Kong. *Proc. 4th Int. Symp. Landslides. Canadian Geotechnical Society, Toronto,* **1**, 399–404

Greenway, D. R. (1987) Vegetation and slope stability. In Anderson, M. G. and Richards, K. S. (eds.), *Slope stability,* Wiley, Chichester, 187–230

Greenwood, J. R. (1983) A simple approach to slope stability. *Ground Engineering,* **16**(4), 45–98

Greenwood, J. R. (1986) Stability analysis of reinforced slopes. *J. Inst. Highways and Transport,* 26–27

Greenwood, J. R., Holt, D. A. and Herrick, G. W. (1985) Shallow slips in highway embankments constructed of overconsolidated clay. *Proc. Symp. Failures in Earthworks,* Paper 6, 79–92, I.C.E., London

Gregory, J. M. and McCarty, T. R. (1986) Maximum allowable velocity prediction for vegetated waterways. *Trans. Am. Soc. Agri. Engnrs.,* **29**, 748–755

Grime, J. P. (1979) *Plant strategies and vegetation processes.* Wiley, Chichester

Grime, J. P., Hodgson, J. G. and Hunt, R. (1988) *Comparative plant ecology.* Allen and Unwin, London

Grindley, J. (1969) *The calculation of actual evaporation and soil moisture deficit over specified catchment areas.* Hydrological Memorandum No. 38, Meteorological Office, Bracknell

Hall, D. G. M., Reeve, M. J., Thomasson, A. J. and Wright, V. F. (1977) *Water retention, porosity and density of field soils.* Technical Monograph 9, Soil Survey of England and Wales, Harpenden

Hammitt, W. E. and Cole, D. N. (1987) *Wildland recreation, ecology and management.* Wiley, Chichester

Haslam, S. M. (1978) *River plants.* Cambridge University Press, Cambridge

Haslam, S. M. and Wolseley, P. A. (1981) *River vegetation: its identification, assessment and management.* Cambridge University Press, Cambridge

Hathaway, R. L. and Penny, D. (1975) Root strength in some Populus and Salix clones. *New Zealand J. Botany,* **13**, 333–344

Hayes, J. C., Barfield, B. J. and Tollner, E. W. (1984) Performance of grass filters under laboratory and field conditions. *Trans. Am. Soc. Agri. Engnrs.,* **27**, 1321–1331

Heede, B. H. (1976) *Gully development and control: the status of our knowledge.* US Department of Agriculture Forest Service Research Paper RM-169, Rocky Mountain Forest and Range Experimental Station, Fort Collins, Colorado

Helliwell, D. R. (1986) The extent of tree roots. *Arboricultural J.,* **10**, 341–347

Hemphill, R. W. and Bramley, M. E. (in press) *Protection of river and canal banks,* CIRIA/Butterworth, London

Hewlett, H. W. M., Boorman, L. A. and Bramley, M. E. (1987) *Design of reinforced grass waterways,* CIRIA Report 116, CIRIA, London

Hiller, H. (1966) Ganzjährige Pflanzzeit für Douglasien-Topfballenpfläzen. *Forstarchiv,* Berlin, FRG, **5**, 93 (data obtained from Schiechtl (1980))

Hillier, H. G. (1974) *A tree for every site.* Leaflet No. 5, Arboricultural Association, Romsey

HMSO (1976) *Specification for road and bridge works,* London

HMSO (1986) *Specification for highway works,* London

Ho, D. Y. F. and Fredlund, D. G. (1982) Increase in strength due to suction for two Hong Kong soils. *Proc. Conf. Engineering and Construction in Tropical Residual Soils,* Honolulu, Hawaii, *ASCE,* 263–295

Hsi, G. and Nath, J. H. (1970) Wind drag within a simulated forest. *J. Appl. Meteorol.,* **9**, 592–602

Hubbard, C. E. (1968) *Grasses* (2nd ed.). Penguin, London

Hudson, N. W. (1981) *Soil conservation.* Batsford, London

Humphries, R. N. (1979) Some alternative approaches to the establishment of vegetation on mined land and on chemical waste materials. In: Wali, M. K. (ed.). *Ecology and coal resource development.* Pergamon Press, New York

I.C.E. (1948) Biology and civil engineering. *Proc. Con., Biology and Civil Engineering,* Institution of Civil Engineers, London

I.C.E. (1976) *Manual of applied geology for civil engineers.* Institution of Civil Engineers, London

Ingold, T. (1982) *Reinforced earth.* Thomas Telford, London

Ito, T. and Matsui, T. (1975) Methods to estimate lateral force acting on stabilizing piles, soils and foundations. *Jap. Soc. Soil Mech. and Found. Engng.,* **15**(4), 43–59

Jacobs, A. (1984) Wind reduction near the surface behind a thin solid fence. *Agricultural and Forest Meteorology,* **33**, 157–162

Janbu, N. (1973) Slope stability computations. In Hirschfield, R. C. and Poulos, S. J. (eds.). *Embankment dam engineering: Casagrande.* Wiley, New York, 47–107

Jarvis, M. G. and Mackney, D. (1979) *Soil survey applications.* Technical Monograph No. 13, Soil Survey of England and Wales, Harpenden

Jefferies, R. A. (1981) Legumes for the reclamation of derelict and disturbed land. *Landscape Design,* May 1981, 39–41

Johnson, P. E. (1985) *Maintenance and repair of highway embankments: studies of seven methods of treatment.* Research Report 30, TRRL, Crowthorne, Berks.

Jones, C. J. F. P. (1985) *Earth reinforcement and soil structures.* Butterworth, London

Kassif, G. and Kopelovitz, A. (1968) *Strength properties of soil root systems.* Technion Institute of Technology, Haifa, Israel

Kirkby, M. J. (1976) Hydrological slope models: the influence of climate. In Derbyshire, E. (ed.). *Geomorphology and climate.* Wiley, London, 247–267

Knutson, P. L. (1977) Designing for bank erosion control with vegetation. *Proc. 5th Symp. Waterway, Port, Coastal and Ocean Div.,* Am. Soc. Civil Eng., New York, 716–733

Koerner, R. M. (1984) In-situ stabilisation using anchored nets. *Proc. Conf. on Low Cost and Energy-saving Construction Methods,* Rio de Janeiro, Envo Publishing, Bethlehem, USA, 465–478

Lee, I. W. Y. (1985) A review of vegetative slope stabilisation. *J. Hong Kong Inst. of Engng.,* **3**(7), 9–21

Lewis, G. and Williams, G. (1984) *Rivers and wildlife handbook.* Royal Society for the Protection of Birds, Sandy, Berks.

Liddle, M. J. (1973) *The effects of trampling and vehicles on natural vegetation.* Unpub. Ph.D. thesis, University College of North Wales, Bangor

Little, M. G. and Jones, H. R. (1979) *The uses of herbaceous vegetation in the drawdown zone of reservoir margins.* Technical Note No. TR105, Water Research Centre, Medmenham

Lowday, J. E. and Wells, T. C. E. (1977) *The management of grassland and heathland in country parks.* CCP 105, Countryside Commission, Cheltenham

Luckman, P. G., Hathaway, R. L. and Edwards, W. R. N. (1981) *Root systems, root strength and slope stability*. Internal Report No. 34, Land Stability Group and Plant Materials Group, Aokautere Science Centre, New Zealand

Luke, A. (1988) Looking to lupins. *Landscape Design,* February 1988, 58–61

Lyles, L. and Allison, B. E. (1981) Equivalent wind erosion protection from selected crop residues. *Trans. Am. Soc. Agri. Engnrs,* **24**, 405–409

M.A.F.F. (1977) *Shelter belts for farmland.* Fixed equipment of the farm, Leaflet 15, Ministry of Agriculture, Fisheries and Food, HMSO, London

Marshall, J. K. (1967) The effect of shelter on the productivity of grasslands and field crops. *Field Crop Abstracts,* **20**(1), 1–14

Marshall, J. K. (1971) Drag measurements in roughness arrays of varying density and distribution. *Agricultural Meteorology,* **8**, 169–292

Matheson, G. D. (1985) *The stability of excavated slopes exposing rock.* Proc. Symp. Failures in earthworks. I.C.E., London, 295–306

McGowan, A., Andrewes, K. Z., and Al-Hasani, M. M. (1978) Effect of inclusion properties on the behaviour of sand. *Geotechnique,* **28**(3), 327–346

Miller, A. (1985) *Windthrow hazard classification.* Forestry Commission Leaflet 85, HMSO, London

Miller, C. R. and Boorland, W. M. (1963) Stabilisation of five-mile and muddy creeks. *J. Hydraulics Div., ASCE,* **89** (HY1), 67–97

Mitchell, R. J. (1983) *Earth structures engineering.* Allen and Unwin, London

Monteith, J. L. (1965) *Evaporation and environment.* Symp. Soc. Exper. Biol., **19**, 205–234

Monteith, J. L. (1973) *Principles of environmental physics.* Edward Arnold, London

Moore, J. E. (1966) *Design for noise reduction.* Architectural Press, London

Moore, P. D. and Chapman, S. B. (1986) *Methods in plant ecology.* 2nd edition, Blackwell, Oxford

Morgan, R. P. C. (1980) Field studies of sediment transport by overland flow. *Earth Surface Processes,* **5**, 307–316

Morgan, R. P. C. (1985) The impact of recreation on mountain soils: towards a predictive model for soil erosion. In Bayfield, N. G. and Barrow, G. C. (eds.). *The ecological impacts of outdoor recreation on mountain areas in Europe and North America.* Recreation Ecology Research Group Report No. 9, 112–121

Morgan, R. P. C. (1986) *Soil erosion and conservation.* Longman, London

Morgan, R. P. C., Finney, H. J. and Williams, J. S. (1988) *Leaf properties affecting crop drag coefficients: implications for wind erosion control.* Paper presented to 5th International Soil Conservation Conference, Bangkok, Thailand

Morgan, R. P. C., Morgan, D. D. V. and Finney, H. J. (1984) A predictive model for the assessment of soil erosion risk. *J. Agric. Engng. Res.,* **30**, 245–253

Morgan, R. P. C. and Finney, H. J. (1987) Drag coefficients of single crop rows and their implications for wind erosion control. In Gardiner, V. (ed.). *International Geomorphology,* Part II, Wiley, Chichester, 449–458

N.C.C. (1983) *Creating attractive grasslands using native plant species.* Nature Conservancy Council, Peterborough

N.C.C. (1986) *Wild flower grasslands from crop-grown seed and hay-bales.* Nature Conservancy Council, Peterborough

N.C.C. (1983) *Nature conservation and river engineering.* Nature Conservancy Council, Peterborough

N.H.B.C. (1985) *Building near trees.* Practice Note 3 National House Building Council, Amersham, Bucks.

Nakamura, H. (1970) Earth pressure acting on piles for the treatment of landslides and their design. *J. Landslides Japan,* **7**(2) (in Japanese)

Nassif, S. H. and Wilson, E. M. (1975) The influence of slope and rain intensity on runoff and infiltration. *Hydrological Sciences Bulletin,* **20**(4), 539–553

Newman, E. I. (1966) A method of estimating the total length of root in a sample. *J. Appl. Ecol.,* **3**(1), 139–146

O.E.C.D. (1971) *Urban traffic noise: strategy for an improved environment.* Report of the Consultative Group on Transportation Research, Organisation for Economic Cooperation and Development, Paris

O'Loughlin, C. L. (1974) The effects of timber removal on the stability of forest soils. *J. Hydrology (New Zealand),* **13**, 121–134

O'Loughlin, C. L. (1984) *Effectiveness of introduced forest vegetation for protecting against landslides and erosion in New Zealand's steeplands.* Symp. Effects of Forest Land Use on Erosion and Slope Stability, Honolulu, Hawaii

O'Loughlin, C. L. and Watson, A. (1979) Root-wood strength deterioration in Radiata pine after clear felling. *New Zealand J. Forestry Sci.,* **9**(3), 284–293

O'Loughlin, C. L. and Watson, A. (1981) Note on rootwood strength deterioration in *Nothofagus fusca* and *N. truncata* after clearfelling. *New Zealand J. Forestry Sci.,* **11**(2), 183–185

O'Loughlin, C. L. and Ziemer, R. L. (1982) The importance of root strength and deterioration rates upon edaphic stability in steepland forests. In *Carbon uptake and allocation in subalpine ecosystems as a key to management,* Proc. I.U.F.R.O. Workshop, Oregon State University, Corvallis, 70–78

Odemerho, F. O. (1986) Variation in erosion-slope relationship on cut-slopes along a tropical highway. *Singapore J. Tropical Geog.,* **7**(2), 98–107

Olesen, F. (1979) *Collective shelterbelt planting.* Hedeselskabet, Viborg

Parr, T. W., Cox, E. and Plant, R. A. (1986) The effects of cutting height on root distribution and water use of Ryegrass (*Lolium Perenne*) turf. *J. Sports Turf Res. Inst.,* **60**, 45–53

Parsons, A. W. and Perry, J. (1985) *Slope stability problems in ageing highway earthworks.* Proc. Symp. Failures in Earthworks, I.C.E. London

Penman, H. L. (1948) Natural evaporation from open water, bare soil and grass. *Proc. Roy. Soc. Lond.* A, **193**, 120–146

Penman, H. L. (1949) The dependence of transpiration on weather and soil conditions. *J. Soil Sci.,* **1**, 74–89

Plate, E. J. (1971) The aerodynamics of shelterbelts. *Agricultural Meteorology,* **8**, 203–222

Ranwell, D. S. and Boar, R. (1986) *Coast dune management guide.* Institute of Terrestrial Ecology, Monks Wood

Raunkiaer, C. (1934) *The life forms of plants and statistical plant geography,* Clarendon Press, Oxford

Reaves, C. A. and Cooper, A. W. (1960) Stress distribution in soil under tractor loads. *Agric. Engng.,* **41**, 20–31

Ree, W. O. (1949) Hydraulic characteristics of vegetation for vegetated waterways. *Agric. Engng.,* **30**, 184–187, 89

Rickson, R. J. (1987) Geotextile applications in steepland agriculture. Paper presented at the International Conference on Steepland Agriculture in the Humid Tropics, Kuala Lumpur, Malaysia

Rickson, R. J. (1988) The use of geotextiles in soil erosion control: comparison of performance on two soils. Paper presented to the 5th International Soil Conservation Conference, Bangkok, Thailand

Rickson, R. J. and Morgan, R. P. C. (1988) *Approaches to modelling the effects of vegetation on soil erosion by water.* Proc. EEC Workshop on Erosion Assessment for the EEC: Methods and Models, Brussels, 237–253

Riestenberg, M. M. and Sovonick-Dunsford, S. (1983) The role of woody vegetation on stabilising slopes in the Cincinnati area. *Bull. Geol. Soc. Am.,* **94**, 506–518

Roberts, R. D. and Bradshaw, A. D. (1985) Hydraulic seeding. *Landscape Design,* **156**, 42–47

Robinette, G. O. (1972) *Plants, people and environmental quality.* US Department of Interior National Park Service, Washington DC

Robson, J. D. and Thomasson, A. J. (1977) *Soil water regimes.* Technical Monograph 11, Soil Survey of England and Wales, Harpenden

Russell, E. W. (1973) *Soil conditions and plant growth.* 10th ed. Longman, London

Sale, J. S. P., Tabbush, P. M. and Lane, P. B. (1983) *The use of herbicides in the forest.* Booklet 51, Forestry Commission, Edinburgh

S.C.A.E. (1979) *When is a slope safe?* Scottish Institute of Agricultural Engineering, Penicuik, Midlothian

Schaller, F. W. and Sutton, P. (eds.) (1978) *Reclamation of drastically disturbed land.* Amer. Soc. Agron., Madison, USA

Schiechtl, H. M. (1973) *Sicherungsarbeiten im Landschaftsbau.* Callway Verlag, Munich, translated as

Schiechtl, H. M. (1980) *Bioengineering for land reclamation and conservation.* University of Alberta Press, Edmonton, Canada

Schmid, A. A. S. (1983) Design in the river landscape. *Landscape Planning,* **10**(1), 31–41

Schwab, G. O., Frevert, R. K., Edminster, T. W. and Barnes, K. K. (1966) *Soil and water conservation engineering.* Wiley, New York

Scott Russell, R. (1977) *Plant root systems, their function and interaction with the soil.* McGraw Hill, New York

Seibert, P. (1968) *Importance of natural vegetation for the protection of the banks of streams, rivers and canals.* Freshwater, Nature and Environment Series No. 2, Council of Europe, Strasbourg, 33–67

Sheldon, J. and Bradshaw, A. D. (1976) The reclamation of slate waste tips by tree planting. *Landscape Design,* **113**, 31–33

Skempton, A. W. (1954) *A foundation failure due to clay shrinkage caused by poplar trees.* Proc. Inst. Civil Eng., part 1, **3**, January, 66–83

Skidmore, E. and Hagen, L. J. (1977) Reducing wind erosion with barriers. *Trans. Am. Soc. Agric. Engnrs.,* **20**, 911–915

Smith, L. P. (1976) *The agricultural climate of England and Wales.* M.A.F.F. Technical Bulletin 35, HMSO, London

Smith, L. P. and Trafford, B. D. (1976) *Climate and drainage.* M.A.F.F. Technical Bulletin 34, HMSO, London

Soane, B. D. (1970) The effects of traffic and implements on soil compaction. *J. and Proc. Inst. Agric. Engnrs.,* **25**, 115

Speight, M. C. D. (1973) Outdoor recreation and its ecological effects; a bibliography and review. Discussion Papers in Conservation No. 4, University College, London

Stiny, J. (1947) *Die Zugfestigkeit von Pflanzenwurzeln* (in German). Data quoted in Schiechtl (1980)

Sutcliffe, J. (1979) *Plants and water.* Studies in Biology No. 14, Edward Arnold, Southampton

Swanston, D. N. (1970) *Mechanics of debris avalanching in shallow till soils of southeast Alaska.* US Department of Agriculture Forest Service Research Paper, PNW-103, Pacific and Northwest Forest and Range Experimental Station, Portland, Oregon

Swanston, D. N. (1974) Slope stability problems associated with timber harvesting in mountainous regions of the Western United States. US Department of Agriculture Forest Service General Technical Report PNW-21. National Technical Information Service, Springfield, VA

Tanner, H. and Naegeli, W. (1947) Wetterbleobachtungen und Untersuchungen über die Windverhältnisse in Bereich von Laub- und Nadelholzstreifen. *Anhang Jahr. Melioraten der Rheinebene* (Schweiz) 28–42

Temple, D. M. (1982) Flow retardance of submerged grass channel linings. *Trans. Am. Soc. Agric. Engnrs.,* **25**, 1300–1303

Temple, D. M., Robinson, K. M., Ahring, R. M. and Davis, A. G. (1987) *Stability design of grass-lined open channels.* Agriculture Handbook No. 667, US Department of Agriculture. National Technical Information Service, Springfield, VA

Thom, A. S. and Oliver, H. R. (1977) On Penman's equation for estimating regional evaporation. *Q.J. Royal Met. Soc.,* **103**, 345–357

Thomasson, A. J. (1975) *Soil and field drainage.* Technical Monograph No. 7, Soil Survey of England and Wales, Harpenden

Tollner, E. W., Barfield, B. J. and Hayes, J. C. (1982) Sedimentology of erect vegetal filters. *J. Hydraulics Div., Am. Soc. Civil Engnrs.,* **108**, 1518–1531

T. R. R. L. (1965) *Soil mechanics for road engineers,* Transport and Road Research Laboratory, Crowthorne

Tsukamoto, Y. and Kusakabe, O. (1984) *Vegetative influences on debris slide occurrences on steep slopes in Japan.* Proc. Symp. Effects of Forest Land Use on Erosion and Slope Stability, Environment and Policy Institute, Honolulu, Hawaii

Turmanina, V. I. (1965) On the strength of tree roots. *Bulletin of the Moscow Society of Naturalists, Biological Section,* **70**(5), 36–45 (in Russian with English summary)

Tuxen, R. (1956) Die heutige potentielle naturliche Vegetation als Gegenstand der Vegetationskartierung. *Angew. Pflanzensoz.,* **13**, Stolenau/Weser

U.S.D.A. (1975) *Engineering field manual for conservation practices.* Soil Conservation Service, US Department of Agriculture, Washington DC

U.S.S.C.S. (1954) *Handbook of channel design for soil and water conservation.* Publication SCS-TP61, US Department of Agriculture, Washington DC

U.S.S.C.S. (1972) *Hydrology: national engineering handbook.* US Department of Agriculture, Section 4, Washington DC

Vaughn, P. R. and Walbanke, H. J. (1973) Pore-pressure changes and delayed failure of cutting slopes in overconsolidated clay. *Geotechnique,* **23**, 531–539

Vidal, H. (1966) La terre armée. *Anns. Inst. Techn. Batim.* Paris, **223–229**. July–August, 888–939

Vidal, H. (1969) *The principle of reinforced earth.* Highway Research Record 282, 1–16

Waldron, L. J. (1977) The shear resistance of root-permeated homogeneous and stratified soil. *Soil Sci. Soc. Am. J.,* **41**, 343–849

Waldron, L. J. and Dakessian, S. (1981) Soil reinforcement by roots: calculation of increased soil shear resistance from root properties. *Soil Sci.,* **132**(6), 427–435

Walker, B. F. and Fell, R. (1987) *Soil slope instability and stabilisation.* Proc. extension course, Sydney, A. A. Balkema, Rotterdam

Wang, W. L. and Yen, B. C. (1974) Soil arching in slopes. *J. Geotech. Eng. Div., A.S.C.E.,* **100**(GT1), 61–78

Water Space Amenity Commission (1980) *Conservation and land drainage guidelines.* W.S.A.C., London

Wells, T. C. E., Bell, S. and Frost, A. (1981) *Creating attractive grasslands using nature plant spaces.* Nature Conservancy Council, Peterborough

Wiersum, K. F. (1985) Effects of various vegetation layers of an *Acacia auriculiformis* forest plantation on surface erosion in Java, Indonesia. In El-Swaify, S.A. Moldenhauer, W. C. and Lo, A. (eds.). *Soil erosion and conservation.* Soil Cons. Soc. Am., Ankeny, IA, 79–89

Wild, A. (ed.) (1988) *Russell's soil conditions and plant growth.* 11th edition, Longman Scientific and Technical, Harlow

Wilson, K. (1985) *A guide to the reclamation of mineral working for forestry.* Forestry Commission Research and Development Paper 141, Forestry Commission, Edinburgh

Winterkorn, A. F. and Fang, H. Y. (eds.) (1975) *Foundation engineering handbook.* Van Nostrand Reinhold, New York

Wischmeier, W. H. and Smith, D. D. (1978) *Predicting rainfall erosion losses.* Agricultural Research Service Handbook 537, US Department of Agriculture, Washington DC

Woodruff, N. P. and Siddoway, F. H. (1965) A wind erosion equation. *Proc. Soil Sci. Soc. Am.* **29**, 602–608

Woodruff, N. P. and Zingg, A. W. (1952) *Wind-tunnel studies of fundamental problems related to windbreaks.* Publication SCS-TP-112, Soil Conservation Service, US Department of Agriculture, Washington DC

Wright, J. L. and Brown, K. W. (1967) Comparison of momentum and energy balance methods of computing vertical transfer within a crop. *Agronomy J.,* **59**, 427–432

Wu, T. H. (1976) *Investigation of landslides on Prince of Wales Island.* Geotechnical Engineering Report 5, Dept. of Civil Engineering, Ohio State Univ., Columbus

Wu, T. H. (1984) *Effect of vegetation on slope stability.* Trans. Res. Record 965, Trans. Res. Board, Washington DC, 37–46

Wu, T. H., McKinnell III, W. P. and Swanston, D. N. (1979) Strength of tree roots and landslides on Prince of Wales Island, Alaska. *Can. Geot. J.,* **16**(1), 19–33

van Kraayenoord, C. W. S. and Hathaway, R. L. (eds.) (1986) *Plant materials handbook for soil conservation. Volume 1: principles and practices.* Water and Soil Miscellaneous Publication No. 93, Natural Water and Soil Conservation Authority (NZ), Water and Soil Directorate, Ministry of Works and Development, Wellington North, New Zealand

van Wijk, A. (1984) Playing conditions and soil construction of winter games pitches. In: Shildrick, J. (ed.) *Proc. Second National Turfgrass Conference,* Keele, September 1983, National Turfgrass Council, Bingley, W. Yorks

Yen, C. P. (1971) Study of the root system form and distribution habit of the ligneous plants for soil conservation in Taiwan (preliminary report), *J. Chinese Soil and Water Conservation,* Taiwan, **3**(2), 179–204

Yen, C. P. (1972) Forest for slope stabilisation. *Q. J. Chinese Forestry,* Taiwan, **4**(4)

Yen, C. P. (1984) Types of the root distribution depth and density of the ligneous plants in Taiwan. Extracted from *J. Chinese Soil and Water Conservation,* **5**(1)

Young, A. (1972) *Slopes.* Geomorphology Text, No. 3, Longman, London

Ziemer, R. R. (1978a) *Logging effects on soil moisture losses.* PhD dissertation, Colorado State University, Ft. Collins

Ziemer, R. R. (1978b) An apparatus to measure the cross-cut shearing strength of roots. *Can. J. Forestry Res.,* **8**(1), 142–144

Ziemer, R. R. (1981a) *Roots and the stability of forested slopes.* Proc. Int. Symp. on Erosion and Sediment Transport in Pacific Rim Steeplands, Christchurch, New Zealand. Int. Assn. of Hydrology Sci. Pub. No. 132, 343–361

Ziemer, R. R. (1981b) *The role of vegetation in the stability of forested slopes.* Ex. Proceedings of XVII Int. Union of Forest Research Organs. World Congress, Japan, 3–18

Ziemer, R. R. and Swanston, D. N. (1977) *Root strength changes after logging in South East Alaska.* Forest Service Research Note PNW-306, Pacific Northwest Forest and Range Experiment Station, US Forest Service, Portland, Oregon, USA

Zulfacar, A. and Clark, C. S. (1974) Highway noise and acoustical buffer zones. *J. Transportation Engng. Div. A.S.C.E.,* **100** (TE2), 389–401

Appendices

A1 Plants with good bioengineering properties suitable for use in the UK

Most species of grasses, herbs, shrubs and trees can fulfil useful functional roles as well as aesthetic ones. This appendix gives some guidance on plants of particular use in bioengineering.

Further advice should be sought on the environmental preferences and tolerances, growth habit, propagation, ecology and management of the species selected. This guide can only indicate the most likely choices based on function. Further information can be obtained from: Schiechtl (1980), Coppin and Bradshaw (1982), Beckett and Beckett (1979), Elias and Chadwick (1979), Hillier (1974), STRI (annual), Countryside Commission (1980), Grime, Hodgson and Hunt (1988).

A1.1 Plants for soil stabilisation, surface protection and erosion control

Functions coded as follows:

SP Surface protection and shallow reinforcement, erosion control
DR Deeper reinforcement and soil strength enhancement
AB Anchoring and buttressing, deep tap-roots
PH 'Phreatophytes' – removal of soil water
BC Bank and channel reinforcement

Species	Functions	Comments
Grasses and sedges		
Agrostis capillaris (Common bent)	SP	Wide soil tolerance, rhizomatous. Many cultivars available including those tolerant of heavy metal contamination.

Species	Functions	Comments
A. castellana (Highland bent)	SP	Cultivar Highland–similar to *A. capillaris* but more strongly rhizomatous
A. stolinifera (Creeping bent)	SP BC	Spreads by stolons, wide soil tolerance. Many cultivars available but prefers damp soils; tolerates occasional flooding and salt.
Ammophila arenaria (Marram grass)	SP	Used for stabilising sand dunes. Propagated by cuttings.
Arrhenatherum elatius (Tall oat grass)	SP	Wide soil tolerance, natural coloniser of embankments and cuttings. Tall.
Carex riparia (Greater pond sedge)	BC	Spreads by extensive rhizomes. Marginal zone (shallow water). Transplant fragments.
C. acutiformis (Lesser pond sedge)	BC	
Elymus (Agropyron) repens (Couch grass)	SP	Deeper soils, not tolerant of extremes; strongly rhizomatous; competitive.
Festuca rubra rubra (Creeping red fescue)	SP BC	Very wide soil tolerance, rhizomatous. Many cultivars available including those tolerant of heavy metals and salt.
F. longifolia (Hard fescue)	SP	Drought tolerant. Wear tolerant. Not rhizomatous.
Glyceria maxima (Reed sweet grass)	BC	Spreading, can be invasive; tolerates damage. Marginal and emergent zones.
Leymus arenarius (Lyme grass)	SP	Sand dunes, salt tolerant.
Lolium perenne (Perennial ryegrass)	SP	Fertile soils, quick–growing, wear tolerant, many cultivars available
L. multiflorum (Italian ryegrass)	SP	Very quick to establish, does not persist long. Westerwold's ryegrass, an annual subspecies, is widely used as a nurse.
Phalaris arundinacea (Reed canary grass)	DR PH	Deep rhizomes, wet soils. No commercial seed, establish as live plants and rhizome fragments.
Poa annua (Annual meadow grass)	SP	Annual, quick to re-colonise bare ground, wear tolerant.
P. compressa (Flattened meadow grass)	SP	Rhizomes, tolerant of very infertile conditions.
P. pratensis (Smooth meadow grass)	SP	Wide soil tolerance, strong rhizomes, wear tolerant. Many cultivars available.

Legumes

Species	Functions	Comments
Coronilla varia (Crown vetch)	SP DR	Wide tolerance, dense growth, slow to establish, particularly in the north.
Lotus corniculatus (Birds-foot trefoil)	SP DR	Wide soil tolerance. Salt tolerant

Species	Functions	Comments
Lupinus polyphyllus (Perennial blue lupin)	SP DR	Wide soil tolerance, but will die out with several hard winters.
Medicago sativa (Lucerne)	SP DR PH	Drought tolerant, neutral/alkaline soils.
Onobrychis vicifolia (Sanfoin)	SP DR	Better soils, neutral/alkaline, drought tolerant.
Trifolium repens (White clover)	SP	Widely used; requires moderate fertility. Many cultivars available.
T. hybridum (Alsike clover)	SP DR	Tolerates waterlogging.

Other herbs

Species	Functions	Comments
Achillea millefolium (Yarrow)	DR	Wide soil tolerance, grows well in grass swards. Spreads by runners/rhizomes. Salt tolerant.
Chrysanthemum leucanthemum (Ox-eye Daisy)	DR	Tall growth; prefers fertile soils. Grows well in grassland.
Plantago lanceolata (Ribwort plantain)	DR	Wide soil tolerance. Short growth.
Poterium sanguisorba (Salad burnet)	DR	Tall growth; prefers lime soils, but tolerates infertile soils. Grows well in grassland.

Shrubs

Species	Functions	Comments
Cotoneaster microphyllous	SP	Wide soil tolerance.
Cytisus scoparius (Broom)	DR	N-fixer, salt tolerant.
Genista tinctoria (Dyers greenweed)	DR	Tall growing, very extensive root system. Prefers heavy soil. N-fixer.
Hedera helix (Ivy)	SP	Good groundcover as well as climber.
Hippophae rhamnoides (Sea buckthorn)	SP DR	Spreads by rhizomes. Sandy soils especially dunes. Tolerant of wind and salt. N-fixer.
Lupinus arboreus (Tree lupin)	SP DR	N-fixer, intolerant of exposure or hard winters. Life span about 7 years. Salt tolerant.
L. perenne (Perennial lupin)	SP DR	N-fixer.
Prunus spinosa (Blackthorn)	DR	Spreads with root suckers, can form dense thickets. Spiny. Salt tolerant.
Rosa rubiginosa (Briar)	DR	Spiny.
R. rugosa (Shrub rose)	DR	Spiny. Salt tolerant.

Species	Functions	Comments
Tamarix spp. (Tamarisk)	SP DR PH	Deep rooted. Tolerant of wind and salt.
Ulex europaeus (Gorse)	DR	N-fixer, fire risk if growing in stands on its own.

Trees

Species	Functions	Comments
Acer pseudoplatanus (Sycamore)	DR AB	Very tolerant of exposure.
Alnus glutinosa (Common alder)	PH DR BC	Can be coppiced, wet sites and derelict land. N-fixer. Salt tolerant.
A. incana (Grey alder)	DR PH	Can be coppiced; drier sites. N-fixer.
Betula spp. (Birches)	SP DR	Tolerant of infertile conditions. Good pioneer species.
Crataegus monogyna (Hawthorn)	DR PH	Can be coppiced; wide soil tolerance. Salt tolerant.
Cupressus macrocarpa	DR PH	Coniferous, evergreen. Salt tolerant.
Larix spp. (Larches)	DR	Coniferous, deciduous.
Populus spp. (Poplars)	PH DR	Extensive deep root system. Roots fairly freely from live wood cuttings, will coppice. Salt tolerant.
Pinus nigra (Corsican and Austrian pine)	DP PH	Coniferous, evergreen.
Quercus robur (Oak)	DR AB PH	Deep tap-root. Salt tolerant.
Robinia pseudacacia (Black locust)	DR SP	Good pioneer species on poor, sandy soils. N-fixer.
Salix cinerea (Sallow)	SP DR PH	Moist or dry sites but select local ectotypes, can coppice but bushy habit not good for channel work.
S. caprea (Goat willow)	SP DR PH	
S. viminalis (Osier)	BC PH	Good for river works, bank repairs. Keep coppiced to prevent larger stems which obstruct flow, grows as thicket.
S. triandra (Almond willow)	BC PH SP	
S. purpurea (Purple willow)	DR PH BC	Bush or shrubby growth, extensive root system, slow growing.
S. alba (White willow)	PH	Larger tree with single trunk, roots at water level. Salt tolerant.
		Note: all willows root freely from live wood cuttings.

A1.2 Grass-based seed mixtures

Seed mixtures should be designed to suit particular circumstances. The following are given only as a guide and should not be taken as prescribed or standard mixtures. Remember that grass-based mixtures are only suitable for surface protection and erosion control; the depth of influence is not very great unless deep-rooting herbs are included.

	Mixture numbers		
	Soil Type		
Use and situation	Free draining (loam)	Prone to waterlogging (clay soil or bank-side)	Prone to drought (sandy)
Wear and damage resistant, vigorous but requiring high maintenance	1	2	3
Wear and damage resistant, not so vigorous, low maintenance	4	5	6
Erosion control and surface binding			
general	7	8	9
saline areas	–	10	–
acid conditions	11	–	11
alkaline conditions	12	–	12
Non aggressive mixture for use with herbs	13	13	13

	Composition of grass-based mixtures, (%)												
Species	1	2	3	4	5	6	7	8	9	10	11	12	13
Perennial ryegrass	25	25	20										
Timothy		10			15			10					
Smooth meadow grass	20	10	25	25	20	25	15	15	15	20		20	15
Rough meadow grass		10			10			10					
Flattened meadow grass			10	10	10	15	10	5	20		30	10	10
Hard fescue				5		10	10		10				10
Chewing's fescue	10				10			10					
Creeping red fescue													
strong type	30	25	30										
slender type				35	35	35	40	40	40	35		55	55
Sheep's fescue											30		
Browntop bentgrass	10	5	10	10	5	10	10	5	10		10		10
Creeping bentgrass		5						10		10		10	
Wavy hair grass											25		
Reflexed salt-marsh grass										35			
White clover	5	5	5	5	5	5	5	5	5	2.5	2.5		
Birdsfoot trefoil		5								2.5	2.5		

1. For suitable cultivars, consult a plant specialist or seed merchant. Lists of cultivar characteristics are published annually by the Sports Turf Research Institute.
2. Sowing rate: 50–200 kg/ha. Use lower rates where soil is fertile or when mixing with herbs, higher rates when full cover is wanted rapidly.
3. Turfgrass cultivars of ryegrass should be selected, which are slower growing, though these may be slower to establish and have less vigorous roots. Agricultural types may be suitable where tall growth is not a constraint, though other species may be shaded out.

A1.3 Trees and shrubs for barriers and general use

The following is a guide to the selection of tree species for different situations (after MAFF, 1977).

Species for providing early rapid growth

Dry soils		Moist soils	
Hardy	Frost-tender	Hardy	Frost-tender
Fertile sites Birch Corsican pine Japanese larch	Cordate-leaved alder	Grey alder Black alder Aspen Japanese larch Hybrid poplars Western red cedar	Norway spruce Sitka spruce
Infertile sites Birch Hybrid larch Japanese larch Scots pine	Monterey pine	Alders Aspen Birch Black locust Japanese larch Sallow	Hybrid larch Sitka spruce

Species for providing longer term growth

Dry soils		Moist soils	
Hardy	Frost-tender	Hardy	Frost-tender
Fertile sites Cherry Cornish elm Wych elm Sessile oak Turkey oak Lime Austrian pine Corsican pine Scots pine	Beech Horse chestnut Monterey pine	Cornish elm Wych elm Lime Sycamore Hybrid poplars Lawson's cypress	Beech Monterey cypress Horse chestnut Pedunculate oak Silver firs Norway spruce Sitka spruce
Infertile sites Sessile oak American red oak Lodgepole pine Mountain pine Scots pine Bishop pine	Evergreen oak Beech	American red oak Western hemlock Lodgepole pine Mountain pine Scots pine	Evergreen oak Noble fir

Trees and shrubs suitable for belts or the margins of plantations

Dry soils		Moist soils	
Hardy	*Frost-tender*	*Hardy*	*Frost-tender*
Fertile sites			
Lime	Laburnum	Hornbeam	Monterey cypress
Cornish elm		Cornish elm	Bird cherry
Whitebeams		Norway maple	
Blackthorn		Lime	
Hawthorn		Lawson's cypress	
		Blackthorn	
		Hawthorn	
		Hazel	
		Snowberry	
		Sycamore	
Infertile sites			
Sea buckthorn		Rowan	Sitka spruce
Broom		Sea buckthorn	White spruce
Tamarisk		Mountain pine	
Mountain pine		Lodgepole pine	
Lodgepole pine			

A2 Geotextiles used in bioengineering

A summary of geotextile types which are used in combination with vegetation for erosion control, surface trafficability and shallow stabilisation

Type	Construction	Materials*
Two-dimensional fabrics and meshes	Woven or knitted textile, small apertures (<25 mm)	Synthetic
		Natural fibres (coir or jute)
	Mini-grids or 'biscuits', of mesh, mixed *in situ* with soil, random orientation	Synthetic
	Filaments blown *in situ*	Fibreglass rovings
	Filaments mixed *in situ* with soil	Synthetic
	Woven or extruded meshes, large apertures	Synthetic; woven types; can be wire-reinforced
Three-dimensional mats	Multi-layer mesh or random-filament matrix	Synthetic
	As above with asphalt	Synthetic, gravel bound with bitumen
	As above but with pre-grown turf	Composite, with soil/compost and grass turf
	Mulch mat	Straw, coir and/or wood shavings in lightweight synthetic mesh
Cellular grids or webs	Honeycomb of hexagonal cells formed from non-woven textile strips	Synthetic
Pocket fabrics	Woven or knitted textile incorporating rows of pockets	Synthetic

* Synthetic materials are polypropylene, polyethylene or polyamide. Most will degrade very slowly in sunlight (u/v). Natural fibres are biodegradable and will last for 1 to 3 years, depending on moisture conditions. They will also absorb water to varying extents, depending on the product.
The physical properties (tensile strength, thickness, etc) vary between proprietary products; reference should be made to manufacturer's literature.

Installation			Function					
Surface laid	Surface buried	Deeper buried	Seed or plant protection	Rainfall and runoff erosion control	Water flow erosion control	Surface reinforcement and trafficability	Soil reinforcement for shallow stabilisation	Gabions and reinforced soil structures
●	●			○	●	●	▲	▲
○			○	○	○			
	●					▲	●	
●			○	●	●			
	●	▲				▲	●	
	●	●					●	●
	●				●	●	●	
●				●	●			
●				●	●	●	●	
○			○	○				
	●						●	
●			●		●			

● Permanent function

○ Temporary function

▲ To some extent or in some situations

A3 Relevant British Standards and West German DIN Standards

A3.1 British Standards

BS 1000(63/632):1981   Universal Decimal Classification. Second English full edition.
Agriculture in general. Forestry. Plant injuries, diseases and pests. Plant protection.

BS 1000(633/635):1985   Universal Decimal Classification. English full edition.
Specific crops. Horticulture.

BS 1192:Part 4:1984   Construction drawing practice. Recommendations for landscape drawings.
Recommendations for the preparation of landscape drawings and schedules. Includes symbols and abbreviations which are used in a series of typical drawings. Appendices include summaries of information commonly used when landscape drawings are being prepared.

BS 3882:1965   Recommendations and classification for topsoil.
Description of topsoil; classification by texture; classification by soil reaction (pH); classification by stone content; size of stones. Notes on method of test for topsoil; designation of topsoil (being extensively revised; draft not available).

BS 3936:Part 1:1980   Nursery stock. Specification for trees and shrubs.
Trees and shrubs including conifers and woody climbing plants, suitable to be transplanted and grown for amenity. Covers origin, root system, condition, dimensions, packaging and labelling and forms and sizes to be supplied for a wide range of species.

BS 3936:Part 4:1984   Nursery stock. Specification for forest trees.
Requirements for origin, dimensions, root and shoot, description, condition and packaging of forest trees for timber production.

BS 3936:Part 5:1985   Nursery stock. Specification for poplars and willows.
Specifies requirements for dimensions, shoot condition and marking for plants to be grown for timber production, shelter belts or for amenity.

BS 3936:Part 10:1981   Nursery stock. Specification for ground cover plants.
Definitions and requirements for origin, root system, condition, dimensions, packaging, designation and labelling. Appendix gives information about minimum spread of 101 types of plant and indication of whether they are deciduous, evergreen or herbaceous.

BS 3969:1965 Recommendations for turf for general landscape purposes.
Common and botanical names of grasses and perennial weeds.

BS 3975:Part 4:1966   Glossary for landscape work. Plant description.
Plant types; plant parts; plant forms; general character; particular character; commercial classes.

BS 3975:Part 5:1969   Glossary for landscape work. Horticultural, arboricultural and forestry practice.

Provides working definitions for terms commonly used in nursery practice, horticultural upkeep and ground maintenance, tree work and forestry.

BS 3998:1966   Recommendations for tree work.

Safety, season and equipment; workmanship; inspection. Individual operations; cuts; pruning; lifting of crown; cleaning out; crown thinning; reducing and reshaping; restoration; repair work; bracing; feeding; tree removal. Appendices cover safety precautions, season, method for protecting a large tree to be used as an anchor, three methods for feeding trees after tree work, examples of methods for treatment of roots with ammonium sulphamate or sodium chlorate (being revised; Draft 86/14078 DC).

BS 4043:1966   Recommendations for transplanting semi-mature trees.

Selection of trees for transplanting, season for transplanting, preparation by root pruning. Tree pits, drainage, tree lifting operations. Lifting, loading and transporting; planting; backfilling and mulching; operational damage. Guying and securing the tree, wrapping, watering and spraying. Appendices classifying trees suitable for transplanting, giving guidance as to the size of prepared root systems, and with examples of guying and securing techniques (being revised; Draft 87/11145 DC).

BS 4156:1967   Specification for peat.

Peat produced for general horticulture and landscape purposes. Requirements as to pH, moisture content, ash, particle size, yield (volume out) and marking.

BS 4428:1969   Recommendations for general landscape operations (excluding hard surfaces).

Deals with the following general landscape operations: preparatory operations, including earthwork, landshaping and drainage; seeding of grass areas; turfing; planting of shrubs, hedges, climbers, herbaceous plants and bulbs; individual tree planting; forestry planting for amenity purposes (being extensively revised to Code of Practice for General Landscape Operations; Draft 87/10155 DC).

BS 5236:1975   Recommendations for cultivation and planting of trees in the advanced nursery stock category.

Recommendations for description, production, preparation for sale, packaging, labelling, planting, mulching and staking. Recommendations on dimensions for trees sold in the form of standards.

BS 5837:1980   Code of practice for trees in relation to construction.

Principles to follow to achieve satisfactory juxtaposition of trees and construction. Recommends types of trees for planting near buildings, structures, plant and services. Advice on planting and maintenance of trees in urban locations and paved areas.

BS 5930:1981   Code of practice for site investigation.

BS 6031:1981   Code of practice for earthworks.
Applies to earthworks forming part of general civil engineering construction such as highways, railways and airfields; bulk excavation for major structures and excavations in pit shafts and trenches for pipelines and drainage works.

BS CP3:Chapter V:Part 2:1972   Buildings - wind loads.
Recommendations and design wind loadings for buildings, but applicable to other structures such as trees.

West German Standards

DIN 18915, 1973   Landschaftsbau: Bodenarbeiten für vegetations-technische Zwecke.
Landscaping; soil working for technical vegetation purposes.
Part 1 Evaluation and grouping of soils.
Part 2 Soil-improving substances, fertilisers.
Part 3 Soil working methods.

DIN 18916, 1973   Landschaftsbau: Pflanzen und Pflanzarbeiten, Beschaffenheit von Pflanzen, Pflanzverahren.
Landscaping, plants and planting; quality of plants and methods of planting.

DIN 18917, 1973   Landschaftsbau: Rasen, Saatgut Fertigräsen-herstellen von Rasenflächen.
Landscaping; turf; seed, sods, turf establishment.

DIN 18918, 1973   Landschaftsbau: Sicherungsbauweisen. Sicherungen durch Ansaaten. Bauweisen mit lebenden und nicht lebenden Stoffen und Bauteilen, kombinierte Bauweisen.
Landscaping; site-stabilisation; stabilisation by seeding, living plant material, dead material and construction elements, combined construction methods.

DIN 18919, 1973   Landschaftsbau: Unterhaltungsarbeiten bei Vegetations-flächen. Stoffe, Verfahren.
Landscaping, maintenance of vegetation areas.

DIN 18920, 1973   Landschaftsbau: Schutz von Bäumen, Pflanzenbeständen und Vegetationsflächen bei Baumassnahmen.
Landscaping, protection of trees, plantations and vegetation areas from construction measures.

DIN 19657, 1973   Sicherungen von Gewässern, Deichen und Kustendunen; Richtlinien.
Protection of watercourses, dikes and coastal dunes; Guidelines.

DIN 19660, 1969   Richtlinien für Landschaftspflege und landwirtschaftlichen Wasserbau.
Guidelines for landscape conservation in agricultural river engineering.

A4 Sources of independent advice and information

ADAS (Agricultural Development and Advisory Service) Local and regional offices are listed under Ministry of Agriculture, Fisheries and Food (England), Welsh Office Agriculture Department and Department of Agriculture and Fisheries for Scotland

Arboricultural Advisory and Information Service, Forestry Commission. Forest Research Station, Alice Holt Lodge, Wrecclesham, Farnham, Surrey GU10 4LH. 0420-22255

Advisory Committee on the Landscape Treatment of Trunk Roads (LAC) Department of Transport, Room G08, 2 Monck Street, London SW1P 2BQ. 01-212 5168

Association of Professional Foresters, Brokerwood House, Brokerwood, Westbury, Wiltshire BA13 4EH. 0373-822238

British Association of Landscape Industries, Landscape House, 9 Henry Street, Keighley, West Yorkshire BD21 3DR. 0535-606139

British Ecological Society, Burlington House, Piccadilly, London W1V 0LQ. 01-434 2641

Committee for Plant Supply and Establishment, c/o Horticultural Trades Association, 19 High Street, Theale, Reading RG7 5AH. 0734-303132

Countryside Commission, John Dower House, Crescent Place, Cheltenham, Gloucestershire GL50 3RA. 0242-521381

Countryside Commission for Scotland, Battleby, Redgorton, Perth PH1 3EW. 0738-27921

European Landscape Contractors Association, Haus der Landschaft, Plitterdorfer Strasse 93 D-5300 Bonn 2, Federal Republic of Germany. 0228/35 40 36-38

Forest Service Department of Agriculture Northern Ireland, Dundonald House, Upper Newtonwards Road, Belfast BT4 3SB

Institute of Biology, 20 Queensferry Place, London SW7 2DZ

Institute of Chartered Foresters, 22 Walker Street, Edinburgh EH3 7HR. 031 225-2705

Institute of Horticulture, PO Box 313, 80 Vincent Square, London SW1P 2PE

Institute of Terrestrial Ecology, 68 Hills Road, Cambridge CB2 1LA. 0223-69745

Institution of Civil Engineers, 1/7 Great George Street, Westminster, London SW1P 3AA. 01-222 7722

Institution of Highways and Transportation, 3 Lygon Place, Ebury Street, London SW1W 0JS. 01-730 5245

Institution of Water and Environmental Management, 15 John Street, London WC1N 2EB. 01-831 3110

Landscape Institute, 12 Carlton House Terrace, London SW1 5AH. 01-839 4044

National Association of Agricultural Contractors, Huts Corner, Tilford Road, Hindhead, Surrey GU26 6SF. 042873-5360

Nature Conservancy Council, Headquarters England: Northminster House, Peterborough PE1 1UA. 0733-40345

Headquarters Scotland: 12 Hope Terrace, Edinburgh EH9 2AS. 031-447 4784

Headquarters Wales: Plas Penrhos, Ffordd Penrhos, Bangor, Gwynedd LL57 2LQ. 0248-355141

Soil Survey and Land Research Centre, Silsoe Campus, Silsoe, Beds MK45 4DT

Sport Turf Research Institute, Bingley, West Yorkshire BD16 1AU. 0274-565131

Transport and Road Research Laboratory, Department of Transport, Crowthorne, Berkshire, RG11 6AU. 0344 773131

Index

Note: information in boxes, illustrations, and tables is indicated by *italic page numbers*.